COMPUTER SCIENC

A First Course in Fo
and its Applications in
Computer Science

R. D. DOWSING
PhD
Senior Lecturer in Computing
University of East Anglia
Norwich NR4 7TJ, UK

V. J. RAYWARD-SMITH
MA, PhD
Senior Lecturer in Computing
University of East Anglia
Norwich NR4 7TJ, UK

C. D. WALTER
BSc, PhD
Lecturer in Computation, UMIST
Manchester M60 1QD, UK

BLACKWELL SCIENTIFIC PUBLICATIONS

OXFORD LONDON EDINBURGH

BOSTON PALO ALTO MELBOURNE

COMPUTER SCIENCE TEXTS

© 1986 by
Blackwell Scientific Publications
Editorial offices:
Osney Mead, Oxford OX2 0EL
8 John Street, London WC1N 2ES
23 Ainslie Place, Edinburgh EH3 6AJ
52 Beacon Street, Boston
 Massachusetts 02108, USA
667 Lytton Avenue, Palo Alto
 California 94301, USA
107 Barry Street, Carlton
 Victoria 3053, Australia

First published 1986

Set by Cotswold Typesetting Ltd
Gloucester and Cheltenham and printed
and bound in Great Britain by
Hollen Street Press Ltd., Slough, Berks.

DISTRIBUTORS

USA and Canada
 Blackwell Scientific Publications Inc
 PO Box 50009, Palo Alto
 California 94303

Australia
 Blackwell Scientific Publications
 (Australia) Pty Ltd
 107 Barry Street,
 Carlton, Victoria 3053

British Library
Cataloguing in Publication Data

Dowsing. R. D.
A first course in formal logic and its
applications in computer science.—
(Computer science texts)
1. Electronic digital computers—
Programming 2. Programming
(Mathematics)
I. Title II. Rayward-Smith, V. J.
III. Walter, C. D. IV. Series
005.13'1   QA76.6
ISBN 0-632-01308-7

Contents

Preface

Mathematical logic provides us with a tool for presenting formal and rigorous arguments both accurately and succinctly. It is surely the most fundamental branch of mathematics since it underpins all mathematical reasoning. This explains why it is accepted as an essential and well-established part of any university course in pure mathematics.

Propositional calculus and Boolean algebra are branches of mathematical logic which have always been included in computer science degree programmes because of their overriding importance in circuit design. We cover this core material in Chapters 1 and 2 of this text.

Predicate calculus is a natural extension of propositional calculus which provides the logician with a much richer language. It is a useful tool for the computer scientist, and we present the fundamentals of predicate calculus in Chapters 3 and 4. As with all logic, it is important to be accurate and precise at all times. This may sometimes strike the reader as overly pedantic but, if mathematical logic is to be the foundation of our reasoning, it is essential that it is soundly based.

In Chapter 5 we present one of the major ways in which a computer scientist uses the tool of mathematical logic. It provides him or her with a formal language in which to reason about computer programs. Proving that a program is correct is usually a highly non-trivial task but it is, nevertheless, very important. If computer programs are going to control our defence systems, be used in the design of major engineering constructions etc., it is vital that they have no bugs. Running a program on test data, however well chosen, is seldom sufficient to locate all such bugs. By using mathematical logic and a good programming style, we can do much better. We apply our techniques to the programming language Pascal. This language was chosen because of its wide use in universities as a teaching tool. It is easy to criticize certain details of its design. Nevertheless, the overall philosophy encourages a disciplined approach to programming. This enables us to reason about Pascal programs using predicate calculus, and the techniques we develop can easily be applied to most other programming languages.

If predicate calculus is such a good formal tool for reasoning, an obvious development is the use of a computer to perform such logical reasoning. In Chapter 6 we explain some techniques for doing this, primarily that of resolution theorem proving. This has wide applications in mathematics, in artificial intelligence and even in programming. The growing interest in logic programming is perhaps one of the most exciting developments in computer science within the last decade. We discuss this topic in Chapter 7 with particular reference to the programming language PROLOG.

Research into the role of formal logic in computer science has been greatly increasing during recent years as the full potential of this tool is being more widely appreciated. However, this text is not aimed at the research student (although it would provide good preliminary reading). We believe that logic and its applications in computer science are core material in an undergraduate programme. We have aimed to produce a textbook which will provide a clear exposition of the subject to a novice. Chapters 1, 2 and, possibly, 3 could be presented in the first year of an undergraduate programme. The remainder of the book is probably best deferred to the second or third year. The material is best studied in the order in which it is presented, although a very detailed reading of Chapters 3 and 4 is not essential for the reader's understanding of the majority of the rest of the book. Exercises are provided at the end of each chapter and any student is strongly advised to complete them before reading on.

Together with *A First Course in Formal Languages* and *A First Course in Computability*, this text provides the undergraduate with a good introduction to the major theoretical topics in computing. Although all these topics are important and every computer scientist should have a thorough understanding of them, formal logic appears to have the greatest potential for a major practical impact. A computer scientist without mathematical logic might find himself isolated from much of computing before the end of this century.

Most of this book was written whilst all three authors were at the University of East Anglia, Norwich. We would like to acknowledge the support provided by members of the Computing Studies Department at that University and, in particular, to thank Ms Carol Bracken and Miss Jane Vergette for some patient typing of difficult manuscripts and Ralph Elliott for help with Chapter 1. Throughout this period our publishers, Blackwell Scientific, were very supportive and the encouragement from their computer science representative, Dominic Vaughan, was much appreciated.

Christmas 1985   R. D. Dowsing, V. J. Rayward-Smith
                                    C. D. Walter

Chapter 1

Propositional Calculus

Introduction

In formal logic we study the principles of valid argument. Thus we are concerned with the structural or formal aspects of arguments rather than the factual content. Consider, for example, the following argument:

'Rome is the capital of Spain or Rome is the capital of France. Rome is not the capital of France. Therefore Rome is the capital of Spain.'

This argument is logically valid, i.e. the conclusion follows from the premises, although anyone with any geographical knowledge knows that the conclusion is incorrect.

Closely related to the notion of a logically valid argument, and forming an integral part of our study, is the notion of a *logically true proposition* (or statement). This type of proposition is one whose truth depends solely on its logical structure rather than its factual content.

In a natural language such as English, propositions are expressed by declarative sentences—as opposed to interrogative or imperative sentences which express questions or commands. It is a crucial distinguishing characteristic of propositions that each is either *true* or *false*, and in logic we say that every proposition has one of the two possible *truth values* which we write as T and F (for truth and falsehood). In propositional logic, the subject of this chapter, we consider the logical structure of propositions at the simplest level, the level at which complex propositions are formed from other simpler propositions using the so-called logical *connectives* or *operators* such as 'and', 'or' and 'not'. In Figs 1.1–1.3 we give examples of the various levels of sentences just described.

From a philosophical point of view the distinction between sentences and the propositions they express is important, but in logic the terms sentence and proposition are used interchangeably. Furthermore, since we

Computers are always right
Logic is easy
Red is a colour

Fig. 1.1. Some examples of simple propositions.

1

A car is not a colour
Propositions are true or propositions are false

Fig. 1.2. Some examples of complex propositions.

Where is the computer?
Put your work on the desk.

Fig. 1.3. Examples of sentences which are not propositions.

are only interested in logical structure rather than factual content, it is a standard technique to represent propositions in an abstract symbolic notation which emphasizes the structure. This formal linguistic framework is the basis of *propositional* calculus. In the following section we describe the linguistic apparatus before considering its application in subsequent sections.

The Linguistic Framework of Propositional Calculus

There is quite a close analogy between the 'language' of arithmetic expressions in elementary algebra and the 'language' of propositions we shall be using in propositional calculus. Indeed the propositional calculus is sometimes referred to as *propositional algebra*. In elementary algebra we use symbols such as letters of the alphabet to stand for numerically valued quantities, and we apply arithmetic operators ($+$, $-$, $\times$, $/$ etc.) to these to form numerically valued expressions, the value of each expression being dependent on its construction. In propositional calculus, by comparison, we use letters of the alphabet to stand for propositions, i.e. for truth-valued quantities, and we apply logical operators ($\sim$, $\wedge$, $\vee$, $\Rightarrow$, $\Leftrightarrow$ etc., representing 'not', 'and', 'or', 'implication', 'equivalence') to these to obtain expressions for more complex propositions. The reader may find this analogy helpful in providing a familiar perspective on the material which follows.

We shall call the basic building blocks of our language of propositions *basic propositions*, and we apply *propositional connectives* (logical operators) to these to build up *composite propositions*. A basic proposition, we shall assume, cannot be decomposed into any simpler propositions. Because of this, and because we are not interested in the specific factual content of any proposition, the precise internal structure and identity of each basic proposition can be ignored, apart from its possession of a truth value and its distinctness from every other basic proposition. Thus we can conveniently represent the distinct basic propositions simply by distinct capital letters A, B, C etc. Each composite proposition is formed by applying a propositional connective to an appropriate number of *operand* propositions. For each connective, the number of operands is fixed: a *unary* connective (e.g. $\sim$ for 'not') takes a single operand, while a *binary* connective (e.g. $\wedge$ for 'and') takes two operands. Each operand of the connective is a composite proposition, which may be either a basic proposition or may itself be a previously constructed composite proposition. In general, we use italic capital letters to stand for propositions; i.e. given any proposition whose precise identity is not fixed by the context or which is not known to be a particular basic proposition, then we use one of the letters A, B, C etc. to stand for that proposition. Given distinct formulations of the same proposition, we use $\equiv$ to denote their identity; for example, we might use $A \equiv B \vee C$ in some context. (Note that $\equiv$ is *not* a propositional connective, since it is not part of our language of propositions.)

For our future convenience we now give a more formal definition of our language of propositions. Such a definition falls naturally into two stages. First the *syntax* (or grammar) is a set of rules defining the construction of all permissible propositions. Second, the *semantics* (or rules of interpretation) is a set of rules ascribing meaning to each of the propositions defined by the syntax.

For the propositional calculus, the syntax implicit in the informal description given earlier is expressed by the following three rules:

(1) There are (*basic*) *propositions* A, B, C etc.

(2) For given propositions A, B, each of the following

$$(\sim A), (A \wedge B), (A \vee B), (A \Rightarrow B), (A \Leftrightarrow B)$$

is a (*composite*) proposition.

(3) There are no propositions in the propositional calculus beyond those determined by the previous two rules.

We point out with regard to rule (2) that in principle it is possible to define and to use other connectives, but we shall concentrate our attention on the five connectives mentioned in rule (2). We also observe in passing that rule (2) specifies one unary connective ($\sim$) and four binary connectives ($\wedge$, $\vee$, $\Rightarrow$, $\Leftrightarrow$).

The precise definition of the semantics of the propositional calculus will be the business of the following sections, but we give here an informal outline of the interpretation we intend to place on our propositions. As we have already stated, beyond their possession of truth values the precise identities of the basic propositions will not concern us. Each connective represents a logical operation determining the meaning of any composite proposition formed with it in terms of its operands. Figure 1.4 shows, for each of the five connectives we use, the operation it represents together with (approximate) equivalents in English and examples.

~ **Negation ('not')**
Example   my tie is not red   ~(my tie is red)

∧ **Conjunction ('and')**
Example   I am a boy and I am naughty
(I am a boy) ∧ (I am naughty)

∨ **Disjunction ('or')**
Example   I will go to bed or I will read a book
(I will go to bed) ∨ (I will read a book)

⇒ **Implication ('implies', 'only if', 'if . . . then . . .')**
Example   if you pay my fare then I will visit you
(you will pay my fare) ⇒ (I will visit you)

⇔ **Equivalence ('is equivalent to', 'if and only if')**
Example   the bill will be paid if and only if the goods are delivered
(the bill will be paid) ⇔ (the goods are delivered)

Fig. 1.4. Examples and meanings of the connectives ~, ∧, ∨, ⇒, ⇔.

Just as in elementary algebra, we can use precedence and other rules to simplify the written form of expressions by omission of brackets in certain circumstances—by writing, for example, $a+b/c+d \times e$ rather than $((a+(b/c))+(d \times e))$. We can apply similar rules and conventions to simplify the written form of the proposition.

(1) The outer brackets of any proposition may be omitted.

(2) The precedence order for the connectives is ~, ∧, ∨, ⇒, ⇔, with ~ having the highest precedence. Any bracket pairs implicit in this order of precedence may be omitted. Hence, we can write ~A ∨ B instead of (~A) ∨ B, but *not* instead of ~(A ∨ B) since ~ has a higher precedence than ∨.

(3) By convention, binary connectives associate to the left. Hence we can write A ∧ B ∧ C instead of (A ∧ B) ∧ C.

When we apply these rules to any particular proposition we obtain, *not* a new proposition, but merely a simpler representation of the original proposition. Thus, for example, the proposition

$$\sim A \vee B \vee \sim C \wedge D \Leftrightarrow (A \wedge C \Rightarrow \sim B)$$

is identical with the proposition

$$((((\sim A) \vee B) \vee ((\sim C) \wedge D)) \Leftrightarrow ((A \wedge C) \Rightarrow (\sim B)))$$

Having completed the linguistic preliminaries, we can now use our language of propositions as a tool in the classification of logical truths and valid patterns of argument. There are two possible approaches to this problem, which we can informally characterize as the 'truth-functional approach' and the 'deductive approach'. In the former we consider issues of logical truth and validity in terms of the possible truth or falsehood of all the basic propositions relevant to any given case, while in the latter approach we try to define rules by means of which we can derive or 'deduce' all the results in which we are interested. Looking ahead for a moment, it turns out that for the propositional calculus both approaches are equally effective. We start by considering the truth-functional approach.

The Truth-Functional Approach

We have already stipulated that each proposition has a truth value (T or F). For the truth-functional approach we make the further stipulation that whenever a connective is applied to suitable operands to form a composite proposition, the truth value of that composite proposition is *completely determined* by the truth values of those operands (and the identity of the given connective). In other words, we stipulate that each connective is *truth functional*. Thus the meaning of any connective can be defined by providing a table which shows, for each possible combination of truth values of its operands, the corresponding truth value for the composite proposition formed by applying the connective to those operands. Such a table is called a *truth table*. The truth table for the negation connective $\sim$ is straightforward and is shown in Fig. 1.5. Being a unary connective it has only one operand, which we call A, and that operand has only two possible values, T or F. Hence its truth table has only two rows, one for each possible

A	$\sim A$
F	T
T	F

Fig. 1.5. Truth table for the negation connective.

value of *A*. Each entry on the right-hand side represents the value of $\sim A$ corresponding to the value of *A* on the left-hand side.

The meaning of the binary connectives described above ($\vee$, $\wedge$, $\Rightarrow$ and $\Leftrightarrow$) can also be described by truth tables. Figure 1.6 shows the truth table for the conjunction connective $\wedge$. This table is constructed using the same principles as the previous one. Since $\wedge$ takes two operands, which we

A	B	A∧B
F	F	F
F	T	F
T	F	F
T	T	T

Fig. 1.6. Truth table for the conjunction connective.

designate *A* and *B*, which may be T or F independently of each other, the table consists of four rows, one for each combination of values for *A* and *B*. As in the previous table the right-hand column specifies the values of $A \wedge B$ for each combination of values for *A* and *B*. From the truth table it can be seen that $A \wedge B$ is true only if both *A* and *B* are true, i.e. the normal English language meaning of 'and'.

The truth table for the disjunction connective $\vee$ is shown in Fig. 1.7.

A	B	A∨B
F	F	F
F	T	T
T	F	T
T	T	T

Fig. 1.7. Truth table for the disjunction connective.

This corresponds to one common interpretation of 'or' in the English language, although there is another possible interpretation called 'exclusive or', where the composite proposition is considered false if *both* constituent propositions are true. Consider the statement 'Jim is writing some computer programs or Jim is playing darts'. The possibility that Jim is performing both actions simultaneously is implicitly excluded. To represent this second meaning we require another connective, known as the 'exclusive or' or 'non-equivalence' ($\not\Leftrightarrow$) which will be mentioned later.

The truth tables for the other two binary connectives $\Rightarrow$ and $\Leftrightarrow$ are shown in Figs 1.8 and 1.9.

A	B	A⇒B
F	F	T
F	T	T
T	F	F
T	T	T

Fig. 1.8. Truth table for the implication connective.

A	B	A⇔B
F	F	T
F	T	F
T	F	F
T	T	T

Fig. 1.9. Truth table for the equivalence connective.

The implication operator ⇒ is used in such forms as 'if A then B', where A is called the *antecedent* and B the *consequent*. If A is true then B determines the truth of the statement, whilst if A is false the statement is deemed to be true. The latter case needs some explanation. Consider the statement

'If the light is switched on, then electricity will be used'.

If the light is switched on the truth or falsity of the statement can be determined but the statement says nothing about the situation where the light is switched off. When the light is switched off, whether electricity is used or not does not contribute to the truth or falsity of the statement. By default the statement is assumed to be true if the antecedent is false.

The truth-functional definition of the connective ⇒, known as material implication, is perfectly valid, although the correspondence between it and 'if . . . then' in normal English usage is weaker than the correspondence between some of the other propositional connectives and their English counterparts. Specifically, the connection between the antecedent and the consequent can be much weaker in material implication than is usually considered proper in normal English usage (e.g. 'If Napoleon lost at Waterloo, then Rome is the capital of Italy').

The equivalence connective ⇔ is used in such forms as 'A if and only if B'. This proposition is true only if A and B have the same truth values, and is false otherwise. An example of the use of this proposition is 'My car will start if and only if there is some petrol in the tank'.

Other Unary and Binary Connectives

Before considering the use of these truth tables, it is worth considering the question 'How many different unary and binary connectives can be defined?'. Since each connective is completely defined by its truth table, this question is equivalent to asking how many different truth tables could be constructed for a given number of operands.

If we regard any unary connective as representing a function $F(A)$ of its operand A, then the right-hand column of the truth table defines the value of the function for each value of its operand A. The question then becomes one of determining how many different ways there are of filling this right-hand column. For the case of unary connectives the answer is four since there are two rows, each of which could contain T or F.

Therefore, in addition to the $\sim$ connective, there are three others whose truth tables are shown in Fig. 1.10. None of these truth tables is of any great interest. The truth table of Fig. 1.10(a) describes the 'identity' operation which leaves the value of its operand unchanged, and Figs 1.10(b) and 1.10(c) describe the 'constant' operations which produce the results T and F regardless of the operand value. Thus the negation operation $\sim$ is the only one of interest.

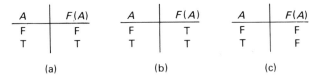

(a)   (b)   (c)

Fig. 1.10. Truth tables for the unary connectives other than $\sim$.

The question of how many binary connectives are possible can be approached in the same way. Each binary connective can be regarded as defining a function $F(A, B)$ where each of the operands A and B and the function itself can take one of two possible values, T or F. As we saw with the connectives $\wedge$, $\vee$ etc., the truth table has four rows since there are $2 \times 2 = 4$ possible combinations of values for the operands A and B. Thus the truth table for a binary connective will consist of four rows with four truth values representing the function values in the right-hand column. Since each value may be T or F, $2^4 = 16$ different truth tables are possible and these are shown in Fig. 1.11. Of these 16 truth tables, six (Figs 1.11(a), 1.11(f), 1.11(h), 1.11(j), 1.11(k) and 1.11(p)) mimic the four unary operations

A	B	F
F	F	F
F	T	F
T	F	F
T	T	F

(a) constant false

A	B	$A \land B$
F	F	F
F	T	F
T	F	F
T	T	T

(b) and

A	B	$A \nRightarrow B$
F	F	F
F	T	F
T	F	T
T	T	F

(c) not implication

A	B	$A \nLeftarrow B$
F	F	F
F	T	T
T	F	F
T	T	F

(d) not reverse implication

A	B	$A \downarrow B$
F	F	T
F	T	F
T	F	F
T	T	F

(e) joint denial, nor

A	B	A
F	F	F
F	T	F
T	F	T
T	T	T

(f) A

A	B	$A \nLeftrightarrow B$
F	F	F
F	T	T
T	F	T
T	T	F

(g) exclusive or, not equivalent

A	B	$\sim A$
F	F	T
F	T	T
T	F	F
T	T	F

(h) not A

A	B	$A \Leftrightarrow B$
F	F	T
F	T	F
T	F	F
T	T	T

(i) biconditional, equivalent, exclusive nor

A	B	B
F	F	F
F	T	T
T	F	F
T	T	T

(j) B

A	B	$\sim B$
F	F	T
F	T	F
T	F	T
T	T	F

(k) not B

A	B	$A \lor B$
F	F	F
F	T	T
T	F	T
T	T	T

(l) or, inclusive or

A	B	$A \Leftarrow B$
F	F	T
F	T	F
T	F	T
T	T	T

(m) reverse conditional, reverse implication

A	B	$A \Rightarrow B$
F	F	T
F	T	T
T	F	F
T	T	T

(n) conditional, implication

A	B	$A \mid B$
F	F	T
F	T	T
T	F	T
T	T	F

(o) alternative denial, nand

A	B	T
F	F	T
F	T	T
T	F	T
T	T	T

(p) constant true

Fig. 1.11. Truth tables for all possible binary connectives.

and we shall not consider them further. A further four (Figs 1.11(b), 1.11(i), 1.11(l) and 1.11(n)) are the binary connectives already discussed. The remaining truth tables are of limited interest, although we shall look at those for alternative and joint denial later.

Truth Tables for Complex Propositions

As we have indicated above, the propositional connectives can be used to construct propositions of arbitrary complexity, as regards both the number of connectives and the number of basic propositions they contain, since the operand(s) of any connective can themselves be composite propositions. For a complex proposition it is useful to be able to construct a truth table which defines its value for each possible combination of operand values, in the same way that the basic truth tables described previously define the values of composite propositions in terms of their immediate operands. We can construct such truth tables in stages, using these basic truth tables. The procedure is best illustrated by an example. Suppose we wish to construct a truth table for the complex proposition P with the definition

$$P \equiv ((A \vee B) \wedge C) \Rightarrow ((\sim A) \vee (B \wedge C))$$

First we observe that just three basic propositions (A, B and C) are used in the construction of P and hence the truth table for P must have $2 \times 2 \times 2 = 2^3 = 8$ rows, representing all possible value combinations for these three propositions, as shown in Fig. 1.12, columns 1–3. We wish to construct a column showing the value of P for each of these eight value combinations. Since P is of the form $A_1 \Rightarrow A_2$, with $A_1 \equiv (A \vee B) \wedge C$ and $A_2 \equiv \sim A \vee (B \wedge C)$, we can use the truth table defining $\Rightarrow$ (Fig. 1.8) to look up values in the column for P if we first establish columns for A_1 and A_2. Similarly, we can use the table for $\wedge$ (Fig. 1.6) to build the column for A_1 if we first establish columns for its operands $A \vee B$ and C. We can pursue this process of decomposition of P until each outstanding operand requirement is for one of the three basic propositions A, B and C. Starting with these three propositions and working in the opposite direction gives us a list of component propositions of P such that each proposition is either one of A, B and C or is formed by applying a single connective to operand propositions occurring earlier in the list. Thus, in addition to columns 1–3

1	2	3	4	5	6	7	8	9
A	B	C	$(A \vee B)$	$((A \vee B) \wedge C)$	$\sim A$	$(B \wedge C)$	$((\sim A) \vee (B \wedge C))$	$((A \vee B) \wedge C) \Rightarrow ((\sim A) \vee (B \wedge C))$
F	F	F	F	F	T	F	T	T
F	F	T	F	F	T	F	T	T
F	T	F	T	F	T	F	T	T
F	T	T	T	T	T	T	T	T
T	F	F	T	F	F	F	F	T
T	F	T	T	T	F	F	F	F
T	T	F	T	F	F	F	F	T
T	T	T	T	T	F	T	T	T

Fig. 1.12. Truth table for $((A \vee B) \wedge C) \Rightarrow ((\sim A) \vee (B \wedge C))$.

already described we obtain the sequence of propositions at the heads of columns 4–9 in Fig. 1.12, ending with the column for P itself. Now we can use the basic truth tables (Figs 1.5–1.9) to look up the values in successive columns. First, we identify the A and B of columns 1 and 2 with the operands A and B in the table for $\vee$ (Fig. 1.7) in which we can then look up values for A $\vee$ B to be entered in column 4. For example, in row 5 A and B have the values T and F, which by row 3 of Fig. 1.7 give the value T for A $\vee$ B, which we enter in column 4, row 5. Similarly, columns 4 and 3 for A $\vee$ B and C provide operand values which we look up in the table for $\wedge$ (Fig. 1.6) to obtain the values in column 5 for (A $\vee$ B) $\wedge$ C. Continuing in this manner column by column, we eventually obtain column 9 for P itself, using columns 5 and 8 and the table for $\Rightarrow$ (Fig. 1.8).

The example illustrates how the truth-functional definitions of the proposition connectives (Figs 1.5–1.9) effectively define the semantics of *every* proposition in the propositional calculus.

Fundamental Logical Properties of Propositions

We can use the truth-functional definition of propositional connectives, and the associated truth table techniques, as a basis for the definition of some fundamental logical properties of propositions.

We say that a proposition A is a *tautology* (is *logically valid*) if A has the value T for *every* possible combination of values of the *basic* propositions used in its construction. Conversely, we say that A is a (logical) *contradiction* if it has the value F for every possible combination of values of its constituent basic propositions.

By this stage it should be apparent to the reader that the above pair of definitions assert that, given the truth table for the proposition A, A is a tautology if and only if (iff) every entry in the column for A is T and, conversely, A is a contradiction iff every entry in the column for A is F. Some examples are shown in Figs 1.13 and 1.14. It should also be apparent, using the truth table defining the connective $\sim$ (Fig. 1.5), that any proposition A is a tautology iff $\sim A$ is a contradiction, and vice versa. We say that a proposition A is logically *consistent* if it is not a contradiction, i.e. if there is at least one T in the truth table for A. Note that it is essential for these definitions that the truth table used should be constructed in terms of all the relevant basic propositions.

Given propositions A, B, if the composite proposition $A \Rightarrow B$ is a tautology, then we say that A *logically implies* B or that B is a *logical*

A∨~A	A	~A	A∨~A
	F	T	T
	T	F	T

A⇔~~A	A	~A	~~A	A⇔~~A
	F	T	F	T
	T	F	T	T

Fig. 1.13. Examples of tautologies.

A∧~A	A	~A	A∧~A
	F	T	F
	T	F	F

A⇔~A	A	~A	A⇔~A
	F	T	F
	T	F	F

Fig. 1.14. Examples of contradictions.

consequence of *A*. Similarly, if *A*⇔*B* is a tautology, then we say that *A* and *B* are *logically equivalent*.

Logical Reasoning

With the propositional connectives we have described previously and the notions of tautology and contradiction it is possible to reason about statements in a natural language such as English using truth tables. The first task is to transform the English statements into the linguistic framework of propositional calculus.

Example 1.1

If I win the race then I will get a prize. This statement can be rewritten as

$$A \Rightarrow B$$

where A represents 'I win the race' and B represents 'I will get a prize', since the form 'if A then B' is one form of implication.

Example 1.2

Either Jill will lose or, if she wins, she will be exhausted. Let A represent 'Jill loses', and B represent 'Jill will be exhausted'. Then the statement can be rewritten as

$$A \vee (\sim A \Rightarrow B)$$

Example 1.3

Either it will be sunny or it will be cloudy but not both. Let A represent 'It will be sunny', and B represent 'It will be cloudy'. Then the statement can be rewritten as

$$(A \vee B) \wedge \sim (A \wedge B)$$

Most of these transformations are straightforward, but the reader should beware of distinctions between 'if', 'if . . . then', 'only if' and 'if and only if'. The statement 'A if B' translates as $B \Rightarrow A$, while 'if A then B' and 'A only if B' both translate as $A \Rightarrow B$. 'A if and only if B' translates as $A \Leftrightarrow B$.

Some synonyms, as far as representing English forms in propositional calculus is concerned, are

A and *B*	*A* but *B*
A and not *B*	*A* never *B*, *A* not *B*
A implies *B*	if *A* then *B*
	A only if *B*
	B if *A*
	A is a sufficient condition for *B*
	B is a necessary condition for *A*
A is equivalent to *B*	*A* if and only if *B* (*A* iff *B*)
	A is a necessary and sufficient condition for *B*
	B is a necessary and sufficient condition for *A*
	if *A* then *B* and if *B* then *A*

Truth of Composite Statements on Given Assumptions

Given a set of simple statements assumed to be true, we can determine the truth of composite statements expressed in terms of those simple statements by using straightforward truth table analysis.

The first step is to translate the statement to symbolic form as shown above and then to use the truth table technique to determine the truth or falsity of the statement.

Example 1.4

Assume the following.
(1) Pascal is a high level programming language.
(2) C is a systems programming language.
(3) Assembler is a low level programming language.
(4) A PDP-11 is a minicomputer.
(5) A Mostek 6502 is a microprocessor.
   Consider the following statements.
(a) If a PDP-11 is a minicomputer then C is a systems programming language.
(b) If either Pascal is a high level programming language or Assembler is a low level programming language then a Mostek 6502 is a microprocessor.
(c) If C is not a systems programming language and a PDP-11 is not a minicomputer then either a Mostek 6502 is not a microprocessor or C is a systems programming language.
(d) Pascal is a high level programming language iff a PDP-11 is a minicomputer and C is a systems programming language.

Solution

(1) Replace the basic propositions (1)–(5) by the symbols A to E.
(2) (a) 'If a PDP-11 is a minicomputer then C is a systems programming language' becomes $D \Rightarrow B$. Assumptions (4) and (1) give D and B as true and the truth table for implication (Fig. 1.8) gives $D \Rightarrow B$ as true for both operands true. Hence the statement is true.

   (b) 'If either Pascal is a high level programming language or Assembler is a low level programming language then a Mostek 6502 is a microprocessor' becomes $(A \vee C) \Rightarrow E$. Assumptions (1), (3) and (5) above give A, C and E as true. Hence we have

A	C	$A \vee C$	$(A \vee C) \Rightarrow E$
T	T	T	T

so the statement is true.

   (c) 'If C is not a systems programming language and a PDP-11 is not a minicomputer then either a Mostek 6502 is not a microprocessor or C is a systems programming language' becomes $(\sim B \wedge \sim D) \Rightarrow (\sim E \vee B)$. Assumptions (2), (4) and (5) above give B, D and E as true. Hence we have

B	D	E	$\sim$B	$\sim$D	$\sim$B$\wedge\sim$D	$\sim$E	$\sim$E$\vee$B	$(\sim$B$\wedge\sim$D$)\Rightarrow(\sim$E$\vee$B$)$
T	T	T	F	F	F	F	T	T

so the statement is true.

(d) 'Pascal is a high level programming language iff a PDP-11 is a minicomputer and C is a systems programming language' becomes $A \Leftrightarrow (D \wedge B)$. Assumptions (1), (2) and (4) above give A, B, D to be true. Hence we have

A	$D \wedge B$	$A \Leftrightarrow (D \wedge B)$
T	T	T

so this statement is true.

Hence all the statements given are true, on the given assumptions.

Analysis of Consistency

We can also use truth table techniques to analyse a set of composite statements for consistency and other properties. The set of statements (propositions) $A_1, A_2, A_3, \ldots, A_n$ are consistent with one another if their conjunction $A_1 \wedge A_2 \wedge A_3 \wedge \ldots \wedge A_n$ is a consistent statement (proposition).

Example 1.5

Three boys, Adam, Brian and Claude, are caught, suspected of breaking the glass in a greenhouse.

> Adam says: 'Brian did it; Claude is innocent'.
> Brian says: 'If Adam is guilty then so is Claude'.
> Claude says: 'I didn't do it; one of the others did'.

Are the statements consistent? Assuming that everyone is innocent, who told lies? Assuming that everyone's statement is true, who is innocent and who is guilty?

Solution. The three statements can be rewritten

$$S_A \equiv \sim B \wedge C$$
$$S_B \equiv \sim A \Rightarrow \sim C$$
$$S_C \equiv C \wedge (\sim B \vee \sim A)$$

where A stands for 'Adam is innocent.', B stands for 'Brian is innocent.' and C stands for 'Claude is innocent.'.

To answer the first question we need to draw the truth table for the conjunction of the three statements.

A	B	C	S_A	S_B	S_C	$S_A \wedge S_B \wedge S_C$
F	F	F	F	T	F	F
F	F	T	T	F	T	F
F	T	F	F	T	F	F
F	T	T	F	F	T	F
T	F	F	F	T	F	F
T	F	T	T	T	T	T
T	T	F	F	T	F	F
T	T	T	F	T	F	F

Statements

Since there is at least one T in the final column, in this case precisely one (in row 6), the statements are consistent, i.e. there is a set of values for A, B and C such that all the boys' statements are true.

The answer to the second question is given in the final row of the truth table. If all the boys are innocent, which is represented by A, B and C all being true, then statements S_A and S_B are false, i.e. Adam and Claude told lies.

The answer to the final question is given by row 6 of the truth table, which is the only row where all the statements are true. For this row the values of A, B and C give Adam and Claude as innocent and Brian as guilty.

Solving this type of problem by means of truth tables is only realistic for small problems; otherwise, the size of the truth table makes this method impractical. For these larger problems deductive reasoning techniques as described later in this chapter are more suitable.

General Results of the Truth-Functional System

Using the definitions of the preceding sections, we are now in a position to establish a number of important general results concerning the truth-functional formulation of the propositional calculus. Before presenting these results we establish some convenient terminological and notational conventions and a few elementary consequences of earlier definitions.

If the proposition A is a tautology we can write $\models A$. (Note that $\models$, like $\equiv$, is *not* a connective in the propositional calculus but is just shorthand notation.) Some further definitions and observations are as follows.

(1) A *primitive truth table* is a truth table constructed exclusively in terms of basic propositions. For example, the truth table of Fig. 1.12 is a basic truth table whilst those of Figs 1.5–1.9 are not.

(2) We say that propositions A and B have the same truth table if, in a suitable primitive truth table, the columns for A and B are identical, i.e. for any row either both columns contain T or both contain F.

(3) For a given assignment of truth values to the relevant basic propositions, the proposition $A \Leftrightarrow B$ has the value T iff A and B have the same truth value. Equivalently, in any given row of a primitive truth table for $A \Leftrightarrow B$, the entry for $A \Leftrightarrow B$ is T iff the entries for A and for B are both T or both F. This is evident from the table defining the connective $\Leftrightarrow$ (Fig. 1.9).

(4) The propositions A and B are logically equivalent iff they have the same truth table. This follows from the previous observation and the definition of logical equivalence.

(5) The relationship of logical equivalence is *reflexive, symmetric* and *transitive*, i.e. it is an *equivalence relation*, in the mathematical sense. Specifically,

(a) any proposition A is logically equivalent to itself,

(b) if A is logically equivalent to B, then B is logically equivalent to A and

(c) if A is logically equivalent to B, and B is logically equivalent to C, then A is logically equivalent to C.

The Principle of Structural Induction

Suppose we are given a general statement concerning some arbitrary proposition A, which we shall call $S(A)$. The *principle of structural induction* states that in order to prove that statement $S(A)$ is true for every proposition A it is sufficient to prove the following pair of statements (in steps).

(1) *Basis step*. When A is an arbitrary basic proposition, e.g. $A \equiv A$, $S(A)$ is true.

(2) *Induction step*. Given arbitrary propositions B and C, and assuming that $S(B)$ and $S(C)$ are true, then each of the statements $S(\sim B)$, $S(B \wedge C)$,

$S(B \vee C)$, $S(B \Rightarrow C)$ and $S(B \Leftrightarrow C)$ is true also. The assumption that $S(B)$ and $S(C)$ are true is called the *induction hypothesis*.

The validity of this principle is implicit in the syntax rules for propositions given in an earlier section.

If we are considering propositions A constructed using only a limited set of connectives, then the list of statements to be proved in the induction step can be correspondingly reduced. For example, if A is constructed using only the connectives $\sim$, $\wedge$ and $\vee$ then we need only prove $S(\sim B)$, $S(B \wedge C)$ and $S(B \vee C)$ in the induction step. It is quite easy to see informally why this is so; we leave it as an exercise for the reader.

Readers familiar with basic mathematical techniques may recognize a strong similarity between the principle of structural induction and the principle of mathematical induction.

Using these definitions and observations we now proceed to establish some general results.

Theorem 1.1 (Substitution rule)

Let A be a proposition constructed from basic propositions A_1, $A_2, \ldots, A_n$. Given an arbitrary list of propositions $A_1, A_2, \ldots, A_n$, let A^* be the proposition derived from A by substituting an occurrence of A_i for each occurrence in A of the corresponding A_i. Then if A is a tautology, A^* is also a tautology, i.e. $\models A$ implies $\models A^*$.

Proof. Consider an arbitrary row l^* in a primitive truth table for A^*. Suppose that for this row each proposition A_i has the truth value v_i. Similarly, in the basic truth table for A, let l be the row for which each basic proposition A_i has the truth value v_i. Since the construction of A^* in terms of the propositions A_i is identical with the construction of A in terms of the basic proposition A_i, the whole of row l^* must be a copy of row l. Hence the entry in row l^* for A^* is the same as that in row l for A, which is T since $\models A$. This argument can be applied to every row of the primitive truth table for A^*, showing that every entry in the column for A^* in this table is T, hence $\models A^*$.

Theorem 1.2 (Replacement rule)

Let C_A be a proposition containing a specified occurrence of the proposition A. Let C_B be the proposition obtained by replacing that occurrence of A by some proposition B. Then we have the following.

(1) If A is logically equivalent to B, then C_A is logically equivalent to C_B.
(2) If A is logically equivalent to B and C_A is a tautology, then C_B is also a tautology (i.e. $|= A \Leftrightarrow B$ implies that $|= C_A \Leftrightarrow C_B$, and $|= A \Leftrightarrow B$ and $|= C_A$ imply that $|= C_B$).

Proof
(1) Let $\mathbf{Z}$ be the set of basic propositions used in the construction of C_A, excluding those which occur in the construction of A alone. Evidently $\mathbf{Z}$ is also the set of basic propositions used in the construction of C_B excluding those used only in constructing proposition B. Consider now a primitive truth table with columns for both C_A and C_B (and hence A and B also); let l be an arbitrary row in this table. Evidently row l includes a sequence of entries, S_A say, reflecting the construction of C_A from A and $\mathbf{Z}$ and also a corresponding sequence of entries, S_B say, reflecting the construction of C_B from B and $\mathbf{Z}$. Since the propositions in $\mathbf{Z}$ are common in both cases, the two sequences S_A and S_B can only differ if the entries for A and B differ in that row of the table. However, this is impossible because A and B are logically equivalent and hence have the same truth table. Hence S_A and S_B are identical and in particular C_A and C_B have the same entry in row l. Application of this argument to every row of the truth table shows that C_A and C_B are logically equivalent.
(2) By the proof above and the logical equivalence of A and B we have the logical equivalence of C_A and C_B. Since C_A is a tautology, C_B must be a tautology also.

Theorem 1.3 (Possible negation and De Morgan's laws)

For arbitrary propositions A, B we have
(1) $|= A \Leftrightarrow \sim \sim A$
(2) $|= \sim (A \wedge B) \Leftrightarrow (\sim A \vee \sim B)$
(3) $|= \sim (A \vee B) \Leftrightarrow (\sim A \wedge \sim B)$

Proof. The truth tables in Figs 1.15–1.17 establish the corresponding results with the basic propositions A, B and C. For the arbitrary propositions A, B, C, Theorem 1.1, with A, B and C substituted for A, B and C, gives the required results.

Theorem 1.4 (Generalized De Morgan's law)

For an arbitrary proposition A constructed using only the connectives $\sim$,

A	$\sim$A	$\sim\sim$A
F	T	F
T	F	T

Fig. 1.15. Truth table showing the equivalence of A and $\sim\sim$A.

A	B	A$\wedge$B	$\sim$(A$\wedge$B)	$\sim$A	$\sim$B	($\sim$A $\vee$ $\sim$B)
F	F	F	T	T	T	T
F	T	F	T	T	F	T
T	F	F	T	F	T	T
T	T	T	F	F	F	F

Fig. 1.16. Truth table showing the equivalence of $\sim$(A $\wedge$ B) and ($\sim$A $\vee$ $\sim$B).

A	B	A$\vee$B	$\sim$(A$\vee$B)	$\sim$A	$\sim$B	($\sim$A $\wedge$ $\sim$B)
F	F	F	T	T	T	T
F	T	T	F	T	F	F
T	F	T	F	F	T	F
T	T	T	F	F	F	F

Fig. 1.17. Truth table showing the equivalence of $\sim$(A $\vee$ B) and ($\sim$A $\wedge$ $\sim$B).

$\wedge$ and $\vee$, let A^* be the proposition obtained by transforming A according to the following rules.

(1) Replace each occurrence of an unnegated basic proposition A_i in A with the proposition $\sim A_i$, and conversely replace each occurrence of $\sim A_i$ with A_i.

(2) Replace each occurrence of $\wedge$ in A with $\vee$ and conversely each occurrence of $\vee$ with $\wedge$.

So, for example, if $A \equiv (A \vee \sim B) \wedge \sim C$ then $A^* \equiv (\sim A \wedge B) \vee C$.

Then, for any such proposition A, the propositions $\sim A$ and A^* are logically equivalent (i.e. $\models \sim A \Leftrightarrow A^*$).

Proof. The proof uses the method of structural induction given previously. BASIS STEP: A is a basic proposition, say $A \equiv A_i$. Then $A^* \equiv \sim A_i$ (by rule (1)) and $\sim A \equiv \sim A_i$ (by definition) and hence $\sim A$ and A^* are logically equivalent.

INDUCTION STEP

Case (a): A ≡ ∼ B for an arbitrary proposition.

   Subcase (1): B is a basic proposition, say $B \equiv B_i$. Then we have $A^* \equiv B_i$ (by rule (1)) and $\sim A \equiv \sim \sim B_i$ (by definition) and so, by Theorem 1.3(1), $\sim A$ and A^* are equivalent.

   Subcase (2): B is not a basic proposition. Then $A^* \equiv \sim(B^*)$ (by definition of the transformation *). But by the induction hypothesis (equivalence of $\sim B$ and B^*) and Theorem 1.2(1) $\sim(B^*)$ is logically equivalent to $\sim \sim B$, i.e. A^* and $\sim \sim B$ are logically equivalent. Moreover, by definition of A, $\sim A \equiv \sim \sim B$ and hence $\sim A$ and A^* are again logically equivalent.

Case (b): A ≡ B ∧ C for arbitrary propositions *B* and *C*. Then $A^* \equiv B^* \vee C^*$ (by definition of *) and so A^* and $(\sim B \vee \sim C)$ are logically equivalent (by the induction hypothesis and Theorem 1.2(1)).
Hence A^* and $\sim(B \wedge C)$ are logically equivalent (by Theorem 1.3(2)). Moreover, $\sim A \equiv \sim(B \wedge C)$, and hence $\sim A$ and A^* are again logically equivalent.

Case (c): A ≡ B ∨ C for arbitrary propositions *B* and *C*. The proof is similar to case (b) except that Theorem 1.3(3) is used instead of 1.3(2). The details are left as an exercise for the reader.

This completes the proof by structural induction.

Theorem 1.5 (Duality)

Let *A* be an arbitrary proposition constructed using only the connectives $\sim$, $\wedge$ and $\vee$. Let A^D (the *dual* of *A*) be the proposition obtained by transforming *A* according to the following rule.

   Replace each occurrence of $\wedge$ in *A* by $\vee$, and each occurrence of $\vee$ by $\wedge$. Then for any such proposition *A*, $\sim A$ is a tautology iff A^D is a tautology, i.e. $\models \sim A$ iff $\models A^D$.

Proof. For an arbitrary proposition *A*, let *A†* be the proposition obtained from *A* by replacing each occurrence of a basic proposition A_i with $\sim A_i$. Let A^* be the proposition obtained from *A* by transforming it as specified in Theorem 1.4. By *A†** we mean $(A†)^*$. It is evident from the definitions of the transformations †, * and ^{D} that, for any proposition *A*, we have

$$A†^* \equiv A^D$$

(1) *Proof that* $|= \sim A$ *only if* $|= A^D$. Assume that $|= \sim A$. Then $|=(\sim A)\dagger$, i.e. $|= \sim(A\dagger)$, by Theorem 1.1. Then $|= A\dagger*$ by Theorems 1.4 and 1.2(2), i.e. $|= A^D$, by the identity above. Hence $|= \sim A$ only if $|= A^D$.

(2) *Proof that* $|= \sim A$ *if* $|= A^D$. Assume that $|= A^D$, i.e. $|= A\dagger*$, by the identity above. Then $|= \sim(A\dagger)$, by Theorems 1.4 and 1.2(2). Then $|= \sim(A\dagger)\dagger$, i.e. $|= \sim(A\dagger\dagger)$, by Theorem 1.1. Then $|= \sim A$, by Theorem 1.3(1) and repeated application of Theorem 1.2(2). Hence $|= \sim A$ if $|= A^D$.

Taking both proofs together gives $|= \sim A$ iff $|= A^D$, as required.

Theorem 1.6 (Modus ponens)

For arbitrary propositions A and B, if A is a tautology and if A logically implies B, then B is a tautology also, i.e. if $|= A$ and $|= A \Rightarrow B$ then $|= B$.

Proof. Consider an arbitrary row l in a primitive truth table for $A \Rightarrow B$. Since $|= A$, A has the value T in this row. From the truth table for implication (Fig. 1.8) the propositions B and $A \Rightarrow B$ must have the same value for this row of the truth table. Moreover, $|= A \Rightarrow B$, so both $A \Rightarrow B$ and B must have the value T for this row of the truth table. Applying a similar argument to each row shows that each entry for B is T, i.e. $|= B$.

Theorem 1.7 (Disjunctive normal form)

Given a list, $A_1, A_2, A_3, \ldots, A_n$ of n basic propositions and an arbitrary truth function $F(A_1, A_2, \ldots, A_n)$ of these propositions, there is a proposition D_F, involving only the propositions $A_1, A_2, \ldots, A_n$ and the connectives $\sim$, $\wedge$ and $\vee$, such that D_F and $F(A_1, A_2, \ldots, A_n)$ are logically equivalent, i.e. $|= D_F \Leftrightarrow F(A_1, A_2, \ldots, A_n)$.

Proof. Consider a primitive truth table containing a column representing the values of $F(A_1, A_2, \ldots, A_n)$ for all possible combinations of truth values for the basic propositions $A_1, A_2, \ldots, A_n$. This table will have 2^n rows. Let $m = 2^n$.

For each row l $(1 \leqslant l \leqslant m)$, define the formula C_l to be the conjunction

$$C_l = A_{l1} \wedge A_{l2} \wedge \ldots \wedge A_{ln}$$

where we define (for $1 \leqslant k \leqslant n$)

$$A_{lk} \equiv A_k \text{ if } A_k \text{ has the value T in row } l$$
$$A_{lk} \equiv \sim A_k \text{ if } A_k \text{ has the value F in row } l$$

Then, from these definitions and the definition of the connectives $\wedge$ and $\sim$, it is evident that each C_l has the value T in row l and F in every other row. Let $l_1, l_2, \ldots, l_p$ be the list of *all* those rows of the table for which $F(A_1, A_2, \ldots, A_n)$ has the value T. Then we define the proposition D_F by the following:

$$D_F \equiv A_1 \wedge \sim A_1 \qquad \text{if } p = 0$$
$$D_F \equiv C_{l_1} \vee C_{l_2} \vee \ldots \vee C_{l_p} \quad \text{if } p \geq 1$$

Now we show that D_F and $F(A_1, A_2, \ldots, A_n)$ are logically equivalent.

Case (1): $p = 0$.
$F(A_1, A_2, \ldots, A_n)$ has the value F in every row of the truth table. Moreover, a simple truth table shows that $D_F \equiv A_1 \wedge \sim A_1$ also has the value F in every row.

Case (2): $p \geq 1$.
We consider an arbitrary row l of the truth table.
    Subcase (a): $F(A_1, A_2, \ldots, A_n)$ has the value T in row l. Then l is included in the list $l_1, l_2, \ldots, l_p$ and hence D_F has the form $D_F \equiv \ldots \vee C_l \vee \ldots$. Our earlier remarks established that C_l has the value T in row l and hence, by the definition of $\vee$, D_F also has the value T in row l.
    Subcase (b): $F(A_1, A_2, \ldots, A_n)$ has the value F in row l. Then l is not included in the list $l_1, l_2, \ldots, l_p$ and hence by our earlier remarks each disjunct C_{l_i} included in D_F has the value F in row l and so, by the definition of $\vee$, D_F also has the value F in row l.

This argument can be applied to every row of the truth table showing that D_F and $F(A_1, A_2, \ldots, A_n)$ have the same value for every row. Hence D_F and $F(A_1, A_2, \ldots, A_n)$ are logically equivalent and evidently D_F has the required form, i.e. it is a disjunction (or) of a set of conjunctions and this form is called *disjunctive normal form*.

Using a similar argument it can be shown that there is an equivalent form called *conjunctive normal form* which is the conjunction of one or more disjunctions in the propositions A_i, $\sim A_i$. The proof is similar to that given above and is left as an exercise for the reader.

These results show that every truth function can be expressed by an equivalent proposition involving only the connectives $\sim$, $\wedge$ and $\vee$.

Theorem 1.8 (Adequate sets of connectives)

Every truth function can be generated using just the connectives $\sim$ and $\wedge$, or $\sim$ and $\vee$, or $\sim$ and $\Rightarrow$.

Proof. First we observe that, by Theorems 1.3(3) and 1.2(1) (twice), we have the equivalence of $\sim\sim(A\vee B)$ and $\sim(\sim A\wedge\sim B)$, and hence by Theorems 1.3(1) and 1.2(1) again we have the equivalence of $A\vee B$ and $\sim(\sim A\wedge\sim B)$. Now Theorem 1.7 shows that any truth function can be expressed by a proposition, P say, involving no connectives other than $\sim$, $\wedge$ and $\vee$. By repeated application of the equivalence just established in conjunction with Theorem 1.2 we can obtain a proposition equivalent to P, P_1 say, in which every occurrence of the connective $\vee$ is removed in favour of occurrences of $\sim$ and $\wedge$. Therefore P_1 generates the given truth function and contains no connectives other than $\sim$ and $\wedge$, as required.

Using Theorem 1.3(2) rather than Theorem 1.3(3), we can similarly establish the equivalence of $A\wedge B$ and $\sim(\sim A\vee\sim B)$. Applying this result in a similar way, we can obtain from P a proposition, P_2 say, which generates the original truth function and which contains no connectives other than $\sim$ and $\vee$.

The truth table in Fig. 1.18 together with Theorem 1.1 establishes the equivalence of $A\vee B$ and $(\sim A)\Rightarrow B$. Applying this result to P_2 in a manner

A	B	$\sim$A	$(\sim$A$)\Rightarrow$B	A$\vee$B
F	F	T	F	F
F	T	T	T	T
T	F	F	T	T
T	T	F	T	T

Fig. 1.18. Truth table showing the equivalence of $(\sim A)\Rightarrow B$ and A$\vee$B.

similar to the treatment of P in the previous two cases, we obtain a proposition, P_3 say, which generates the original truth function and which contains no connectives other than $\sim$ and $\Rightarrow$, thus completing the proof.

Referring to the truth tables of the binary connectives, there are two more which are of interest in connection with Theorem 1.8. These are joint denial, $\downarrow$, which is shown in Fig. 1.11(e), and alternative denial, $|$, which is shown in Fig. 1.11(o).

Joint denial $\downarrow$, which is also known as nor (not or), is the name of the binary connective which gives a true value only when both of its operand propositions are false. From this the following tautologies can be established:

$$\models\;\sim A\Leftrightarrow A\downarrow A$$
$$\models A\wedge B\Leftrightarrow((A\downarrow A)\downarrow(B\downarrow B))$$

These equivalences show that the ↓ connective alone is sufficient to generate any truth function.

Alternative denial, |, which is also known as nand (not and), is the binary connective which gives a true value when either or both of its constituent propositions are false. From this the following tautologies can be established:

$$|= \sim A \Leftrightarrow A|A$$
$$|= A \vee B \Leftrightarrow ((A|A)|(B|B))$$

This shows that the | connective is also sufficient by itself to generate any truth function.

Theorem 1.9 (Single adequate connectives)

The only binary connectives which are sufficient by themselves to generate all truth functions of two operands are ↓ and |.

Proof. If we assume that f(A, B) is a function which will generate any truth function, then f(T, T)=F and f(F, F)=T must hold for it to be possible to generate the ∼ connective.

There are four possible truth functions, shown in Fig. 1.19, which conform to this. Figure 1.19(a) represents ∼A and Fig. 1.19(c) represents ∼B. Since ∼ is a unary connective it is not sufficient by itself to reflect dependences on both A and B simultaneously, and hence alternative denial (Fig. 1.19(b)) and joint denial (Fig. 1.19(d)) are the only binary connectives which could possibly be sufficient to generate any truth function. Since we have already established their sufficiency above, this completes the proof.

A	B	f(A,B)
F	F	T
F	T	T
T	F	F
T	T	F
	(a)	

A	B	f(A,B)
F	F	T
F	T	T
T	F	T
T	T	F
	(b)	

A	B	f(A,B)
F	F	T
F	T	F
T	F	T
T	T	F
	(c)	

A	B	f(A,B)
F	F	T
F	T	F
T	F	F
T	T	F
	(d)	

Fig. 1.19. Truth tables for functions f with f(T, T)=F and f(F, F)=T.

Chapter 1

Formal Theories: The Deductive Approach

So far we have worked with a truth-functional formulation, or model, of the propositional calculus. We now consider an alternative approach—the deductive approach—to the study of the propositional calculus. In this approach we locate our propositions in the context of a *formal theory* which provides formalisms for the notions of *proof* and *theorem*. The intention is that the notion of a theorem should play the same role in this approach as the notion of a tautology played in the truth-functional approach. Thus we have an alternative approach which we can use when the truth-functional method seems unwieldy.

A *formal theory* is characterized by the following three components.
(1) The *syntax rules* of the theory, which define the permissible constructs of the theory (propositions in this case).
(2) A set of constructs (propositions) which form the *axioms* of the theory. If it can be decided whether a proposition is or is not an axiom then the theory is said to be an *axiomatic theory*.
(3) A (finite) set of *rules of inference* for the theory. Each such rule R specifies the circumstances in which the relation of *direct consequence* can hold between some fixed number of formulae and another formula.

Given this framework we can then define the notions of *proof*, *theorem* and *valid consequence* within a formal theory.

A *proof* of B in the theory is a sequence of one or more propositions

$$C_1, C_2, \ldots, C_l$$

with $C_l \equiv B$, such that each formula C_i in the sequence satisfies one or other of the following two conditions:
(a) C_i is an axiom;
(b) C_i is a direct consequence (according to some rule of inference) of an appropriate number of propositions $C_m, \ldots, C_p$, each of which occurs *earlier* in the sequence.

A *theorem* of the theory is a proposition for which there is a proof. If it is possible to decide by some mechanical procedure whether or not any given proposition A is a theorem, the theory is said to be *decidable*. We write $\vdash A$ if the proposition A is a theorem.

We say that a proposition B is a (*valid*) *consequence* of a list of *assumption* propositions $A_1, A_2, \ldots, A_k$ if there is a list of propositions

$$C_1, C_2, \ldots, C_l$$

with $C_1 \equiv B$, such that each proposition C_i in the sequence satisfies one of the following three conditions:

(a) C_i is an axiom;

(b) $C_i \equiv A_j$ for one of the assumptions A_j;

(c) C_i is a direct consequence of propositions $C_m, \ldots, C_p$ occurring *earlier* in the sequence.

Such a sequence is called a *deduction* of B from the formulae $A_1, A_2, \ldots, A_k$ and we write $A_1, A_2, \ldots, A_k \vdash B$. Thus finding a deduction is equivalent to finding a proof in a theory whose axioms have been extended with the specified assumptions. In the case where the list of assumptions is empty, the notions of deduction and consequence reduce to those of proof and theorem.

We can best see how these definitions operate in practice by applying them to the propositional calculus, which we shall do in the rest of this chapter. The propositional calculus is characterized as follows.

(1) The *syntax rules* of the theory are those already specified at the beginning of this chapter, with the proviso that we shall henceforth limit ourselves to the propositional connectives $\sim$ and $\Rightarrow$. Theorem 1.8 suggests that we can avoid any sacrifice of expressive power due to this restriction if we define the connectives $\wedge$, $\vee$ and $\Leftrightarrow$ as follows:

$$A \wedge B \equiv \sim (A \Rightarrow \sim B)$$
$$A \vee B \equiv \sim A \Rightarrow B$$
$$A \Leftrightarrow B \equiv (A \Rightarrow B) \wedge (B \Rightarrow A)$$

(2) The axioms of the theory are all those propositions conforming to one of the following three *axiom schemata*:

(A1) $A \Rightarrow (B \Rightarrow A)$

(A2) $(A \Rightarrow (B \Rightarrow C)) \Rightarrow ((A \Rightarrow B) \Rightarrow (A \Rightarrow C))$

(A3) $(\sim B \Rightarrow \sim A) \Rightarrow ((\sim B \Rightarrow A) \Rightarrow B)$

By saying that each of the above is an axiom schema we mean that any proposition of the specified form is an axiom. Hence the following propositions are all axioms according to schema (A1):

$$A \Rightarrow (B \Rightarrow A)$$
$$A \Rightarrow ((B \Rightarrow \sim B) \Rightarrow A)$$
$$\sim A \Rightarrow ((\sim B \Rightarrow B) \Rightarrow \sim A)$$
$$(A \Rightarrow B) \Rightarrow (\sim C \Rightarrow (A \Rightarrow B))$$

(3) There is just one *rule of inference* which is called *modus ponens* (MP).

This is analagous to Theorem 1.6 and states that, for any propositions A and B, the proposition B is a direct consequence of the two propositions A and $A \Rightarrow B$.

We now develop two simple proofs in this theory.

Example 1.6

Show that $\mid\!-A \Rightarrow A$ for any proposition A.

Proof

(1) $(A \Rightarrow ((A \Rightarrow A) \Rightarrow A)) \Rightarrow ((A \Rightarrow (A \Rightarrow A)) \Rightarrow (A \Rightarrow A))$	by axiom schema (A2)
(2) $A \Rightarrow ((A \Rightarrow A) \Rightarrow A)$	by axiom schema (A1)
(3) $(A \Rightarrow (A \Rightarrow A)) \Rightarrow (A \Rightarrow A)$	by rule MP with (2), (1)
(4) $A \Rightarrow (A \Rightarrow A)$	by axiom schema (A1)
(5) $A \Rightarrow A$	by rule MP with (4), (3)

Example 1.7

Show that $\mid\!-(\sim B \Rightarrow B) \Rightarrow B$ for any proposition B.

Proof

(1) $(\sim B \Rightarrow ((\sim B \Rightarrow \sim B) \Rightarrow \sim B)) \Rightarrow ((\sim B \Rightarrow (\sim B \Rightarrow \sim B)) \Rightarrow (\sim B \Rightarrow \sim B))$
                                                      by axiom schema (A2)

(2) $\sim B \Rightarrow ((\sim B \Rightarrow \sim B) \Rightarrow \sim B)$	by axiom schema (A1)
(3) $(\sim B \Rightarrow (\sim B \Rightarrow \sim B)) \Rightarrow (\sim B \Rightarrow \sim B)$	by rule MP with (2), (1)
(4) $\sim B \Rightarrow (\sim B \Rightarrow \sim B)$	by axiom schema (A1)
(5) $\sim B \Rightarrow \sim B$	by rule MP with (4), (3)
(6) $(\sim B \Rightarrow \sim B) \Rightarrow ((\sim B \Rightarrow B) \Rightarrow B)$	by axiom schema (A3)
(7) $(\sim B \Rightarrow B) \Rightarrow B$	by rule MP with (5), (6)

By using the result of Example 1.6 this proof could be shortened to the final three steps.

Before proceeding to establish some important general results about our formal system in the following section, let us pause to observe some distinctive features of our formal notions of proof and theorem. Firstly, it is apparent that the notion of proof in a formal system does not conform very closely to our informal conception of a proof as an 'intuitively convincing demonstration'; given the proofs above, most readers would regard the conclusions on their own as a good deal more convincing and obvious than the 'proofs' which are intended to establish them. However, for the logician, the formal notion of proof has the advantage that it is both rigorously defined and mechanically checkable in any given case.

   It is important to observe that there is an essential distinction between a theorem *in* the formal theory and the familiar notion of a theorem as a general result *about* the formal theory. We have used the term theorem in the latter sense in the present section and will continue to do so in the following sections, although in more technical works the distinct term *metatheorem* is used for this latter sense. Which of the two meanings is intended in any particular case is usually obvious from the context.

General Results about the Formal Theory

Using the axiom schemata and rules of inference defined previously for the propositional calculus we can prove some general results about our formal system.

Theorem 1.10 (Deduction theorem)

If, for arbitrary propositions $A_1, A_2, \ldots, A_m$ and B, we have $A_1, A_2, \ldots, A_{m-1}, A_m \vdash B$, then also $A_1, A_2, \ldots, A_{m-1} \vdash A_m \Rightarrow B$ and, in particular, if $A \vdash B$ then $\vdash A \Rightarrow B$.

Proof. Since $A_1, A_2, \ldots, A_{m-1}, A_m \vdash B$, there is a sequence of propositions

$$C_1, C_2, \ldots, C_n \equiv B$$

which is a deduction of B from $A_1, A_2, \ldots, A_{m-1}, A_m$. We show how this sequence can be expanded and modified by replacing each successive proposition C_i with a sequence of propositions

$$S_i \equiv D_{i'}, D_{i'+1}, \ldots, D_{i'+x_i}$$

such that $D_{i'+x_i} \equiv (A_m \Rightarrow C_i)$ and such that the new sequence of propositions (formed by concatenating the sequences $S_1, S_2, S_3, \ldots, S_n$) constitutes a deduction of its final proposition $D_{n'+x_n} \equiv (A_m \Rightarrow C_n) \equiv (A_m \Rightarrow B)$ from the (reduced list of) assumptions $A_1, A_2, \ldots, A_{m-1}$. For each i, the sequence S_i depends on the grounds of inclusion of the corresponding proposition C_i in the original deduction. Together with the specification of S_i in each case, we present its *analysis*, i.e. the grounds of inclusion of each proposition of S_i in the *new* deduction.

Case (a): C_i is an axiom.

Then the sequence S_i contains three propositions:

(i')	C_i	axiom
$(i'+1)$	$C_i{\Rightarrow}(A_m{\Rightarrow}C_i)$	axiom schema (A1)
$(i'+2)$	$A_m{\Rightarrow}C_i$	MP with (i'), $(i'+1)$

Case (b): $C_i \equiv A_j$ for one of the assumptions A_j $(1 \leqslant j \leqslant m)$.

Subcase (1): $j < m$. Therefore $C_i \equiv (A_j)$ is still an assumption for the new deduction. Then the sequence S_i is just as in case (a) above except that the grounds of inclusion of line (i') is 'assumption' rather than 'axiom'.

Subcase (2): $j = m$. Therefore $C_i \equiv A_m$ is not an assumption for the new deduction. Then S_i consists of five lines, with analysis, copied directly from the proof of $|{-}A{\Rightarrow}A$ given in Example 1.6 except that A is replaced by $A_m ({\equiv} C_i)$ throughout, and thus the final line is

$(i'+4)\ A_m{\Rightarrow}C_i$

as required.

Subcase (3): C_i is a direct consequence by MP of (earlier) propositions C_j, C_k, with $j, k < i$. Then either $C_k \equiv (C_j{\Rightarrow}C_i)$ or $C_j \equiv (C_k{\Rightarrow}C_i)$ (by MP). We need only consider the former case since the latter can be converted to it by a simple renaming of indices j and k. Since $j, k < i$, the revised sequence of propositions must already include the two lines

$(j'+x_j)\ A_m{\Rightarrow}C_j$

.

.

.

$(k'+x_k)\ A_m{\Rightarrow}(C_j{\Rightarrow}C_i)$

with both $j'+x_j$, $k'+x_k < i'$. Then we can define the sequence S_i of three lines:

(i')	$(A_m{\Rightarrow}(C_j{\Rightarrow}C_i)){\Rightarrow}((A_m{\Rightarrow}C_j){\Rightarrow}(A_m{\Rightarrow}C_i))$	axiom schema (A2)
$(i'+1)$	$(A_m{\Rightarrow}C_j){\Rightarrow}(A_m{\Rightarrow}C_i)$	MP with $(k'+x_k)$, (i')
$(i'+2)$	$A_m{\Rightarrow}C_i$	MP with $(j'+x_j)$, $(i'+1)$

From the analysis given in each of the above cases it is apparent that the new sequence of propositions

$$D_{1'}, \ldots, D_{1'+x_1}, D_{2'}, \ldots, D_{2'+x_2}, \ldots, D_{n'}, \ldots, D_{n'+x_n}$$

is a deduction of $D_{n'+x_n} \equiv (A_m{\Rightarrow}B)$ from assumption propositions $A_1, A_2,$ $\ldots, A_{m-1}$, as required.

The remaining results in this section show the 'equivalence' between the truth-functional and formal-theoretic interpretations of the propositional calculus. Although they are not particularly difficult to follow, the proofs of these results are fairly lengthy and so we omit them for reasons of space, referring the interested reader to any standard logic text (e.g. Kleene, 1967; Mendelson, 1979) for these proofs.

Theorem 1.11 (Consistency or Soundness)

Any proposition A is a (formal) theorem only if it is a tautology, i.e. $\vdash A$ only if $\models A$. (In other words, the formal theory for the propositional calculus is consistent with respect to the truth-functional notion of a tautology. A proposition can be formally proved only if it is also a tautology.)

Theorem 1.12 (Completeness)

Any proposition A is a (formal) theorem if it is a tautology, i.e. $\vdash A$ if $\models A$. (In other words, the formal theory is complete with respect to the tautologies of the truth-functional formulation. Thus every proposition which is a tautology can also be proved in the formal system.)

Theorem 1.13 (Equivalence)

Any proposition A is a (formal) theorem iff it is a tautology, i.e. $\vdash A$ iff $\models A$. (In other words, the notions of formal theorem and tautology both characterize the same set of propositions, although the meanings of the two notions are quite distinct.)

Proof. Conjunction of the results of Theorems 1.11 and 1.12.

This last result is a major landmark in the history of formal logic and it has some practical significance for us also, for it assures us that any result (tautology or theorem) obtained by either the truth-functional or the deductive approach is equally valid by the criteria of the other approach. Hence the results of one approach can be carried over to the other. Thus we have two independent but mutually consistent routes to the notion of *logical truth*, since we can safely identify this notion with both of the notions *tautology* and *formal theorem*.

Applications of the Formal Theory

In the final section of this chapter we consider, with examples, some techniques which facilitate the process of establishing new results (theorems and consequence relations) in the formal theory presented in the previous section. Although techniques of this sort can be formalized into a *natural deduction system*, we shall confine ourselves here to an informal treatment. In what follows we shall write $A_1, \ldots, A_m \vdash B_1, \ldots, B_n$ as an abbreviation for the n assertions

$$A_1, \ldots, A_m \vdash B_1$$

$$\cdot$$
$$\cdot$$
$$\cdot$$

$$A_1, \ldots, A_m \vdash B_n$$

We make the following observations in relation to the formal theory for the propositional calculus; they can be seen as useful rules. They are all straightforward consequences of the definitions and results of the previous section; we leave the proofs of most of them as a simple exercise for the reader.

(1) $A \vdash A$ (by a trivial one-line proof).

(2) Introduction of redundant assumptions: If $A_1, \ldots, A_{m-1} \vdash B$, then also $A_1, \ldots, A_{m-1}, A_m \vdash B$, for arbitrary A_m.

(3) Reordering of assumptions: The list of assumptions in a deduction can be reordered without compromising the validity of that deduction.

(4) Concatenation of deductions: If both $A_1, \ldots, A_m \vdash B_1, \ldots, B_n$ and $B_1, \ldots, B_n \vdash C_1, \ldots, C_p$, then also $A_1, \ldots, A_m \vdash C_1, \ldots, C_p$.

(5) Elimination of proven assumptions: If both $A_1, \ldots, A_{m-1}, A_m \vdash B$ and $A_1, \ldots, A_{m-1} \vdash A_m$, then also $A_1, \ldots, A_{m-1} \vdash B$. (This follows from rules (1) and (4).)

(6) Finally we remind ourselves that, by the deduction theorem (Theorem 1.10), we can always proceed from $A_1, \ldots, A_{m-1}, A_m \vdash B$ to $A_1, \ldots, A_{m-1} \vdash A_m \Rightarrow B$; conversely, by the rule of inference MP—together with rules (1), (2) and (4)—we can always proceed from $A_1, \ldots, A_{m-1} \vdash A_m \Rightarrow B$ to $A_1, \ldots, A_{m-1}, A_m \vdash B$.

(Any mention in the above rules of a consequence relation, such as $A_1, \ldots, A_m \vdash B$, is intended—if this is permitted by the context—to include the limiting case of a theorem such as $\vdash B$, i.e. the case where $m = 0$.)

It must be emphasized that when rules such as the above are applied to establish a new result (theorem or consequence relation) of the formal theory on the basis of previously established results we are *not*, in the formal sense, *proving* the new result; rather, we are proving, in the ordinary informal mathematical sense, that a proof, in the formal sense, *can* be constructed. In practice, it is usually a lengthy and tedious business to construct a formal proof on the basis of the informal proof, even if various obvious short-cuts are exploited, which fact serves to emphasize the merits of the informal techniques. As an example, it is a simple matter, by means of two applications of the rule MP followed by a reordering of assumptions and two applications of the deduction theorem, to show informally that $A \Rightarrow (B \Rightarrow C) \vdash B \Rightarrow (A \Rightarrow C)$. The reader may find it instructive, however, to construct a formal deduction for this result employing the techniques used in the proof of the deduction theorem.

We conclude with some examples illustrating the application of these informal methods, including their deployment in checking the validity of arguments presented in natural language. We sometimes employ rules (1)–(6) above without explicitly mentioning them; the reader should attempt to recognize such occasions as they occur. We also use the following abbreviations: Ax.A1 etc. for axiom schema (A1), MP for rule MP and Ded.Thm. for deduction theorem.

Example 1.8

Show that $\sim \sim A \vdash A$.

Solution. Ax.A3 with two applications of MP gives $\sim A \Rightarrow \sim A$, $\sim A \Rightarrow \sim \sim A \vdash A$; hence, using the result of Example 1.6 $\sim A \Rightarrow \sim \sim A \vdash A$. Ax.A1, with an application of MP, gives $\sim \sim A \vdash \sim A \Rightarrow \sim \sim A$. Hence, concatenating these two results, $\sim \sim A \vdash A$, as required.

Example 1.9

Examine the validity of the following argument:

> 'I will pay the garage provided that the repair work is successful. My car still does not work. Therefore, I will not pay.'

Solution. If we define propositions P and R by

> P ≡ 'I will pay the garage.'
> R ≡ 'The repair work is successful.'

then the sense of the argument above is conveyed formally by

$$P \Rightarrow R, \ \sim R \vdash \sim P$$

Let us try to establish this assertion in a general form. By Example 1.8 we have $A \Rightarrow B, \ \sim \sim A \vdash A \Rightarrow B, A$, and, by an application of MP, $A \Rightarrow B, A \vdash B$. Concatenating these results gives, with Ded.Thm., $A \Rightarrow B \vdash \sim \sim A \Rightarrow B$; by Ax.A1, with an application of MP, $\sim B \vdash \sim \sim \sim A \Rightarrow \sim B$. Combining these two results, we have $A \Rightarrow B, \ \sim B \vdash \sim \sim A \Rightarrow \sim B, \ \sim \sim A \Rightarrow B$; by Ax.A3, with two applications of MP, $\sim \sim A \Rightarrow \sim B, \ \sim \sim A \Rightarrow B \vdash \sim A$. Concatenating these two results, we have $A \Rightarrow B, \ \sim B \vdash \sim A$. Since $P \Rightarrow R, \ \sim R \vdash \sim P$ is a particular instance of this valid deduction $A \Rightarrow B, \ \sim B \vdash \sim A$, we conclude that the original argument is indeed valid.

Example 1.10

Evaluate the following argument:

'If this is August, last month was July. If last month was July then 6 months ago it was February. If 6 months ago it was February then 11 months ago it was September. If next month will be September then this is August. Last month was July. Therefore, this is August.'

Solution. We make the following translation into formal notation:

$S_{11} \equiv$ '11 months ago it was September.'
$S_1 \equiv$ 'Next month will be September.'
$A \equiv$ 'This is August.'
$J \equiv$ 'Last month was July.'
$F \equiv$ '6 months ago it was February.'

Then the formal translation of the argument above is

$$A \Rightarrow J, \ J \Rightarrow F, \ F \Rightarrow S_{11}, \ S_1 \Rightarrow A, \ J \vdash A$$

First we establish a useful general consequence relation. By an application of MP, $A \Rightarrow B, \ B \Rightarrow C, \ A \vdash B \Rightarrow C, B$, and by another application of MP, $B \Rightarrow C, \ B \vdash C$; concatenating these results, we have $A \Rightarrow B, \ B \Rightarrow C, \ A \vdash C$, and hence, by Ded.Thm., $A \Rightarrow B, \ B \Rightarrow C \vdash A \Rightarrow C$.

Applying this result, to the assumptions of the argument we are considering, we have

$$A \Rightarrow J, \ J \Rightarrow F, \ F \Rightarrow S_{11}, \ S_1 \Rightarrow A, \ J \vdash J \Rightarrow S_{11}, \ S_1 \Rightarrow A, \ J$$

and an application of MP gives

$$J \Rightarrow S_{11}, S_1 \Rightarrow A, J \vdash S_{11}, S_1 \Rightarrow A$$

so, by concatenation, we have

$$A \Rightarrow J, J \Rightarrow F, F \Rightarrow S_{11}, S_1 \Rightarrow A, J \vdash S_{11}, S_1 \Rightarrow A$$

which appears to be as far as we can proceed with the stated assumptions. However, we observe that an application of our earlier result, together with an application of MP, gives

$$S_{11}, S_1 \Rightarrow A, S_{11} \Rightarrow S_1 \vdash A$$

and so, by concatenation with the previous result, we have

$$S_{11} \Rightarrow S_1, A \Rightarrow J, J \Rightarrow F, F \Rightarrow S_{11}, S_1 \Rightarrow A, J \vdash A$$

which has the required conclusion but which employs the additional assumption $S_{11} \Rightarrow S_1$. Hence we conclude that, while the argument as originally stated is (as far as we can discover) not proven, it can be regarded as valid, given the additional assumption $S_{11} \Rightarrow S_1$, i.e. it is valid given the presupposition that, if 11 months ago it was September, then next month will also be September.

Exercises

1 Which of the numbered statements follow from the initial one in each group?
   (a) Children enjoy games but not computing.
      (1) No children enjoy games and computing.
      (2) Anyone who enjoys games and computing cannot be a child.
      (3) Children only enjoy games if they do not like computing.
   (b) The result of execution of the program is either 2 or 3.
      (1) Neither 2 nor 3 is the answer.
      (2) The answer is not 2 or not 3.
      (3) The answer is not 2 and it is not 3.
   (c) Computers are large and coloured blue.
      (1) Computers are large and computers are blue.
      (2) Computers are either large or blue.
      (3) Computers are large only if they are blue.

2 Translate the following sentences in English into symbolic notation using capital letters to stand for basic component statements.
  (a) Neither paper tape readers nor card readers are output devices.
  (b) If the electricity is turned off then the computer will not operate.
  (c) If my program is large and the computer's memory is small then I will not be able to run my program.
  (d) If and only if your computer is identical with mine will the result of running my program be identical on both machines.

3 John, Alan and Robert are considering going to a party. John says that he will go if Robert goes and Alan does not. Alan says that he will only go if both John and Robert attend. Robert asserts that he will go only if an even number of them go. Using truth table techniques
  (a) determine whether their statements are consistent,
  (b) determine who goes to the party,
  (c) assuming that John told lies, determine how this affects the situation.

4 Construct truth tables for the following propositions:
  (a) $A \lor (\sim A \land \sim B)$
  (b) $(A \lor B) \Rightarrow (A \land \sim B)$
  (c) $A \Rightarrow B \Rightarrow ((A \lor C) \Rightarrow (B \lor C))$

5 Determine a proposition P whose truth table is shown below:

A	B	C	P
F	F	F	T
F	F	T	T
F	T	F	F
F	T	T	F
T	F	F	T
T	F	T	F
T	T	F	T
T	T	T	T

6 John said that Jack and Jill never tell the truth. Jack said that if John told the truth Jill did not. Jill said that Jack only told the truth if John told lies. Are these statements compatible?

7 What conclusions can you draw from the following collection of statements?
  (a) I only use computers that can be programmed in C.
  (b) Microcomputers are always coloured orange.

(c) I use a terminal to talk to a computer.

(d) Computers coloured orange which can be programmed in C are microcomputers.

8 Assertions in computer programs are statements inserted by the programmer which must be true whenever their points of insertion are reached in execution. If, at the start of a piece of program, you wished to assert that the truth value of logical variable A must be true, that of logical variable B false and that of logical variable C true, write the required assertion in symbolic form.

9 Prove that $(\sim B \wedge (A \Rightarrow B)) \Rightarrow \sim A$ is logically true:
   (a) using truth table techniques;
   (b) using the formal theory defined in this chapter.

10 Prove that the pair of connectives $\Rightarrow$ and $\wedge$ are not sufficient to generate all truth functions.

11 'If and only if John's program executes without errors and his program is correct and it is given the correct data can he be pleased with the result. If the computer has failed then John's program will not execute without errors. In fact the computer has not failed. Therefore John is pleased with the results of his program.' Is this argument logically valid?

12 Using the formal theory defined in this chapter prove the following theorems:
   (a) $\sim \sim P \Rightarrow P$
   (b) $\sim P \Rightarrow (P \Rightarrow Q)$
   (c) $(\sim Q \Rightarrow \sim P) \Rightarrow (P \Rightarrow Q)$
   (d) $(Q \Rightarrow P) \Rightarrow (\sim P \Rightarrow \sim Q)$

Chapter 2

Logic and Digital Electronic Circuits

Boolean Algebra

The ideas of propositional calculus as outlined in Chapter 1 are very similar to those of Boolean algebra, which is an algebra over the alphabet 0 and 1. The similarities between them are very strong and the reader should recognize many of the results from Chapter 1 in a different form in this chapter.

Boolean algebra forms the basis for the analysis and design of digital electronic circuits. These circuits comprise components such as storage devices capable of storing representations of the binary digits 0 and 1, and logic elements which can perform simple processing on these values. Since computers comprise a large amount of digital electronics, Boolean algebra is one of the fundamentals of computer design. We consider the design and analysis of digital electronic circuits in this chapter purely from the logic point of view; details of the physical realization of such circuits are not considered.

In logic a statement is either true or false, which can be represented mathematically by 1 or 0 respectively. Many physical systems can be represented or modelled by two-state logic. For example, in an electrical system a light is ON or OFF and a switch is OPEN or CLOSED; the state of a computer is described by the set of binary digits stored in its memory.

The mathematics of two-state logic, now called Boolean algebra, was developed by the mathematician George Boole in the 1840s. It was then applied to switching circuits by Claude Shannon, an American mathematician, in the 1930s. He used two-element Boolean algebra since he was interested in networks of switches which could be in one of two states, ON or OFF.

Definitions

A *Boolean algebra* is a set of two elements, denoted 0 and 1, together with two operations + and . , called addition and multiplication, for which the following rules hold:

$$0+0=0$$
$$0+1=1+0=1$$
$$1+1=1$$

and

$$0.0=0$$
$$0.1=1.0=0$$
$$1.1=1$$

Notice that these rules are identical with those for propositional calculus if 1 and 0 are substituted for true and false together with $\wedge$ being substituted by . and $\vee$ substituted by $+$.

A *Boolean variable* is a symbol such as A, B or C, representing one of the values 0 or 1. A *Boolean expression* is an expression containing Boolean variables, the constant values 0 and 1, and Boolean operators such as $+$ and . . As in normal algebra functions can be defined on variables, e.g.

$$F(X, Y)=X.Y$$

Since each Boolean variable can take one of two values, 1 or 0, a Boolean function can be expressed in terms of a truth table where the values of all possible combinations of the function variables are tabulated against the function value. The truth table for the function given above is shown in Fig. 2.1. Since each Boolean variable can assume one of two different values the truth table will contain 2^n rows, where n is the number of input variables.

X	Y	X.Y
0	0	0
0	1	0
1	0	0
1	1	1

Fig. 2.1. Truth table for the function $X.Y$.

To compute a more complex function is no more difficult, but it may be helpful if some of the intermediate values are calculated as well. For example, the truth table shown in Fig. 2.2 could be utilized to compute

$$F(X, Y, Z)=X.Y+Y.Z$$

This is exactly analogous to the use of truth tables in propositional calculus. Two Boolean functions are *equal* if, for the same inputs, they produce the same outputs. In implementing logic circuits it is frequently necessary to

X	Y	Z	X.Y	Y.Z	F(X,Y,Z)
0	0	0	0	0	0
0	0	1	0	0	0
0	1	0	0	0	0
0	1	1	0	1	1
1	0	0	0	0	0
1	0	1	0	0	0
1	1	0	1	0	1
1	1	1	1	1	1

Fig. 2.2. Truth table for the function $X . Y + Y . Z$.

implement the circuit which performs the given function for the minimum cost. In order to do this a function which is equal to that given but which minimizes the number of operators used is required. For example, the logic function

$$G(X, Y, Z) = (X + Y) . (X + Z)$$

is equal to the function

$$F(X, Y, Z) = X + Y . Z$$

as can be seen from the truth table in Fig. 2.3, although the function G contains three operators whereas F contains only two. Thus function F can be implemented using less logic as will be shown later.

X	Y	Z	X+Y	X+Z	(X+Y).(X+Z)	Y.Z	X+Y.Z
0	0	0	0	0	0	0	0
0	0	1	0	1	0	0	0
0	1	0	1	0	0	0	0
0	1	1	1	1	1	1	1
1	0	0	1	1	1	0	1
1	0	1	1	1	1	0	1
1	1	0	1	1	1	0	1
1	1	1	1	1	1	1	1

Fig. 2.3. Truth table for the function $(X + Y) . (X + Z)$ and $X + Y . Z$.

Basic Algebraic Properties

As shown earlier in this chapter the operations . and + are equivalent to the propositional connectives AND and OR respectively defined over truth values true and false. A third operation, complementation, is equivalent to the NOT connective. It is represented by a bar over the symbol or group of symbols, e.g. $\bar{A}$, which is the notation used here, or by a prime as in A'.

Hence, the Boolean functions defined in the last section could be implemented by logic elements of the type AND, OR and NOT. As mentioned previously, it is not usually the case that a given function is implemented as defined but rather as an equal function which uses less logic or logic of a different type. As seen in Chapter 1 a proposition can be implemented by $\sim$ and $\wedge$, or by $\sim$ and $\vee$, or just $\downarrow$ or just $|$. There are equivalents to this in Boolean algebra. In order to manipulate functions before implementation some basic properties of Boolean algebra can be used. Some of the most important relationships are shown below (cf. propositional calculus).

Distribution	$X \cdot (Y + Z) = X \cdot Y + X \cdot Z$
	$X + Y \cdot Z = (X + Y) \cdot (X + Z)$
Association	$X + Y + Z = (X + Y) + Z = X + (Y + Z)$
	$X \cdot Y \cdot Z = (X \cdot Y) \cdot Z = X \cdot (Y \cdot Z)$
Complementation	$X \cdot \bar{X} = 0$
	$X + \bar{X} = 1$
	$\bar{\bar{X}} = X$
Commutation	$X + Y = Y + X$
	$X \cdot Y = Y \cdot X$
Zero	$X \cdot 0 = 0$
	$X + 1 = 1$
Identity	$X + 0 = X$
	$X \cdot 1 = X$
Idempotence	$X + X = X$
	$X \cdot X = X$
Absorption	$X + X \cdot Y = X$
	$X \cdot (X + Y) = X$
	$X + \bar{X} \cdot Y = X + Y$
De Morgan's law	$\overline{X + Y + Z} \ldots = \bar{X} \cdot \bar{Y} \cdot \bar{Z} \ldots$
	$\overline{X \cdot Y \cdot Z} \ldots = \bar{X} + \bar{Y} + \bar{Z} \ldots$

Some of these relationships are obvious from the truth tables of the Boolean operators given in the last section, and some are not so obvious but can be shown to be correct using the truth table method outlined earlier. To show,

for example, that

$$X + \bar{X} . Y = X + Y$$

we draw the truth table showing all possible values of the variables X and Y and the corresponding value of the expressions on the left- and right-hand sides of the equals sign as shown in Fig. 2.4. Hence we have shown that the above identity holds.

X	Y	$\bar{X}.Y$	$X+\bar{X}.Y$	$X+Y$
0	0	0	0	0
0	1	1	1	1
1	0	0	1	1
1	1	0	1	1

Fig. 2.4. Truth table for the functions $X + \bar{X} . Y$ and $X + Y$.

All the above relationships are useful in manipulating logic expressions, and De Morgan's law is especially so, since it gives a method of changing expressions containing $+$ into those containing . and vice versa.

Switches

Perhaps the best example of a physical device which obeys the rules of Boolean algebra is a switch, and hence the term *switching circuits* is used. A switch can exist in one of two states as shown below:

open switch   closed switch
$S = 0$ $S = 1$

Switches can be joined together to form networks such as

both switches open   both switches open

The example on the left above illustrates the AND or . function as both switches have to be closed for the input to be connected to the output, as shown in Fig. 2.5. The other circuit given represents the OR or $+$ function since either or both switches closed will cause the input to be connected to the output, as shown in Fig. 2.6.

S1	S2	AND gate output
0	0	0
0	1	0
1	0	0
1	1	1

Fig. 2.5. Truth table for the AND switch circuit.

S1	S2	OR gate output
0	0	0
0	1	1
1	0	1
1	1	1

Fig. 2.6. Truth table for the OR switch circuit.

Similarly other switching circuits can be produced to mimic other Boolean expressions. This is the basis of the use of logic in designing electronic circuits. In this case electronic rather than mechanical switches are used as we describe in the following sections.

Electronic Logic

The logic values 0 and 1 are usually represented in electronic logic by different voltage levels. The exact voltages used depend on the type of logic, but for transistor–transistor logic (TTL) they are nominally 0 V and +5 V. This gives rise to two different types of logic: positive logic, where logic 0 is represented by 0 V and logic 1 by +5 V, and negative logic, where logic 0 is represented by +5 V and logic 1 by 0 V. This does not give rise to two different schemes of logic design and analysis since, by the principle of duality explained in Chapter 1, every device in positive logic has its dual in negative logic. For the examples we consider in this chapter, considerations of positive and negative logic are irrelevant. Similarly, we ignore other problems which arise owing to the physical properties of flow of electric current, such as noise and timing delays through components. We refer the interested reader to Mano (1984) for the practical details of circuit implementation.

Logic Gates

A *logic gate*, or gate, is an electronic component which performs a Boolean operation on one or more inputs. A *digital circuit* comprises a network of such logic gates. Whilst there are a great many types of logic circuit marketed, we confine our discussion to a few of them. We have already seen the AND, OR and NOT functions, and these are represented by the logic symbols shown in Fig. 2.7. A wider variety of gates are available, corresponding to more of the possible two-input one-output functions; NAND and NOR are the two most common ones and are shown in Figs 2.8 and 2.9. Gates are also available with more than two inputs.

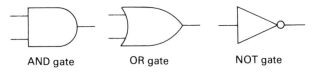

AND gate   OR gate   NOT gate

Fig. 2.7. The logic symbols for AND, OR and NOT gates.

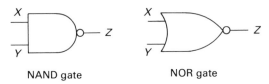

     NAND gate   NOR gate

Fig. 2.8. NAND and NOR gate logic symbols.

NAND gate truth table			NOR gate truth table		
X	Y	Z	X	Y	Z
0	0	1	0	0	1
0	1	1	0	1	0
1	0	1	1	0	0
1	1	0	1	1	0

Fig. 2.9. NAND and NOR gate truth tables.

By the property of association given before, an n-input logic gate can be implemented by one or more two-input gates of the same type. For example, $A . B . C$. which can be drawn as

$$
\begin{array}{c}
A \\
B \\
C
\end{array} \!\!\!\!\!\!\!\Big)\!\!\!-
$$

is equivalent to $(A . B) . C$ or the circuit

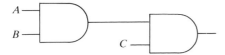

In the chapter on propositional calculus we showed that any truth function could be implemented using only joint denial ↓ or else using just alternative denial |. These are equivalent to NOR and NAND gates respectively. Thus any digital circuit can be constructed from only NAND or only NOR gates. For example, an inverter, which is a circuit performing the NOT operation, can be obtained by using either of the circuits shown in Fig. 2.10.

or

Logic 1

Fig. 2.10. Two circuits implementing a NOT operation.

Using the relationships defined above it is possible to implement a Boolean expression by different types of gates and by gates containing different numbers of input signals.

Combinatorial Logic

Combinatorial logic, which is also called combinational logic, is logic whose outputs depend solely on the inputs to the circuit. These circuits do not contain any storage or memory elements since the outputs cannot depend on any previous actions.

In the earlier part of this chapter we described the technique used to analyse combinatorial circuits, namely the use of truth tables. This technique is illustrated here on a larger example, shown in Fig. 2.11 in diagrammatic form and Fig. 2.12 in truth table form. This circuit can be described in Boolean algebra by

$$M = \overline{A \cdot B} \qquad N = \overline{M \cdot C} \qquad Q = N \cdot \bar{B} \qquad Z = Q \cdot \bar{C} \cdot D$$

and substituting we get

$$Z = \overline{A \cdot B \cdot C} \cdot \bar{B} \cdot \bar{C} \cdot D$$

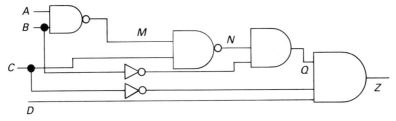

Fig. 2.11. Example circuit in logic diagram form.

A	B	C	D	M	N	Q	Z
0	0	0	0	1	1	1	0
0	0	0	1	1	1	1	1
0	0	1	0	1	0	0	0
0	0	1	1	1	0	0	0
0	1	0	0	1	1	0	0
0	1	0	1	1	1	0	0
0	1	1	0	1	0	0	0
0	1	1	1	1	0	0	0
1	0	0	0	1	1	1	0
1	0	0	1	1	1	1	1
1	0	1	0	1	0	0	0
1	0	1	1	1	0	0	0
1	1	0	0	0	1	0	0
1	1	0	1	0	1	0	0
1	1	1	0	0	1	0	0
1	1	1	1	0	1	0	0

Fig. 2.12. Truth table for the circuit of Fig. 2.11.

Using the relationships given before, this expression can be simplified by

(a) using De Morgan's law

$$Z = \overline{(\overline{A \cdot B} + C)} \cdot \bar{B} \cdot \bar{C} \cdot D$$
$$= (A \cdot B + \bar{C}) \cdot \bar{B} \cdot \bar{C} \cdot D$$

(b) using distribution

$$Z = A \cdot B \cdot \bar{B} \cdot \bar{C} \cdot D + \bar{C} \cdot \bar{B} \cdot \bar{C} \cdot D$$

(c) using complement and idempotence

$$Z = 0 + \bar{B} \cdot \bar{C} \cdot D$$

(d) using the identity law

$$Z = \bar{B} \cdot \bar{C} \cdot D$$

Hence the above circuit could be simplified to that shown in Fig. 2.13. This may be verified by inspection of the truth table.

A combinatorial circuit can therefore be analysed by the use of truth tables or Boolean algebra. For large circuits the analysis may not be as simple or straightforward as in the above example and we require some method of deriving a circuit which performs the given function using the minimal number of gates. This is shown in the next section.

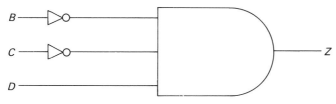

Fig. 2.13. Reduced circuit for the truth table of Fig. 2.12.

Design of Combinatorial Circuits

The designer is normally presented with a truth table or logic expression and asked to produce a cheap, or the cheapest, solution in logic, often with constraints about what type of gates can be used. A systematic method of designing such circuits is required. One method starts by producing the truth table, if not given, and then expressing it in a particular logic expression form. This is best explained using an example.

Example 2.1

Design a circuit to implement the truth table shown in Fig. 2.14.

Inputs				
A	B	C	Output = Z	Minterms
0	0	0	0	$\bar{A}.\bar{B}.\bar{C}$
0	0	1	1	$\bar{A}.\bar{B}.C$
0	1	0	0	$\bar{A}.B.\bar{C}$
0	1	1	1	$\bar{A}.B.C$
1	0	0	0	$A.\bar{B}.\bar{C}$
1	0	1	0	$A.\bar{B}.C$
1	1	0	1	$A.B.\bar{C}$
1	1	1	1	$A.B.C$

Fig. 2.14. Example truth table.

Solution. There are many different logic expressions which can be written corresponding to this truth table. A systematic one is required for logic design and the one based on minterms is used here. This is analogous to the disjunctive normal form in propositional calculus. A *minterm* corresponds to each row of the truth table and is the AND expression of the input variables in true or complemented form which gives the value 1. For the first row of the example above the minterm would be $\bar{A} \cdot \bar{B} \cdot \bar{C}$ since this is the only AND expression involving a single A, B and C which gives the value 1 for $A=0$, $B=0$ and $C=0$. Similarly the minterm for the last row is $A \cdot B \cdot C$. The output for the required function is obtained by ORing together the minterms whose output is a 1 in the truth table since if the value of any of the minterms in this expression is 1 the circuit output Z is required to be 1. Hence the required logic expression for the truth table above is

$$Z = \bar{A} \cdot \bar{B} \cdot C + \bar{A} \cdot B \cdot C + A \cdot B \cdot \bar{C} + A \cdot B \cdot C$$

Having produced this expression it has to be transformed into an equivalent expression which can be implemented by a reduced number of logic gates, if possible. This can be done using Boolean algebra as shown in the last section, but the reductions are not always obvious and hence we require some systematic method of simplification. For a small number of input variables the *Karnaugh map* method is normally used. A Karnaugh map consists of a set of squares formed into a rectangle or square. Each square represents a minterm and adjacent squares, sharing an edge, represent minterms which only differ in one variable. This leads to many representations partly because this arrangement is really a toroid (doughnut) but has to be presented in two dimensions. Thus in Fig. 2.15 we should consider that the right- and left-hand sides are connected as are the top and bottom rows. One common representation for three input variables is shown in Fig. 2.15.

Each square in the Karnaugh map represents one minterm value. We use a Karnaugh map to simplify the logic expression by first marking the squares. Those corresponding to terms in the logic expression are marked

$A.B.C$	$A.\bar{B}.C$	$\bar{A}.\bar{B}.C$	$\bar{A}.B.C$
$A.B.\bar{C}$	$A.\bar{B}.\bar{C}$	$\bar{A}.\bar{B}.\bar{C}$	$\bar{A}.B.\bar{C}$

Fig. 2.15. Karnaugh map representation for three input variables.

with a 1 and the others are marked with a 0. Use of the example above and the representation of Fig. 2.15 results in the map shown in Fig. 2.16.

To simplify the expression the 1s in the map have to be grouped using the following rules.

(1) Each group must be of size $2^a \times 2^b$, i.e. square or rectangular with each side of size a power of 2.

(2) Each 1 must be included in at least one group.

(3) Each group must be as large as possible.

(4) A 1 may only be included in more than one group if it enlarges the size of one of the groups.

(5) There should be the minimum number of groups.

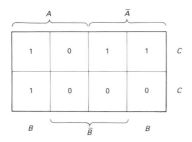

Fig. 2.16. Karnaugh map of $Z = \bar{A} . \bar{B} . C + \bar{A} . B . C . + A . B . \bar{C} . + A . B . C.$

During this grouping process it must be remembered that the map is really toroidal shaped so that moving off one edge is equivalent to moving on to the opposite edge, i.e. the right-hand side connects with the left-hand side and the top with the bottom.

It is interesting to see the basis on which these rules work. Adjacent squares vary in a single variable so, for example, could represent $A . B . C$ and $A . B . \bar{C}$. Combining these two together is equivalent to

$$A . B . C + A . B . \bar{C} = A . B(C + \bar{C})$$
$$= A . B . 1$$
$$= A . B$$

Larger groups are amalgamated using similar rules. Hence the use of Karnaugh maps is a simple application of the rules of Boolean algebra. Its power lies in the observation that human beings can group 1s together in maps using the rules outlined above much more easily than they can see in what order to apply the reduction rules of Boolean algebra directly.

By grouping the 1s in the map of Fig. 2.16 we obtain the map of Fig. 2.17

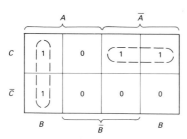

Fig. 2.17. Karnaugh map showing groups.

which exhibits two groups of a pair of 1s. There are several other possible groupings but they do not conform to the rules given above. For example, the map of Fig. 2.18 contravenes rule (3) since the single groups could be combined into larger ones as in the former map and it also contravenes rule (5) since there are three groups in this map rather than the two of the original map. The map shown in Fig. 2.19 contravenes rule (5) since the group containing $\bar{A} . B . C$ and $A . B . C$ does not contain any terms not included in other groups and is therefore redundant. The grouping of 1s in a Karnaugh map is not a simple task and it is easy to make mistakes. Experience and practice are required to find the correct grouping quickly.

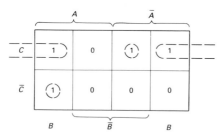

Fig. 2.18. Illegal Karnaugh map.

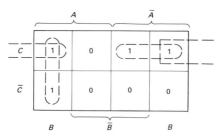

Fig. 2.19. Illegal Karnaugh map.

The simplified logic expression can now be read from the map by ignoring those variables which change within a group. For example, in Fig. 2.17 in the left-hand group C changes for the two squares but the other variables do not, so this group represents $A \cdot B$. Similarly the other group represents $\bar{A} \cdot C$. Hence the simplified logic expression is

$$Z = A \cdot B + \bar{A} \cdot C$$

The Karnaugh map technique can only be applied when the circuit has a small number of input variables (five or less). For a larger number of variables other techniques, such as the Quine–McCluskey method described below, have to be used.

Quine–McCluskey Minimization Technique

The Quine–McCluskey method is based on the same idea as Karnaugh maps, i.e. that of reducing the expression by recognizing terms differing in only a single variable. Instead of relying on maps the Quine–McCluskey method organizes the information in tabular form so that the search for terms differing in only a single variable is easy. The method is a two-stage process, firstly grouping the terms and secondly eliminating redundant groups. We illustrate the technique with the same example as that used to illustrate Karnaugh maps.

Example 2.2

Minimize the logic required to implement the following:

$$Z = \bar{A} \cdot \bar{B} \cdot C + \bar{A} \cdot B \cdot C + A \cdot B \cdot \bar{C} + A \cdot B \cdot C$$

This function corresponds to the truth table in Fig. 2.20.

A	B	C	Z
0	0	0	0
0	0	1	1
0	1	0	0
0	1	1	1
1	0	0	0
1	0	1	0
1	1	0	1
1	1	1	1

Fig. 2.20. Truth table for the Quine–McCluskey example.

Solution: The first step in the Quine–McCluskey procedure is to draw up a table of those minterms which give a function value of 1 separated into groups depending on the number of 1s in each minterm. For the example above this leads to the table shown in Fig. 2.21. Since terms differing in a single variable will be in adjacent groups this grouping simplifies the search process. The terms differing in a single variable are linked together as shown in Fig. 2.22 where the symbol * represents the value which differs. The right-hand table in Fig. 2.22 has been regrouped on the number of 1s in each row. This process is continued until none of the rows can be coalesced into another row. For the next iteration patterns have to have * in the same place and only differ by a single variable. In this simple example no further coalescing of the rows is possible. In Fig. 2.22 terms which have no arrows leading from them are irreducible.

The second step is to determine which terms are necessary in the reduced expression. The simplest way to do this is by means of a table listing the irreducible against the original terms. For the example above this table is shown in Fig. 2.23. A tick indicates that there is an arrow or, in a more

A	B	C
1	1	1
1	1	0
0	1	1
0	0	1

Fig. 2.21. Quine–McCluskey minimization—first stage.

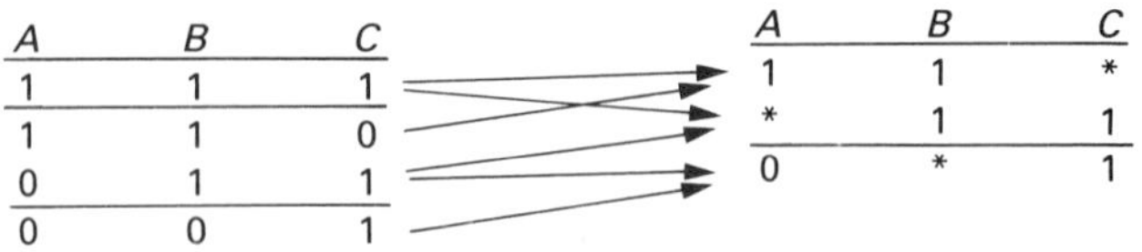

Fig. 2.22. The first stage of the reduction process.

	111	110	011	001
11*	✓	✓		
*11	✓		✓	
0*1			✓	✓

Fig. 2.23. Reducible versus irreducible terms.

complicated example, a chain of arrows from the original to an irreducible term. The reduced expression is obtained by including (ANDing) a set of irreducible terms such that the combination covers (has ticks in) every column, i.e. it includes all the original terms. For example, the single tick in the 110 column indicates that the term 11∗, i.e. $A . B$, has to be included in the final expression. Similarly the term 0∗1, i.e. $\bar{A} . C$, has to be included to cover 001. Since these two irreducible terms cover every column no other terms are necessary. If this were not the case then additional terms would have to be included so that every column was covered. Discovering the optimal covering is a non-trivial problem.

Hence we obtain the simplified form of the original equation:

$$Z = A . B + \bar{A} . C$$

Normally Karnaugh maps are used for simplifying expressions containing a small number of variables and the Quine–McCluskey method is only used for larger examples. The Quine–McCluskey method can be used with truth functions of any number of input variables but for large numbers the process becomes extremely tedious and computer assistance is highly desirable. Thus the Quine–McCluskey and similar methods form the basis of computer methods of logic minimization.

Circuit Implementation

Having produced a simplified logic expression the implementer has to design a circuit to achieve this using the desired logic gates. De Morgan's law can be used to convert a circuit from an AND to an OR gate representation or vice versa, and the distribution laws can be used to convert to logic gates with different numbers of inputs if required. A further complication for the logic designer today is the fact that integrated circuits do not contain a single gate but several, typically four or six in the case of AND, OR and NOT gates. The designer now wishes to minimize the number of integrated circuits rather than gates and so he will often manipulate the logic expression to use groups of four or six of a particular type of gate. We show below, using examples, some equivalent implementations and the reason why the designer might choose them.

$$Z = A . B + \bar{A} . C$$

can be implemented directly by the circuit shown in Fig. 2.24. This implementation of the logic expression requires two AND gates, one OR

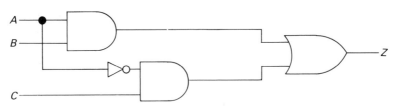

Fig. 2.24. A direct implementation of $Z = A \cdot B + \bar{A} \cdot C$.

gate and one NOT gate. But

$$A \cdot B + \bar{A} \cdot C = \overline{\overline{A \cdot B + \bar{A} \cdot C}}$$
$$= \overline{\overline{A \cdot B} \cdot \overline{\bar{A} \cdot C}}$$

by De Morgan's law. Implementing this results in the circuit shown in Fig. 2.25. This NAND implementation uses three NAND gates and one NOT gate which can be produced from a NAND gate by tying both inputs together. Alternatively,

$$A \cdot B + \bar{A} \cdot C = \overline{\overline{A \cdot B}} + \overline{\overline{\bar{A} \cdot C}}$$
$$= \overline{\bar{A} + \bar{B}} + \overline{A + \bar{C}}$$

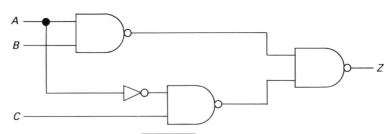

Fig. 2.25. Implementation of $\overline{\overline{A \cdot B} \cdot \overline{\bar{A} \cdot C}}$.

by De Morgan's law. This expression results in the circuit shown in Fig. 2.26. This NOR implementation uses two NOR gates, one OR gate and three NOT gates. Since a NAND integrated circuit contains four NAND gates the designer would almost certainly choose the NAND implementation shown in Fig. 2.25, given a choice, since it uses a single integrated circuit whereas the others use at least two integrated circuits.

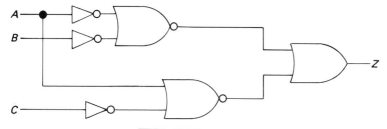

Fig. 2.26. Implementation of $\overline{\overline{A}+\overline{B}}+\overline{\overline{A}+\overline{\overline{C}}}$.

Structured Combinatorial Circuit Design

Today, circuit design differs somewhat from that presented in the previous sections. Whereas in the past components were expensive and the designer's aim was to minimize the component cost for a circuit, these costs are now small and the aim is to limit the design time costs since, for small production runs, these will outweigh the component costs by several orders of magnitude. In the search to reduce costs many more structured components have been produced. Their use greatly reduces the design time as we show in the examples below.

One of the devices which has made combinatorial logic design simpler is the *multiplexer* or data selector. This component acts as a multiposition electronic switch whose position is determined by a number of control (select) inputs. The output of the circuit shown in Fig. 2.27 will be one of the input values, which one depends on the values of the select inputs S_1 and S_2. If the select input is regarded as being a binary value, the input corresponding to that value will be selected for output. For example, in Fig.

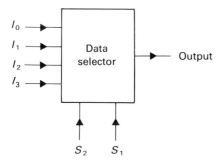

Fig. 2.27. Data selector or multiplexer.

2.27 the output will be

$$I_0 \text{ if } S_2 S_1 = 00$$
$$I_1 \text{ if } S_2 S_1 = 01$$
$$I_2 \text{ if } S_2 S_1 = 10$$
$$I_3 \text{ if } S_2 S_1 = 11$$

The number of data inputs on a data selector will be 2^s where s is the number of select signals. Discrete components are available with s values of 1, 2, 3 and 4, and larger ones can be fabricated as part of a design in large-scale integration. To illustrate the technique used in designing with data selectors we consider the example used earlier to illustrate simplification by Karnaugh maps. The truth table for this example is shown in Fig. 2.28.

Inputs			Output
A	B	C	Z
0	0	0	0
0	0	1	1
0	1	0	0
0	1	1	1
1	0	0	0
1	0	1	0
1	1	0	1
1	1	1	1

Fig. 2.28. Truth table for the data selector example.

No design time is required to implement this truth table using a data selector. Since the select inputs determine which input is routed to the output, the required circuit is a data selector with eight inputs to carry the eight values of Z. This data selector will have three select lines and these can be directly connected to A, B and C to select the required value of Z. The required circuit is shown in Fig. 2.29.

This produces a very quick design but, because of technology limitation, can only be adopted for a small number of input variables using discrete components. It is possible to implement a data selector very simply in very-large-scale integrated (VLSI) circuits using a regular structure. This has led to a widespread use of this type of circuitry in VLSI design.

Multiple-Output Combinatorial Circuits

All the circuits we have described so far have only a single output. To design circuits with multiple outputs the methods for circuits with single outputs can be used, duplicated for each output.

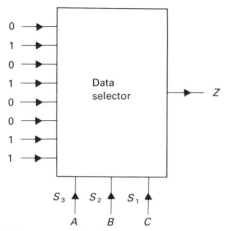

Fig. 2.29. Data selector circuit.

Example 2.3

Design the combinatorial circuit required to perform the function specified by the truth table of Fig. 2.30.

Inputs			Outputs		
A	B	C	X	Y	Z
0	0	0	0	1	1
0	0	1	1	0	0
0	1	0	1	0	1
0	1	1	1	1	0
1	0	0	1	1	1
1	0	1	0	0	0
1	1	0	0	0	1
1	1	1	0	1	0

Fig. 2.30. Truth table for a multiple-output circuit.

Solution. The Karnaugh map for the X output is shown in Fig. 2.31. The minimized function is $X = \bar{A} . C + \bar{A} . B + A . \bar{B} . \bar{C}$. Similarly the Karnaugh map for Y, shown in Fig. 2.32, gives $Y = B . C + \bar{B} . \bar{C}$. By inspection $Z = \bar{C}$. Putting these three circuits together we obtain the composite circuit shown in Fig. 2.33.

Designing in this manner for a number of different outputs becomes lengthy and the layout of the resulting circuit takes a considerable time. In order to reduce the design time some more structured devices can be used, and the two considered here are the programmable logic array (PLA) and the read-only memory (ROM).

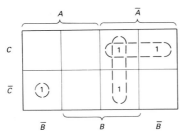

Fig. 2.31. Karnaugh map for the *X* output.

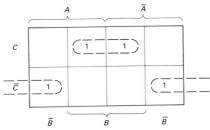

Fig. 2.32. Karnaugh map for the *Y* output.

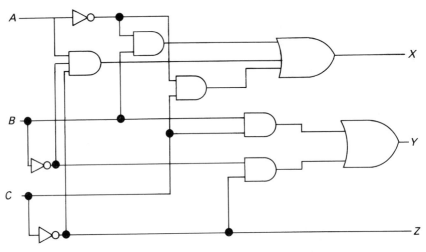

Fig. 2.33. Combined circuit.

Programmable Logic Array

As we proved in the previous chapter on propositional calculus any truth function can be represented using only the connectives $\lor$, $\land$ and $\sim$. In Boolean algebra this corresponds to saying that any logic expression can be implemented using only AND, OR and NOT gates. A PLA is an integrated circuit containing a collection of AND, OR and NOT gates which can be connected (programmed) into one of a number of different circuits. A block diagram of a PLA is shown in Fig. 2.34. All the inputs and their complements are presented to links at the inputs of the AND gates. The particular links made determine which AND functions are performed. Similarly the outputs of all the AND gates are presented to links at the inputs of the OR gates. Again, the particular links made determine which OR functions are performed.

The size of the PLA is specified in terms of the number of inputs, the number of product terms (AND gates) and the number of outputs. A typical PLA has 16 inputs, 48 product terms and eight outputs. The structure of a smaller PLA consisting of two inputs, two product terms and two outputs is shown in Fig. 2.35. The links, shown in regions P, Q, R and S in the figure, determine the function performed by the circuit. The simple function illustrated is $O_2 = A \cdot B + \bar{A} \cdot \bar{B}$. In order to use a PLA, we require a design technique to decide which links need to be made to implement a particular

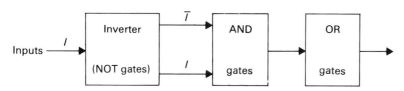

Fig. 2.34. Block diagram of a PLA.

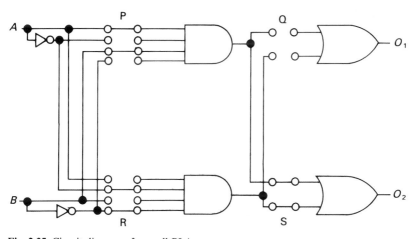

Fig. 2.35. Circuit diagram of a small PLA.

logic function. This design technique has to be flexible so that it can be adapted to varying combinations of product terms.

The basic design technique is to simplify the logic required using one of the techniques described previously. Having produced the simplified logic expression, a straightforward implementation proceeds by mapping the product (AND) terms onto the AND gates and the OR terms onto the OR gates. This assumes that the PLA contains enough AND and OR gates.

Example 2.4

Implement the logic required for Example 2.3 in a PLA.

Solution. The simplified expressions were

$$X = \bar{A} . C + \bar{A} . B + A . \bar{B} . \bar{C}$$
$$Y = B . C + \bar{B} . \bar{C}$$
$$Z = \bar{C}$$

In order to implement these expressions directly a three-input PLA is required with six AND gates, one for each of the six terms, and three outputs.

In many cases several of the product terms are identical and can be implemented by a single AND gate whose output is connected to several of the OR gates. In order to program the PLA a table is required specifying which links are to be formed. The actual programming of a PLA is either performed in manufacture or, in a field-programmable logic array (FPLA), by appropriate laboratory equipment.

To make the best use of a PLA the number of product terms needs to be minimized. The number of terms in each product is not important since all the input variables and their complements are available at each AND gate. Both the true and complemented values of the functions, obtained from the Karnaugh maps, are examined to see which combinations can be implemented using the least number of product terms. We show below a simple example, too simple to need PLA implementation, to illustrate this procedure.

Example 2.5

Implement the following functions using a PLA with four product terms:

$$X = A . B . C + \bar{A} . B . C + A . \bar{B} . C + A . B . \bar{C}$$
$$Y = A . B . C + A . \bar{B} . \bar{C} + \bar{A} . B . \bar{C} + \bar{A} . \bar{B} . \bar{C}$$

Solution. First, we simplify using Karnaugh maps as shown in Figs 2.36 and 2.37. From these maps

$$X = A \cdot C + B \cdot C + A \cdot B$$

and

$$Y = \bar{A} \cdot \bar{C} + \bar{B} \cdot \bar{C} + A \cdot B \cdot C$$

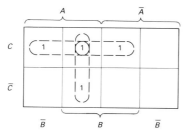

Fig. 2.36. Karnaugh map for X.

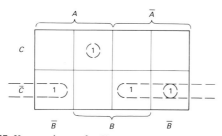

Fig. 2.37. Karnaugh map for Y.

In the same way that the 1s in Karnaugh maps can be taken to produce the sum of products for the function, the 0s can be taken to produce the sum of products for the complement of the function. This follows since those rows of the truth table giving the value 0 for the function do not contribute to the function and hence must contribute to its complement. Using this method we could simplify the above maps to those shown in Figs 2.38 and 2.39. These maps lead to

$$\bar{X} = \bar{A} \cdot \bar{B} + \bar{B} \cdot \bar{C} + \bar{A} \cdot \bar{C}$$

or

$$X = \overline{\bar{A} \cdot \bar{B} + \bar{B} \cdot \bar{C} + \bar{A} \cdot \bar{C}}$$

and

$$\bar{Y} = \bar{A} \cdot C + \bar{B} \cdot C + A \cdot B \cdot \bar{C}$$

or

$$Y = \overline{\bar{A} \cdot C + \bar{B} \cdot C + A \cdot B \cdot \bar{C}}$$

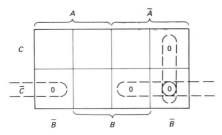

Fig. 2.38. Karnaugh map for $\bar{X}$.

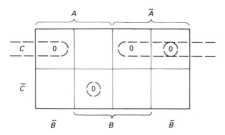

Fig. 2.39. Karnaugh map for $\bar{Y}$.

The combination of expressions for X and Y which involve the minimum number of distinct product terms is

$$X = \overline{\bar{A} \cdot \bar{B} + \bar{B} \cdot \bar{C} + \bar{A} \cdot C}$$
$$Y = \bar{A} \cdot \bar{C} + \bar{B} \cdot \bar{C} + A \cdot B \cdot C$$

To implement these functions a PLA with four product terms is required. The product terms implement $\bar{A} \cdot \bar{C}, \bar{B} \cdot \bar{C}, A \cdot B \cdot C$ and $\bar{A} \cdot \bar{B}$. In order to implement the expression for X the output from the PLA has to be inverted. Many PLAs include an extra inversion stage on the output so that either the sum of products or its complement can be directly produced depending on the links made.

A typical commercial PLA will have many more inputs, product terms and outputs, and the simplification of the Boolean expressions will not be as straightforward as shown above. In this case computer aids are invaluable to simplify the expression for each function and to select the minimum number of product terms.

A PLA is used to implement a set of logic functions where the number of product terms is small. As the number of product terms increases it becomes more likely that a ROM would be used instead.

Read-Only Memory

A ROM is frequently described as a form of memory although it is actually a combinatorial circuit, i.e. the outputs are solely a function of the current inputs and the device does not store any information. As a combinatorial circuit it is most easily thought of as being an extension of a PLA with all the input variables being fully decoded so that all the product terms are available inside the device and subsets of these can be ORed together to produce the required outputs. The ORing together can be performed in the manufacturing process or, in a programmable read-only memory (PROM), by means of suitable laboratory equipment. Since a ROM is more often described as a memory device we shall also give this form of description here.

If we consider a ROM as a memory, it consists of n words each of m bits. Each word of memory has an address and the m bits contained in a word are read by using that address. The ROM acts as a table look-up device, where the address is the position in the table and the content of that word is the required information, as illustrated in Fig. 2.40.

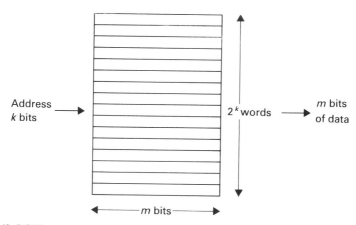

Fig. **2.40**. ROM structure.

ROMs are available in a range of sizes, the most common being 8 bits wide ($m=8$). When a ROM is used to implement a truth table, the truth table outputs are assigned to different bit positions in each word of the ROM and the address inputs to the ROM are the inputs to the truth table. The ROM contents can be written down immediately from the truth table and so no design time is required.

Example 2.6

Implement the circuit specified in Fig. 2.41.

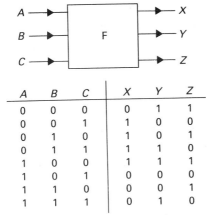

A	B	C	X	Y	Z
0	0	0	0	1	1
0	0	1	1	0	0
0	1	0	1	0	1
0	1	1	1	1	0
1	0	0	1	1	1
1	0	1	0	0	0
1	1	0	0	0	1
1	1	1	0	1	0

Fig. 2.41. Specification of the required circuit.

Solution. To implement this circuit in a ROM, an 8×3 ROM would be required as shown in Fig. 2.42.

The devices described here are only some of those used to implement combinatorial logic quickly. As has always been the case, the design engineer has to produce logic at an economic price. The techniques and devices used depend upon the cost of components and labour, the design time required, the complexity of the design and the number of circuits to be produced. The data selector, PLA and ROM all have disadvantages, the data selector and PLA because they are too small to implement large circuits and the ROM because it is too expensive, but they are in common use since, for many applications, their advantages outweigh these disadvantages.

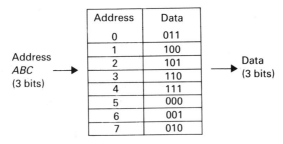

Fig. 2.42. ROM for Example 2.6.

Applications of Combinatorial Logic to Computers

A computer contains a considerable amount of combinatorial logic. This combinatorial logic is now implemented using structured design techniques and large-scale integrated circuits as described earlier in this chapter but, for illustrative purposes, we consider below the design of an adder circuit using discrete components.

Half Adder

A half adder circuit is a circuit which sums two single-bit inputs and produces as output their sum and carry as shown by the truth table of Fig. 2.43. The circuit required to implement this function is given by the expressions

$$\text{carry} = A \cdot B$$
$$\text{sum} = \bar{A} \cdot B + A \cdot \bar{B}$$

Inputs		Outputs	
A	B	Carry	Sum
0	0	0	0
0	1	0	1
1	0	0	1
1	1	1	0

Fig. 2.43. Truth table of the half adder circuit.

and these lead to the circuit of Fig. 2.44. This circuit can be redrawn as shown in Fig. 2.45 where the circuit symbol ⊐D— stands for an exclusive-OR (XOR) gate which has the truth table shown in Fig. 2.46 and is represented by the operator $\oplus$, e.g. sum $= A \oplus B$.

Full Adder

In a computer, multiple-bit quantities rather than single bits are normally added together. To implement a multiple-bit adder, several single-bit adders have to be connected. Since a single-bit adder produces two outputs, a sum and a carry, the single-bit adder required as the component for a multiple-bit adder needs to input the carry from the previous bit position. The truth table for the required 1 bit adder, called a full adder, is given in Fig. 2.47.

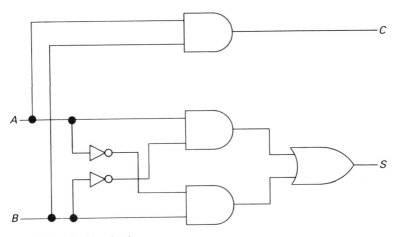

Fig. 2.44. Half adder circuit.

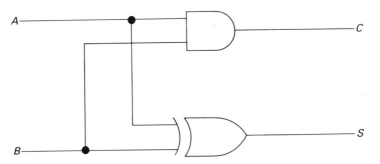

Fig. 2.45. Half adder circuit.

Inputs		Output
A	*B*	
0	0	0
0	1	1
1	0	1
1	1	0

Fig. 2.46. Truth table for an exclusive OR gate.

As might be expected the full adder can be produced by a modification of the half adder circuit. Consider a half adder with inputs A and B and outputs C_h and S_h. The circuit required to implement a full adder, using the C_h and S_h outputs from a half adder and the C_{in} input from a previous stage,

Inputs			Outputs	
A	B	C_{in}	C_{out}	Sum
0	0	0	0	0
0	0	1	0	1
0	1	0	0	1
0	1	1	1	0
1	0	0	0	1
1	0	1	1	0
1	1	0	1	0
1	1	1	1	1

Fig. 2.47. Truth table for a 1 bit full adder.

is given in truth table form in Fig. 2.48. From this, using the technique described previously, the required circuits are

$$C_{out} = C_h + S_h \cdot C_{in}$$
$$\text{sum} = S_h \oplus C_{in}$$

which leads to the complete circuit shown in Fig. 2.49. However, the circuit

Inputs			Outputs	
C_h	S_h	C_{in}	C_{out}	Sum
0	0	0	0	0
0	0	1	0	1
0	1	0	0	1
0	1	1	1	0
1	0	0	0	1
1	0	1	1	0
1	1	0	1	0
1	1	1	1	1

Fig. 2.48. Modified truth table for a 1 bit adder.

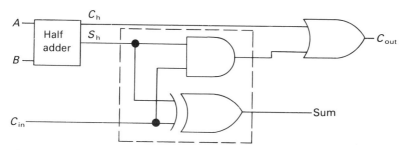

Fig. 2.49. 1 bit full adder circuit.

enclosed in broken lines in the diagram above is the circuit for a half adder so the complete full adder circuit can be redrawn as shown in Fig. 2.50.

A multiple-bit full adder can be implemented by linking several 1 bit full adders together as shown in the example of a 4 bit full adder in Fig. 2.51. This circuit will add two 4 bit binary numbers, represented by $A_3A_2A_1A_0$ and $B_3B_2B_1B_0$, together producing as their sum the binary number $S_3S_2S_1S_0$ and the carry value C_{out}.

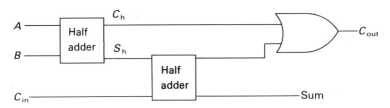

Fig. 2.50. Final 1 bit full adder circuit.

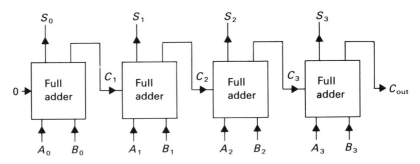

Fig. 2.51. 4 bit full adder circuit.

Structured Computer Organization by Tanenbaum (1984) is an excellent book which describes the application of logic to computers in detail.

Sequential Logic

Unlike combinatorial circuits, the outputs from sequential logic circuits depend not only on the present inputs but also on the past history of the circuit. Thus an important component of sequential logic circuits is some form of memory, and most sequential circuits consist of memory elements together with some combinatorial logic.

Types of Sequential Logic

There are two basic types of sequential logic components, clocked and unclocked. *Unclocked* circuits act in the same way as combinatorial logic in that changes of the inputs to the components cause them to change their state and hence their outputs. Since circuits are built from many components the only way to ensure that all the circuit elements change state at once is to change all the inputs at the same time. However, this can be difficult since external events determine when some inputs change. It is usually more convenient to add a control signal to each element which determines when it is active. To produce a *synchronous* circuit (i.e. a circuit which is controlled by a single signal) from such elements simply involves connecting all the control signals from all the elements to a single common point. The control signal on each component is called a clock signal and determines when the circuit elements change state. *Asynchronous* circuits use components with no clock signal or the individual components are controlled by several different clock signals. Examples of synchronous and asynchronous circuits are given later in this chapter.

A clock signal is a signal which changes its logic level with time as shown in Fig. 2.52. Clock signals need not be regular or periodic: sequential logic

Fig. 2.52. A typical clock signal.

components controlled by a clock signal are sensitive either to a change of logic level, when they are called *level sensitive*, or to the actual transition from 0 to 1 or vice versa, when they are called *edge triggered*. In most of the examples considered in this chapter the type of control is irrelevant but for those where it does matter edge triggering on the transition from 1 to 0 has been assumed.

Flip-Flops

The simplest sequential logic element is the 1 bit memory element called a flip-flop. There are many different types of flip-flop differing in the number of inputs and the conditions under which the stored value changes. The two most important types, the D-type and *JK* flip-flops, are discussed here.

D-type flip-flop (clocked)

The D-type flip-flop has a single input, stores a single bit and outputs the value of this single bit together with its inverted value as shown in Fig. 2.53. Since the clock signal determines when the flip-flop stores its data input, its mode of action is described by the state table given in Fig. 2.54. The left-hand side of the table describes all the possible states of the flip-flop, i.e. its

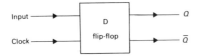

Fig. 2.53. D-type flip-flop.

Input	Q	Next Q	Next $\bar{Q}$
0	0	0	1
0	1	0	1
1	0	1	0
1	1	1	0

Fig. 2.54. State table for a D-type flip-flop.

input is 0 or 1 and its stored value Q is 0 or 1. The columns on the right show the resulting state, or value stored, for each of the possible present states when the next clock transition occurs. For example, from row 1, if the input was 0 and the stored value was 0 (i.e. $Q=0$) then, on the next clock transition, there would be no change in the stored value, so the next $Q=0$. From the complete table we can see that, no matter what the stored value is, the resulting stored value at the next clock transition is a copy of the input.

JK flip-flop

This is probably the most widely used flip-flop. Its mode of action is described in Fig. 2.55. We can summarize the action of this circuit as shown in Fig. 2.56. The important action to note is the toggle action when $J=K=1$. If the inputs to the flip-flop are both 1 when the next clock transition occurs the value stored in the flip-flop, reflected in the Q output, changes from 0 to 1 or 1 to 0, i.e. it toggles. This action makes the *JK* flip-flop extremely useful in sequential logic design, as will be described later. From the action table of the *JK* flip-flop given in Fig. 2.56 we can determine

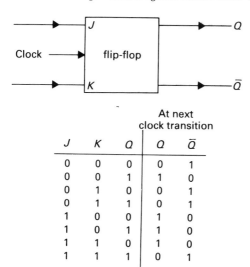

J	K	Q	Q	Q̄
0	0	0	0	1
0	0	1	1	0
0	1	0	0	1
0	1	1	0	1
1	0	0	1	0
1	0	1	1	0
1	1	0	1	0
1	1	1	0	1

Fig. 2.55. Block diagram and truth table for a *JK* flip-flop.

J	K	Action on next clock transition
0	0	None
0	1	Reset, $Q = 0$
1	0	Set, $Q = 1$
1	1	Toggle, new Q = old $\bar{Q}$

Fig. 2.56. Action table for a *JK* flip-flop.

the *excitation table* of the *JK* flip-flop. This table, which is shown in Fig. 2.57, lists the values of *J* and *K* required on a flip-flop to change the *Q* output from one value to another. The table is used later in this chapter to show how sequential circuits based on *JK* flip-flops are designed.

Present state	Next state	Required J	K
0	0	0	X
0	1	1	X
1	0	X	1
1	1	X	0

Fig. 2.57. Excitation table for a *JK* flip-flop (*X* stands for 'don't care', i.e. 1 or 0).

Design of Sequential Circuits

The design of sequential circuits is quite complex, and we shall only consider a few simple examples here to show how sequential circuits can be constructed using *JK* flip-flops. *Analysis and Design of Sequential Digital Systems* by Lind and Nelson (1977), is just one of the more detailed textbooks covering this subject.

One of the more frequently used sequential circuits is a *counter*. This is a circuit which has one or more outputs which continuously cycle through a given set of values. A counter whose outputs produced the sequence 0, 1, 2, 3, 4, 5, 6, 7, 0, 1 etc. would be called a divide-by-8 up counter since it counts upwards and repeats itself every eight values. Similarly a counter whose outputs produce the sequence 2, 1, 0, 2, 1 etc. would be called a divide-by-3 down counter. The design of counters is relatively straightforward. The simplest type is called an *asynchronous counter* since there is no common clock signal to all the stages.

Example 2.7

Design an asynchronous divide-by-8 counter.

Solution. The design of asynchronous counters using *JK* flip-flops is based on the toggle action. If $J=1$ and $K=1$ then on the next clock cycle the output will change (toggle). If a number of *JK* flip-flops are connected together as shown in Fig. 2.58 with all the *J* and *K* inputs set to 1 but with the clock input connected to the *Q* output of the previous stage, a binary counter will be formed, i.e. a counter whose outputs change on a power of 2. Three *JK* flip-flops are required for a divide-by-8 counter since $8=2^3$.

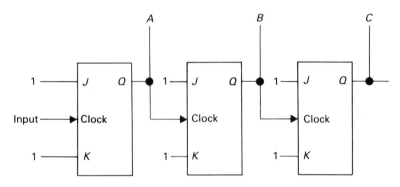

Fig. 2.58. Asynchronous divide-by-8 counter.

The simplest way of explaining the action of this circuit is in terms of a waveform diagram as shown in Fig. 2.59. Tabulating the values for A, B and C for every clock pulse we obtain the table shown in Fig. 2.60. This is the binary pattern for 0, 1, 2, 3, 4, 5, 6, 7, 0. Hence the circuit output cycles from 0 to 7. The circuit then acts as a counter, counting up on every clock pulse. Since it counts modulo 8 it is known as a modulo 8 counter. It is sometimes also referred to as a divide-by-8 counter since the output performs one cycle for every eight input clock signals.

This type of circuit is the basis of a number of sequential circuits, where, as well as *JK* flip-flops, some combinatorial logic is necessary to produce the required output signals.

The general design procedure for sequential circuits is based on a state approach. Each distinct state of the system can be represented by a number of flip-flops, each capable of representing two states. In the above counter example the number of distinct states required is eight, which is the number

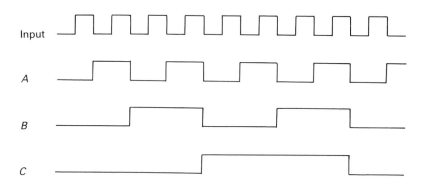

Fig. 2.59. Waveform diagram for an asynchronous divide-by-8 counter.

C	B	A
0	0	0
0	0	1
0	1	0
0	1	1
1	0	0
1	0	1
1	1	0
1	1	1
0	0	0

Fig. 2.60. Values of the outputs of a divide-by-8 counter.

of different outputs. The procedure details the method of designing the combinatorial logic necessary to drive the *JK* inputs of the flip-flops to produce the required outputs. The steps in this general design procedure are outlined below.

Step (1): Decide the number *s* of states required to solve the problem. Each state corresponds to a unique set of outputs and examination of the required outputs from the circuit leads to the number of states required.

Step (2): Determine the number *n* of *JK* flip-flops required where $2^n \geqslant s > 2^{n-1}$.

Step (3): Devise a state allocation table to allocate sets of outputs to states. The actual allocation is arbitrary but it is common in circuits such as counters to allocate states to the numeric value of the outputs, e.g. state 0 has an output of 0, state 1 has an output of 1 and so on.

Step (4): Allocate values of the control inputs for all the input conditions.

Step (5): Draw a state diagram for the required circuit. This is a graph with the nodes representing states and the edges representing transitions. From this state diagram a state table giving the conditions for each transition is produced.

Step (6): Use the *JK* excitation table to produce an excitation table for the circuit under consideration which gives the required inputs to the *JK* flip-flops to produce each transition.

Step (7): Design the combinatorial circuit required to produce the desired *JK* inputs specified in step (6) from the flip-flop outputs and control inputs.

Step (8): Draw the required circuit diagram.

We illustrate this general design procedure by means of an example.

Example 2.8

Design a divide-by-3 up–down counter.

Solution. This is a counter with a control input which determines whether the counter counts up or down. The counter will either count 0, 1, 2, 0 etc. or 2, 1, 0, 2 etc. depending on the control input.

Step (1): The system has three states, corresponding to the three different output values.

Step (2): The number of flip-flops required is 2 since $2^2 \geqslant 3 > 2^1$. The flip-flops are labelled A and B.

Step (3): Let S_0, S_1, S_2 represent the states whose outputs are 00, 01 and 02 respectively.

Step (4): Let the control input I be 0 to count up and 1 to count down.

Step (5):

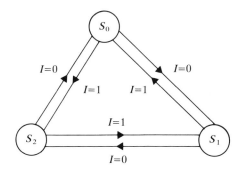

| Current state | | | Next state | |
A	B	I	A	B
0	0	0	0	1
0	0	1	1	0
0	1	0	1	0
0	1	1	0	0
1	0	0	0	0
1	0	1	0	1
1	1	0	X	X
1	1	1	X	X

where $X =$ 'don't care' since this should not arise (no state 3).

For synchronous design it is the J and K inputs which have to be designed since all the clock signals are tied together. The excitation table states what values of J and K are required to change state for each row of the table. It is produced using the JK excitation table shown in Fig. 2.57 and the state table derived above.

Step (6): Excitation table for the required circuit.

| Current state | | Input | Next state | | | Required | | |
A	B	I	A	B	J_A	K_A	J_B	K_B
0	0	0	0	1	0	X	1	X
0	0	1	1	0	1	X	0	X
0	1	0	1	0	1	X	X	1
0	1	1	0	0	0	X	X	1
1	0	0	0	0	X	1	0	X
1	0	1	0	1	X	1	1	X
1	1	0	X	X	X	X	X	X
1	1	1	X	X	X	X	X	X

At this stage the circuit shown in Fig. 2.61 has been designed.

We now require the combinatorial circuit to connect to the J and K inputs of flip-flops A and B as given by the truth table (excitation table) above.

Step (7): By inspection $K_A = K_B = 1$ (let all $X = 1$). The Karnaugh maps for J_A and J_B are shown in Fig. 2.62. The reduced expression for J_A is $I \cdot \bar{B} + B \cdot \bar{I}$ and that for J_B is $\bar{I} \cdot \bar{A} + I \cdot A$. Note the use of 'don't care' states in the Karnaugh maps. We can consider them to be 0 or 1 depending on our design. Those included in the groups are assumed to be 1 and the others 0. The two expressions above are the exclusive OR and exclusive NOR operations and so we arrive at the final circuit shown in Fig. 2.63.

This example shows clearly that so-called sequential logic circuits are usually a mixture of sequential and combinatorial logic.

Analysis of Sequential Circuits

Synchronous Circuits

The simplest circuits to analyse are synchronous circuits, controlled by a single clock signal, and we illustrate the technique with the example below.

Example 2.9

Analyse the action of the circuit shown in Fig. 2.64.

Solution. This is a synchronous circuit since all the flip-flops are controlled by the same clock signal. The circuit contains no external input so we

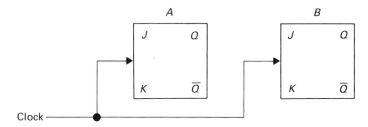

Fig. 2.61. Partial counter circuit.

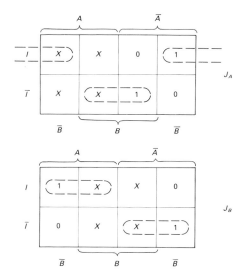

Fig. 2.62. Karnaugh maps for J_A and J_B.

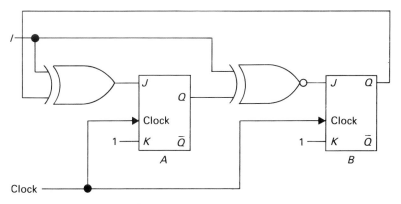

Fig. 2.63. Final counter circuit.

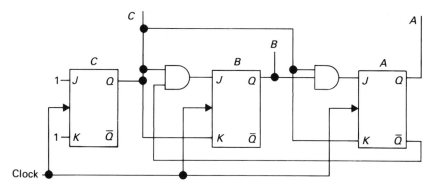

Fig. 2.64. Synchronous counter circuit for Example 2.9.

proceed with the analysis by considering all the possible states of the flip-flops, i.e. eight (2^3) since there are three flip-flops, and the changes which occur on the next clock pulse. We start by considering the case where all the flip-flops are in their 0 state, i.e. all the Q outputs are 0. On the application of a clock pulse flip-flop C will change to a 1 since both its J and K inputs are 1, and this is the condition for the toggle action as stated in the JK action table above. Flip-flop B takes its K value from Q_C, the previous Q-value of C, which was 0, and its J value from the AND of this previous value and the complement of A. Since $Q_C=0$ both J_B and K_B are 0, the no-action condition for B. Hence the next value of B is the same as its present one, namely 0. By a similar argument A is also kept at the same state, namely 0. Hence if the flip-flops were in state (0, 0, 0), on the application of a clock pulse the next state would be (0, 0, 1). By applying this procedure to all the other possible states we can produce the state table of Fig. 2.65.

This circuit is a *modulo 6 counter* since it will count in the sequence 0, 1, 2, 3, 4, 5, 0, 1 etc. Note that states 7 and 8 are not used in this circuit but if the

	Current state			Next state		
	A	B	C	A	B	C
1	0	0	0	0	0	1
2	0	0	1	0	1	0
3	0	1	0	0	1	1
4	0	1	1	1	0	0
5	1	0	0	1	0	1
6	1	0	1	0	0	0
7	1	1	0	0	0	1
8	1	1	1	0	0	0

Unused states (rows 7 and 8)

Fig. 2.65. State table for the example circuit.

circuit starts in one of these states it will jump into the divide-by-6 sequence on the next clock pulse. We can use the same principles as described here to analyse circuits with external inputs except that all possible values of the external inputs have to be considered as well as all possible internal states.

Example 2.10

Determine the action of the circuit shown in Fig. 2.66.

Solution. In this circuit B toggles on every clock pulse and A either stays the same or toggles depending on whether $J_A = K_A = 0$ or $J_A = K_A = 1$. We can describe the action of this circuit by the state table of Fig. 2.67. It is a divide-by-4 up–down counter since it repeats its sequence every four clock pulses with the Z control input determining whether it counts up (0) or down (1).

Asynchronous Circuits

Asynchronous circuits can be more difficult to analyse because the flip-flops change state at different times. The technique we use in this case is similar to that described above, i.e. the clock signal on one of the flip-flops is taken to be the reference and the changes invoked by this are evaluated throughout the circuit. We have to evaluate all the outputs resulting from different combinations of this clock signal and the external inputs to decide upon the action of the circuit.

Example 2.11

Determine the function of the circuit shown in Fig. 2.68.

Solution. This circuit is a mixture of two flip-flops which are synchronous and a third which changes state as a result of a change in the second flip-flop. Flip-flops change state on a change in the clock signal from 0 to 1 or vice versa. For the analysis below we assume that these flip-flops, or more specifically flip-flop A, changes state on a change in the clock signal from 1 to 0. Producing the state table as before gives the table of Fig. 2.69.

Considering the first row of the truth table, the input J_C is 1 so the C flip-flop toggles to a new value of 1. At the same time $K_B = 0$ and $J_B = 0$, the no-change condition, so the B flip-flop stays at 0. Since there is no change in B, flip-flop A will not change even though J_A and K_A are both 1 (the toggle

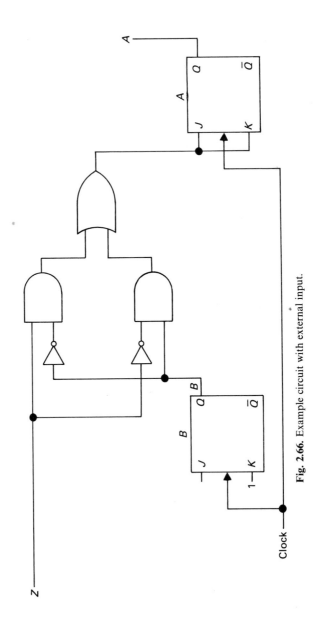

Fig. 2.66. Example circuit with external input.

Current state		Input	Next state	
A	B	Z	A	B
0	0	0	0	1
0	0	1	1	1
0	1	0	1	0
0	1	1	0	0
1	0	0	1	1
1	0	1	0	1
1	1	0	0	0
1	1	1	1	0

Fig. 2.67. State table for Example 2.10.

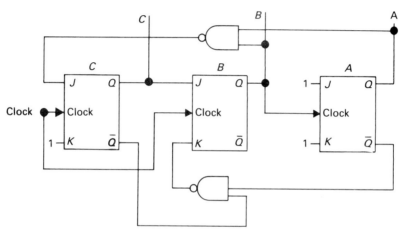

Fig. 2.68. Circuit of Example 2.11.

Present state			Next state		
A	B	C	A	B	C
0	0	0	0	0	1
0	0	1	0	1	0
0	1	0	0	1	1
0	1	1	1	0	0
1	0	0	1	0	1
1	0	1	1	1	0
1	1	0	0	0	0
1	1	1	0	0	0

Fig. 2.69. State table for Example 2.11.

action) because the clock signal does not change. The fourth line of the state table shows a situation where A does change. For this starting state J_C is 1 so C toggles to 0; J_B and K_B are both 1 so B toggles to 0. This change of B from 1 to 0 initiates a change of A from 0 to 1, since J_A and K_A are both 1 (the toggle condition). The circuit given is a divide-by-7 up counter.

Applications of Sequential Logic to Computers

In the same way that combinatorial logic is implemented in present day computers using large-scale integration and structured design techniques, sequential logic is also implemented by structured devices rather than the discrete flip-flops described in the previous sections. These structured techniques for sequential devices are outside the scope of this text but to indicate the type of sequential logic component inside computers we illustrate the design of a register using *JK* flip-flops.

A Register

The central processing unit (CPU) of a computer typically contains a set of registers. Each of these registers is an *n* bit memory, and appropriate control signals allow the value stored to be changed and sent to other components of the computer.

An *n* bit register consists of a set of *n* flip-flops with their clock inputs tied together so that they all change state at the same time. Since each flip-flop stores a single bit, which is either 1 or 0, the inputs are configured to be $J=0, K=1$, the reset condition, which causes a 0 value to be stored, or $J=1$, $K=0$, the set condition, which causes a 1 value to be stored.

The basic register structure is shown in Fig. 2.70 which illustrates a 4 bit register. However, this register has no control on its input and output. The

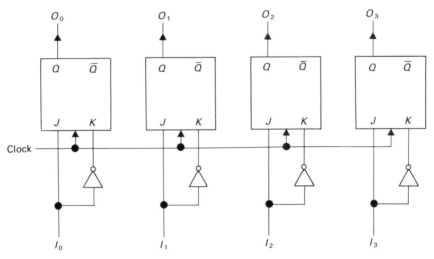

Fig. 2.70. A 4 bit register.

input could be controlled by the clock signal but the clock signal used is normally a high frequency clock used to control all the actions of the CPU. The clock signal sent to the flip-flops is produced by ANDing this system clock signal with an input enable signal, thus allowing input to the register only when both the system clock signal and the input control signal are active. To provide output control the output signals from the flip-flops are ANDed with an output control signal. This output control is necessary since the outputs from several registers flow along a common transmission medium (a bus) and thus only a single register may output at once to avoid signal corruption. This structure is shown in Fig. 2.71.

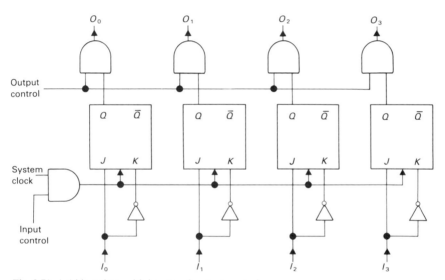

Fig. 2.71. A 4 bit register with input and output control.

The registers in the CPU are connected in parallel via a pair of buses which are simply a collection of wires. The buses connect similar bit positions in all the registers together, one bus for the input and one for the output. This structure, which is shown in Fig. 2.72, is called a register stack and forms a subsystem within the CPU. The diagram only shows the data routes to and from the registers. Signals providing the input and output control for each register are generated by other logic inside the processor.

Structured Design Techniques

As we showed earlier for combinatorial logic elements, modern techniques

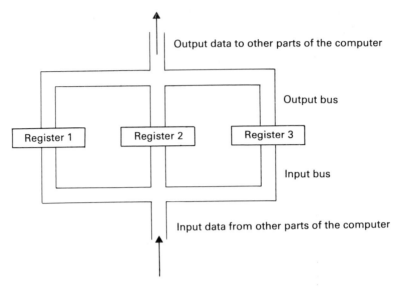

Fig. 2.72. Register stack.

do not use discrete components but regular structures which are simple to design. Memory elements are no exception; they are one of the easiest components to fabricate in regular structures. These regular structures are rather different from the *JK* flip-flop and are closer to the D-type flip-flop in operation in that they store the value given on their input. These types of memories together with the regular forms of combinatorial elements form the basis of sequential logic design for VLSI, the best example of which is the microprocessor or microcomputer. The reader should consult Mavor *et al.* (1983) or Mead and Conway (1980) for more details.

Exercises

1 Draw the truth table corresponding to the following Boolean expressions:

(a) $X = A \cdot \bar{B} \cdot C + \bar{A} \cdot \bar{B} \cdot C + \bar{A} \cdot B \cdot \bar{C} + A \cdot B$
(b) $Y = P \cdot \bar{Q} + P \cdot Q \cdot R + \bar{P} \cdot \bar{Q} \cdot \bar{R}$
(c) $Z = E \cdot F \cdot G \cdot H + \bar{E} \cdot \bar{F} \cdot \bar{G} \cdot \bar{H} + \bar{E} \cdot \bar{F} \cdot G \cdot \bar{H}$

2 Using Boolean algebra simplify the expressions given in Exercise 1.

3 Confirm the simplifications of Exercise 2 using Karnaugh maps.

4 Draw the circuit for an OR function of two inputs using only (a) NAND gates and (b) NOR gates.

5 Using gates design the combinatorial logic required to produce a circuit whose action is given by the following truth table:

Inputs			Outputs		
A	B	C	X	Y	Z
0	0	0	0	1	1
0	0	1	1	0	0
0	1	0	1	0	1
0	1	1	1	1	0
1	0	0	1	1	1
1	0	1	0	0	0
1	1	0	0	0	1
1	1	1	0	1	0

6 Find the simplified circuit corresponding to

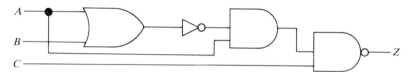

7 Simplify the following logic expression:

$$A . B . C + \bar{A} . \bar{C} + B + \bar{A} . \bar{B} . \bar{C}$$

8 Using the Quine–McCluskey method simplify the following Boolean expression:

$$X = \bar{A} . B . \bar{C} . \bar{D} + \bar{A} . B . C . D + A . \bar{B} . \bar{C} . D$$

$$+ A . \bar{B} . C . \bar{D} + A . B . \bar{C} + A . B . C$$

9 Convert the following circuit into one using only NAND gates:

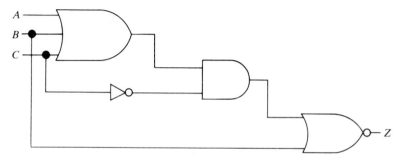

10 Convert the circuit above into one using only two input NAND gates.

11 Design an adder whose input is two 2 bit binary numbers and whose output is 3 bits.

12 How would you implement the following truth table using an eight-input data selector? Can you suggest a method by which it could be implemented using a four-input selector instead? (Hint: the inputs do not have to be constants.)

A	B	C	Output
0	0	0	0
0	0	1	1
0	1	0	1
0	1	1	0
1	0	0	0
1	0	1	1
1	1	0	1
1	1	1	0

13 Devise the implementation of the functions

$$X = A \cdot \bar{B} + A \cdot B \cdot C$$
$$Y = A \cdot C + B \cdot C$$

using a PLA with three product (AND) terms and two outputs (OR gates). (Hint: some rearrangement of the terms is necessary.)

14 Design a divide-by-5 count down counter using JK flip-flops.

15 A set of traffic lights sequence through the colours red, red/amber, green, amber, red etc. Design the logic to control the traffic lights.

16 The opening of a safe is controlled by a set of buttons, representing digits, which must be pressed in a particular order (the correct combination) for the safe to open. If an incorrect sequence is pressed the cancel button must be operated before the next sequence is attempted. Design the logic required to interface the buttons to the door-opening mechanism.

17 What function does the following circuit represent?

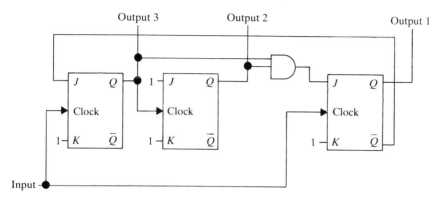

Chapter 3

Predicate Calculus

Introduction

Before defining what we mean by predicate calculus we show why propositional calculus is not adequate for some purposes.

An important use of predicate calculus is in the formal specification of a piece of code. This is done by writing down conditions which must hold before and after the code is executed. Formality is necessary to ensure a precise definition, and this can be achieved by writing these *pre-* and *post-conditions* as formulae in a predicate language. This is clearly useful for describing the semantics of a programming language or for stating the functional behaviour of a procedure or program.

A programming language is just an executable specification language because the code of a program specifies its behaviour and can also be run on a machine. More abstract specification languages say less about *how* a computation is to be performed and concentrate on a precise statement of *what* must be achieved. If they give insufficient information about how to compute something then they are non-executable specification languages. Some subsets of predicate calculus are executable and have been developed into languages called logic programming languages. This is the topic of Chapter 7. However, if programs can be specified properly in a language such as predicate calculus, then their external behaviour as black boxes should be clearer because the description is not so confused with implementation details of algorithms. It ought then to be easier to verify that the code performs according to its specification. We consider this in detail in Chapter 5.

A trivial example of specifying code by the use of predicate calculus is the following.

```
{Power ≥ 0}
Term := 1;
for i := 1 to Power do Term := Term * Base;
Answer := Term
{Answer = Base ** Power}
```

In this we have inserted two *assertions*, i.e. facts which hold when control passes those points in the code. These assertions on their own represent pre- and post-conditions for a section of code which must be written and form a specification against which the code can be verified. The choice of algorithm is then an implementation detail. These two assertions are examples of predicates which contain variables and are either true or false, depending on the values of the variables. Propositional calculus, which gives us no access to program variables, is much more restrictive than we require.

Therefore propositional calculus is rather limited in its applicability. Many of the propositions we would like to write down and make use of in programs depend on variables which are measurements of quantities like time, weight or money. An example is a computer monitoring a rocket launch: the proposition 'the rocket is able to lift off' is true or false depending on the thrust developed by the engines and the weight of the rocket. In data processing also, any program should commence by checking the validity of the input data: the proposition 'the item just entered is valid' will depend on computations performed on the item such as matching a cashcard personal number with that stored in the bank's database. These propositions which depend upon variables are called predicates. The word 'proposition' is only used for predicates which do not (explicitly) depend on any variables. We need to extend propositional calculus in this way, keeping the logical connectives such as 'not', 'and' and 'or' to bind the new predicates together. These predicates, some variables and functions of variables together with the quantifier 'for all' mentioned below and the previous logical connectives are the building blocks of predicate calculus, which we define formally in the next section.

Before this, let us consider one or two simple examples. In a conditional statement it is easy to write down assertions which must be true:

```
if BoolExp then
begin
        {BoolExp}
        Statement1
end
else
begin
        {not BoolExp}
        Statement2
end
```

Here the uses of 'and', 'or' and 'not' in the assertions correspond, of course, to the appropriate connectives as in propositional calculus. The two assertions illustrate that documenting programs with pre- and post-conditions written in a predicate language will involve the use of variables and operators that are used in programs. In fact, Boolean-valued functions in a programming language are examples of predicates. To check their truth, the values of the parameters are input and the result true or false is returned. Consider the predicate

P(x, y, z) = 'A triangle with sides x, y, z has a right angle opposite side z.'

To establish the truth of this, a Boolean function might use Pythagoras' theorem and calculate

Sqr(z) − Sqr(x) − Sqr(y)

If this is zero then P(x, y, z) is true, and if not it is false. The expression is a *function* of the three *variables* x, y and z; moreover, it is composed of several functions, i.e. − and Sqr. We therefore want to include both functions and variables in the definition of predicate calculus. An example *formula* of predicate calculus is the following:

(Sqr(z) = Sqr(x) + Sqr(y)) ⇒ P(x, y, z)

On the left-hand side is a predicate, the equality predicate, which takes two arguments. In this case these arguments are both functions, namely Sqr(z) and Sqr(x) + Sqr(y), with the second being made up of the functions Sqr and +. We know that the truth of this formula is independent of the values chosen for x, y and z, i.e. that 'for all x, y and z, z∗z = x∗x + y∗y implies P(x, y, z)' is true. This *quantified* formula whose truth we assert is written

∀x∀y∀z ((Sqr(z) = Sqr(x) + Sqr(y)) ⇒ P(x, y, z))

Its truth is independent of any values which may have been assigned to the variables somewhere else. Alternatively, it may be that we require the existence of a value for z which will give a right-angled triangle for any pre-assigned values of x and y, i.e. that 'there is a z such that P(x, y, z)' is true. The expression in quotes is written

∃z P(x, y, z)

The symbols ∀ and ∃ which we have just introduced are called *quantifiers* and are always associated with a variable. The first, i.e. ∀, is the *universal* quantifier and the second, i.e. ∃, is the *existential* quantifier. Both are so named for obvious reasons, and the notation is derived from the initial characters of the words 'all' and 'exists'.

The truth of the formula $\exists z\, P(x, y, z)$ depends on the values of the *free* variables x and y, i.e. on the values of the variables which are not associated with any quantifier. A corresponding formula in which we have no such free variables is

$$\forall x \forall y \exists z\, P(x, y, z)$$

which is read as 'for all x and y there exists a z for which $P(x, y, z)$'. In the power example earlier in the section we could have quantified the formula:

```
{Power ⩾ 0}
Term := 1;
for i := 1 to Power do Term := Term * Base;
Answer := Term
{∀ Base (∀ Power ((Power ⩾ 0) ⇒ (Answer = Base ** Power)))}
```

A useful feature we shall allow is that our variables, functions and predicates can be named just like variables, functions and procedures in a programming language such as Pascal; any alphanumeric string not commencing with a digit should be acceptable. This has already been done with the function Sqr above and in the power example. This enables us, for example, to take the Boolean expressions found in program control statements and interpret them directly as predicate formulae.

Any such formula is constructed at the lowest level from variables, which are examples of *terms*. Any function of terms is itself another term and can be used as a parameter of another function. Therefore $(3 + (4 * Pi)) - (5 * Ln(2))$ and $Max((2 * Exp(Side1)) + SqRt(Side2), Ln(Side3))$ are terms. Indeed, any arithmetic expression in a programming language is a term. Terms constructed in this way are the actual parameters allowed for predicates and functions.

The notation used above for $*$ and $+$ is called *infix* notation because the symbol appears between the operands. However, most functions are written in prefix notation, like Max. Even the common arithmetic operations can be written in the standard way used for other functions, replacing, for example, $x + y$ by $Add(x, y)$. Hence we can assume that all terms can be written in such prefix notation.

At the moment no restriction has been placed on the set of values which the variables can assume. In the above examples the intention is to have real or integer-valued variables but no mention was explicitly made to this effect. There is an underlying universal set in which all the variables will have values and the choice of this *universe* forms part of an *interpretation*. When a program is run on a machine we have to consider the implementation interpretation in which the universal set is created explicitly and consists of the binary strings which can be held in the memory locations of the computer. However, we can also consider the abstract intended interpretation specified by the definition of the programming language for which the universe consists essentially of the union of the various types declared in the program.

In addition to specifying a universe, an interpretation makes the decision about how to implement the basic functions and predicates which will be used, such as $<$, $+$, $*$, $=$ etc. This decision made by the interpretation determines the truth values of the basic predicates which we wish to use when the values of the variables are known. We hope that they will have their usual mathematical meanings, but they never do on real machines. For example, in Pascal adding two numbers which have a sum greater than MaxInt will not produce the required result. The more complex predicates which we build up from the basic predicates are called *formulae* and have their truth values automatically determined from the atomic values just as in the case of propositional calculus.

All the ingredients for developing first-order predicate calculus are now present—it is just a generalization of propositional calculus.

The Language

The first-order predicate calculus is a class of languages, called predicate languages, each of which is tailored to the particular use that is envisaged by making a choice of the predicates and functions. It includes propositional calculus and the languages of set theory and arithmetic in exactly the form that we already know. If, say, a Pascal program were to be studied using a predicate language, then the function symbols in the language would include all those function identifiers in the program under consideration. Clearly we would want to keep the same names, which will be strings of alphanumeric characters. Thus Sqr, $+$, $*$ etc. would be the names of functions in the set FN of function symbols in the predicate language. Variables such as Side1, Side2 and Sum might also retain the same names in the set VAR of variables in the language, and similarly for predicates like $=$, $<$, Odd etc. in the set PRED of predicate symbols.

The *alphabet* of a predicate language consists of five disjoint subsets:

(i) the connectives $\vee$, $\wedge$, $\sim$, the quantifier $\forall$, parentheses ( ) and comma , ;

(ii) the set PRED of predicate symbols (or relations);

(iii) the set FN of function symbols (or operations);

(iv) the set CONST of constant identifiers;

(v) the set VAR of variable identifiers.

In all of these but the first it is possible, and sometimes necessary, to have arbitrarily many elements. Since in practice only finitely many symbols or letters are available for naming these elements, the identifiers adopted are usually finite strings of characters from some alphabet such as the set of alphanumeric characters. In this case such names are immediately distinguishable from those in the first set. As in Pascal we could write the symbols $\vee$, $\wedge$, $\sim$ as 'or', 'and', 'not' respectively, in which case we need the concept of reserved words to distinguish them from the identifiers used for elements of the other sets. The non-punctuation symbols in the first set are called *logical connectives*.

The elements in the five sets of the definition are just identifiers which we shall string together mechanically according to certain rules, which are called syntactic rules because they do not require any meaning to be attached to the symbols. Later on we shall define interpretations and valuations which will ascribe meaning to the symbols, such as associating a function to each function symbol.

For the language of integer arithmetic as implemented in Pascal we have

$$\text{PRED} = \{=, <, >, <=, >=, <>, \text{Odd}\}$$
$$\text{FN} = \{\text{Div, Mod, Abs, Sqr, *, +, }-\}$$
$$\text{CONST} = \{0, 1, 2, \ldots\}$$

These sets may vary if arithmetic is studied in some other environment such as another programming language or mathematics. The names at least may be different, and perhaps also the sets of functions and predicates will not correspond. There may be extra predicates such as | (divides) or functions like ! (factorial). Indeed, anyone studying arithmetic is at liberty to define more of these as required. The predicate language used should have all the function, variable, predicate and constant symbols which are needed.

With each function and predicate symbol is associated a non-negative integer, i.e. the number of formal parameters (terms or arguments) which each takes. Let n be this number for the predicate P in PRED. Then P is called an *n-place* or *n-ary* predicate. In Chapter 1 every predicate had $n=0$ and was called a *proposition*. A *unary* predicate has $n=1$ and a *binary* predicate has $n = 2$. Thus Odd is unary and $<$ is binary in Pascal. Similarly, to each function f in FN there is an associated number n of variables or operands; f is a function of n variables or an *n-ary* function. The functions Abs and Sqr are unary, whereas $*$ and Div are binary. For any given predicate P or function f we shall write the associated numbers of formal parameters as n_p and n_f respectively to show their dependence on P and f.

For both predicates and functions we allow the possibility of no variables. For example, True and False are Pascal predicates of no variables and 0, 1, 2, ... are functions of no variables. They require no arguments before they can be evaluated, unlike $<$, $=$, Odd and Sqr. The functions of null arity are called *constants*, and for convenience we have separated them from the other functions into the set CONST. However, in most respects they behave in the same way as functions.

It is possible to use the same name for functions and predicates of different arities, and this is common when the definition is essentially identical for any number of parameters. An example of this is Add(a, b, ... , c) standing for $(... ((a + b) + ... + c))$. However, if the arity is different for two functions or predicates we regard them as being distinct members of FN or PRED.

Before progressing to the construction of the formulae of predicate languages, observe that great freedom exists within the set of connectives and punctuation to rename, add and remove symbols just as is the case for the predicates and functions of arithmetic. The set chosen above in (i) is easy for describing a language and for proofs because it is so limited in its alphabet, but for that reason it entails hard work in practical use; usually all the symbols listed in Fig. 3.1 are required. Extra connectives, among others,

Symbol	Alternatives	Read	Name
$\wedge$	$\cdot$, $\cap$	and	conjunction
$\vee$	$+$; $\cup$	or	disjunction
$\sim$	$\neg$ $-$	not	negation
$\Rightarrow$	$\rightarrow$ $>$ $\supset$	implies	implication
$\Leftarrow$	$\leftarrow$ $<$ $\subset$	if	reverse implication
$\Leftrightarrow$	$\leftrightarrow$ $\equiv$	if and only if	equivalence
$\forall$	A	for all	universal quantification
$\exists$	E	there is a	existential quantification
(	[{	open brackets	left parenthesis
)	] }	close brackets	right parenthesis
,		comma	comma
$=$	$\cdot$	is equal to	equality predicate
$\neq$	$<>$	is not equal to	inequality predicate

Fig. 3.1. Some symbols of predicate calculus with their common alternatives.

can be added without difficulty by defining them in terms of existing connectives.

A predicate language has strings of two types: the terms and the formulae. The terms include variables; they are used as arguments of functions and predicates and are constructed by noting that any function of terms is again a term. Thus, terms are defined recursively as compositions of a finite number of functions. An example of a term is

Chr(Add(Ord(Ch), Sbt(Ord('A'), Ord('a'))))

where 'A' and 'a' are constant symbols (elements of CONST), Ch is a variable (an element of VAR), Chr and Ord are unary function symbols, and Add and Sbt are binary function symbols.

The formal definition of a term is as follows. *Terms* are those finite strings generated by repeated application of the following rules:
(i) if x is in VAR then x is a term;
(ii) if c is in CONST then c is a term;
(iii) if f in FN is an n-ary function symbol and $t_1, t_2, \ldots, t_n$ are terms then $f(t_1, t_2, \ldots, t_n)$ is a term.
The set of all terms in a given language will be denoted TERMS. The convention is not always to use prefix notation for functions as in the definition. Shortly we shall introduce a relaxation of this constraint by which infix notation will be allowed so that we can recognize First + Second and $a * b * c$ as valid terms.

In a manner similar to that for the construction of terms, the formulae of the language are also defined recursively starting with predicates evaluated on terms. These are the *atomic* formulae, so called because they cannot be decomposed into smaller formulae. The connectives are then used to create the other formulae from the atomic formulae. There are no strings in common between the terms and the formulae. The latter must contain predicate symbols but the former cannot. The predicates are the strings to which we shall assign truth values.

The *formulae* of a predicate language are those finite strings generated from the alphabet according to the following rules
(i) if P in PRED is an 0-ary predicate symbol then P is a formula
(ii) if P in PRED is an n-place predicate symbol with $n > 0$ and $t_1, t_2, \ldots, t_n)$ are terms then $P(t_1, t_2, \ldots, t_n)$ is a formula
(iii) if U, V are formulae then so are $(U \wedge V), (U \vee V)$ and $\sim U$
(iv) if W is a formula and x is in VAR then $\forall x (W)$ is a formula.

The strings of symbols which are formulae are also called *well-formed formulae* (WFFs). The *atomic* formulae are those generated by rules (i) and (ii). If $\mathscr{L}$ is the language being considered then we shall write $W \in \mathscr{L}$ when W is a formula of $\mathscr{L}$. Note that after a quantifier only a variable is possible. This is the characteristic property of first-order predicate calculus. The higher-order languages also allow quantification over function symbols and predicate symbols, but we are not interested in them in this book. $\forall x\,(W)$ is read as 'for all x, W holds', which is a predicate that may or may not be true; truth values still have to be assigned.

Examples of atomic formulae include Gt(Abs(x), Sqr(y)) and Eq(Cos(Pi), Sin(0)) where Gt and Eq are the binary predicates $>$ and $=$ written in prefix notation, Cos and Sin are functions of one variable, and 0 and Pi are constants. In general, as remarked earlier, the Boolean expressions of a programming language are all WFFs, but they do not usually contain quantifiers.

At the moment nothing is claimed about the truth or falsehood of formulae; that depends on their interpretation. As in the case of terms, some concessions need to be made to allow standard mathematical notation to be accepted in the above definition. We want to treat $\text{Cos}(\text{Pi}) = \text{Sin}(0)$ as a respectable formula in the language. This requires a list of conventions by which letters in the alphabet can be deleted from or reordered within formulae, thereby extending the language.

Conventions and Extensions

The economy of symbols used in predicate languages as described in the last section is balanced by its lack of expressive power. To gain even a part of the richness of mathematics or the power of a high level programming language without making formulae impractically long or unreadable it is necessary to have the freedom to add new symbols such as some of the logic symbols listed in Fig. 3.1.

There are two aspects to extending the alphabet. First, a syntactic rule is required for constructing formulae or terms with each new symbol. Second, a semantic rule may be needed for transforming such terms and formulae into those using the original language. In the former the translation rule must allow unique decipherability into the constituent subformulae. In the latter the transformation rule defines the meaning of the formula. The rules for constructing terms and formulae with a new symbol are similar to those used before. For example, if the connectives $\Rightarrow$, $\Leftarrow$ and $\Leftrightarrow$ are added then the new syntactic rules if U, V are formulae then so are

$(U \Rightarrow V)$, $(U \Leftarrow V)$ and $(U \Leftrightarrow V)$

are included, and the semantic rules are that

$(U \Rightarrow V)$ means $(\sim U \vee V)$ *False implies true*

$(U \Leftarrow V)$ means $(U \vee \sim V)$ *If u true then v false*

$(U \Leftrightarrow V)$ means $((U \Rightarrow V) \wedge (U \Leftarrow V))$ *u is true if & only if V is true.*

The first of these leads to the algorithm 'replace every subformula $(U \Rightarrow V)$ by $(\sim U \vee V)$'. The unique decipherability ensures that this algorithm is unambiguous, and repetition of the replacement procedure will convert any formula (which may use $\Rightarrow$ several times) into a formula which does not use $\Rightarrow$. In this way all formulae using the new alphabet can be rewritten in the original language. In the same way we add the existential quantifier to the universal quantifier already in the language by including $\exists x(U)$ in the syntax and the semantic rule that this means $\sim \forall x(\sim U)$. In Chapter 1 we used the symbol $\equiv$ to denote this equivalence and wrote, for example,

$$(U \Rightarrow V) \equiv (\sim U \vee V)$$

New symbols and their syntactic rules lead to a higher-level predicate language in exactly the same way as they do for a programming language where, for example, a **case** statement is superior to the more primitive **if** . . . **then** . . . **else if** . . . **then** . . . **else if** . . . . The rules by which we add extra structuring connectives to a predicate language and what the connectives mean in terms of the basic connectives are mirrored in the work of a compiler. A high level programming language is defined similarly using such rules of syntax, and a compiler for it performs the translation via semantic rules into the lowest-level language, i.e. the computer's machine code. Via such construction rules arithmetic operators in a predicate language can be defined to obtain the infix notation typical of arithmetic expressions in most programming languages. In this way

$$(3 + (2 * (5 - ((10 * \text{Pi})/3))))$$

becomes an acceptable term. Because of the semantic transformation rules, when it comes to proving results about terms and formulae it can always be assumed that the string is in one of the restricted forms defined initially; if it is not, the added symbols should be replaced appropriately by the more primitive ones.

The other manner in which formulae tend to stray from the initial very restricted form is in the inclusion, change or exclusion of brackets. It is already possible by using the above to allow different brackets such as { } and [ ]. Any pair of brackets can be added around a term or formula, and this is particularly useful for clarity when it becomes a substring of a larger string. As an example, there may be a subset of FN corresponding to arrays in a Pascal program for which square brackets would be appropriate. (An array can be regarded as a function defined on the index set and yielding the value of the appropriate element in the array.) Then SomeArray[$I+1, J+2$] should be a respectable term.

Deletion of parentheses is possible provided that there is a similar convention to that in arithmetic where multiplication is always done before addition. With suitable syntactic and semantic rules we can write the example term above as

$$3+2*(5-10*Pi/3)$$

which is standard notation. A similar order of priorities exists for logical operators showing which must act first and it is given in Fig. 3.2. This order

Fig. 3.2. Order of precedence for operators.

is exactly the same as in propositional calculus with the additional logical operators, i.e. the quantifiers, at the top of the list with the highest priority. Thus, quantifiers are always performed first, i.e. they operate over the smallest possible subformulae, followed by $\sim$, $\wedge$, $\vee$ in that order. Note that the unary operators always have a higher priority than any of the binary operators. Brackets can now be inserted as long as we know how to deal with operators of equal priority. This is done by applying the leftmost such operator first. Typically we assume the construction rules

if U, V are formulae then so are $U \vee V$ and $U \wedge V$

The resulting formula $U \vee V \vee W$, say, needs to be bracketed. The parentheses can be inserted by a rule which deals with the rightmost ambiguous operator of lowest priority first (or, equivalently, the leftmost ambiguous operator of highest priority) and inserts brackets to make it unambiguous at that point, i.e. by an 'association from the left' transformation rule. The rule is as follows.

Suppose $*$ is the rightmost operator of lowest priority which is still unbracketed and $(U * V)$ is the smallest bracketed substring containing it. Then this substring means $((U)*(V))$.

By convention the outermost pair of brackets is omitted and must be replaced first before applying the rule. Doing this to $U \lor V \lor W$ yields first $(U \lor V \lor W)$ and then $((U \lor V) \lor (W))$, which is unambiguous. A more complicated example is $\exists x U \Rightarrow V \land W_1 \Rightarrow W_2 \land \forall x \sim W$ which becomes $(((\exists x(U)) \Rightarrow (V \land W_1)) \Rightarrow (W_2 \land (\forall x(\sim W))))$. Make sure that you understand why it is bracketed in this way.

Apart from the two special cases of omitting brackets for arithmetic and logical operators it is sometimes unwise to try to reduce the number of other parentheses beyond omitting the outermost pair. An example will illustrate the dangers. Suppose function names were to include SqrRoot, Sqr and Root, and the latter pair could be concatenated in some formula. Then Sqr(Root(x)) and SqrRoot(x) could not be distinguished if brackets were to be omitted.

Quantifiers

Much of computing is concerned with data processing. A simple problem in this area might be when a bank searches its files for a record with a particular account number, say using a Pascal function with heading

> **function** ThereIsAnAccount(GivenAcNo: AcNoType): Boolean;

Clearly it will need a local variable, say

> **var** AcNo: AcNoType;

and it will check all values of AcNo to see whether any matches GivenAcNo. The value of the Boolean function is then precisely the truth value of

> $\sim \forall \text{AcNo} (\text{AcNo} \neq \text{GivenAcNo})$

or of

> $\exists \text{AcNo} (\text{AcNo} = \text{GivenAcNo})$

there exists AcNo (if AcNo=Gi---) holds

in the obvious sense. It is quite possible that AcNo is not the best identifier for the local variable; perhaps CurrentAcNo might be more precise. The change in the program is easily made using an editor to change all

occurrences of AcNo to CurrentAcNo in the Boolean function. Assuming
there is no other variable CurrentAcNo in the function, this change does
not affect the result of the program at all; the same numbers and characters
are being processed as before, and there is just a different logical name for
the local variable. The formula corresponding to the altered program is
now

$$\sim \forall \text{CurrentAcNo} \; (\text{CurrentAcNo} \neq \text{GivenAcNo})$$

with every occurrence of AcNo also having been changed to CurrentAcNo,
and we would expect its truth value to remain the same as before. This is an
example of *alphabetic substitution*, and when a truth value is defined we
shall ensure that such substitutions in quantified formulae do not alter
truth values.

   To make such changes we need to distinguish which occurrences of a
variable are attached to a given quantifier over that variable. This is
achieved in the same way as in programming languages by having scope
rules. These rules will bind the given occurrences to a particular quantifier
symbol just as occurrences ·in programs are attached to a certain
declaration. There is no problem when all the variables have distinct
names, as in the formula

$$\forall x \, (x < 3 \Rightarrow \forall y \, (z = \text{Sqr}(x) + \text{Sqr}(y)))$$

Every x is bound by the initial quantifier, and every y by the other
quantifier. However, suppose that all occurrences of y are changed into x to
obtain

$$\forall x \, (x < 3 \Rightarrow \forall x \, (z = \text{Sqr}(x) + \text{Sqr}(x)))$$

Both quantifiers are now over the same variable. With what quantifier do
you associate each occurrence of x? In fact the last x in the first formula has
changed allegiance. Each quantifier will assign a value to its own variable
and those occurrences bound to it by the scope rules. Effectively we have a
different variable for each quantifier although the names might be identical.
To decide what quantifier any particular instance of a variable is bound to,
we just look outside more and more enclosing pairs of brackets (. . .) around
the occurrence until a quantifier of that name is found. This is what happens
in Pascal programs where we look just above the bodies of larger and larger
procedures containing the variable occurrence until a declaration of that
variable is found. Therefore in the formula $\forall x \, (x < 3 \Rightarrow \forall x \, (z = \text{Sqr}(x) +$
$\text{Sqr}(x)))$ the occurrences of x governed by the second quantifier are those xs

within the bracketed subformula of $\forall x\,(z = \text{Sqr}(x) + \text{Sqr}(x))$ and they take the same value as the x attached to that quantifier. The instance of x in $x < 3$ is governed by the first quantifier and receives the value of the x attached to that quantifier.

As a further example we could write a pseudo-Pascal procedure for making a formula true, e.g.

$$\forall i \forall j\,((\text{Matrix}[i, j] = i + 3j) \wedge \forall i\,(\text{Vector}[i] = 2j))$$

In this WFF we have variables Matrix and Vector to initialize, and we are given a binary function _ [_] and a ternary function _ [_ , _] which we shall interpret in our pseudo-Pascal as functions for accessing arrays. A procedure is required for each quantifier, their declarations being nested in the same way as are the quantified subformulae in the main formula. The formula translates easily into the code of Fig. 3.3. In the code each quantifier yields a local declaration of its variable, and the scope of that variable coincides with the scope of the corresponding variable in the predicate formula.

We can now give the scope rules for the variables of quantifiers. First, the *scope* of the intial quantifier in a subformula $\forall x\,(W)$ is contained within

```
procedure WholeFormula(var Matrix, Vector : Universe);
{Post-condition: ∀i ∀j [(Matrix(i,j)=i+3j) ∧ ∀i (Vector (i)=2j))}
    var   i,j : Universe;
    procedure Subformula1(i,j : Universe; var Matrix,Vector : Universe);
    {Post-condition: (Matrix[i,j]=i+3j) ∧ ∀i (Vector[i]=2j)}
        procedure SubFormula2(j : Universe; var Vector : Universe);
        {Post-condition: ∀i (Vector[i] = 2j) }
            var i : Universe ;
        begin {SubFormula2}
            ForAll i do Vector[i] := 2 * j
        end ; {SubFormula2}

    begin { SubFormula1}
        Matrix[i,j] := i + 3 * j ;
        SubFormula2(j,Vector)
    end ; {SubFormula1}

begin   {WholeFormula}
        ForAll i do  ForAll j do  SubFormula1 (i,j,Matrix,Vector)

end ; {WholeFormula}
```

Fig. 3.3. A procedure to make a certain formula hold.

the subformula (W), and secondly it is outside any smaller subformula $\forall x\,(V)$ within W where the quantified variable is the same. All such occurrences of x, including the explicitly mentioned one attached to the quantifier in $\forall x\,(W)$, are *bound by* or *governed by* the initial quantifier. Occurrences of x are called *free* if they are not bound, i.e. not within the scope of a quantifier over the same variable.

In the example illustrated in Fig. 3.3 the free variables for each subformula have been entered as parameters of the procedures, and the bound variables are governed by the quantifier associated with the declaration of the given variable in the code. Here occurrences of variables are free in a formula if and only if they are not declared in the code for the corresponding procedure.

The definition of bound and free variables can be recast as follows, in the same manner as the recursive definition for constructing formulae.

(i) Every occurrence of every variable in an atomic formula is *free*.

(ii) No occurrence of the variable x in $\forall x\,(W)$ is free.

(iii) The occurrences of the variable x which are free in U and V remain free in $\sim U$, $U \vee V$, $U \wedge V$ and $\forall y\,(U)$ where y is a variable not equal (as an element of **VAR**) to x.

(iv) Occurrences of a variable which are not free by the above rules are *bound*.

It is clear that the only way in which an occurrence of a variable x can become bound in a formula is via rule (ii) by appearing in a subformula of the form $\forall x\,(W)$. The quantifier in the smallest such subformula containing the occurrence is the quantifier which binds or governs it. Note also that the explicitly mentioned x in $\forall x\,(W)$ is itself bound and that any instance of x which is bound by the initial quantifier of $\forall x\,(W)$ becomes free in W. For example, in

$$\forall i \forall j\,((\text{Matrix}(i, j) = i + 3j) \wedge \forall i\,(\text{Vector}(i) = 2j))$$

the first three occurrences of i in the WFF are bound to the initial quantifier and the last two occurrences are bound under the final quantifier. As all occurrences of j are bound by the second quantifier, there are no free occurrences of any variable if the other identifiers denote functions.

In practice the predicate formulae of greatest interest are those for which every instance of each variable is bound. Such formulae are called *sentences*. The above example

$$\forall i \forall j\,((\text{Matrix}(i, j) = i + 3j) \wedge (\forall i\,(\text{Vector}(i) = 2j)))$$

is a sentence. If a formula does have a free variable x and is true for the arbitrary value x might take, it will be true for all values. Therefore adding ∀x to bind the variable will not change its truth. Doing this for each variable usually enables us to consider only sentences. We shall need sentences with all the quantified variables distinct when we come to theorem-proving techniques later.

Interpretations

Certain parallels have already been observed between programs and formulae. For example, the choice of names for the classes VAR, CONST and FN was deliberate to emphasize these connections. The equivalents of predicates are Boolean-valued functions which have no side effects (i.e. which do not alter any non-local variables). Quantifiers arise naturally with loops; for example, ∀x (Property(x)) is an assertion that can be made at the end of a loop which ensures the truth of Property(x) for each consecutive value of x.

However, nothing has been said so far about the definitions of the functions and predicates (how are they to be evaluated?) or about the values which the variables may take (what is their type?). Just as these must all be specified in a program the same is true for a predicate language, and this is done by an *interpretation*. Variables in predicate languages do not have a predeclared type as do those in programming languages. We are free to choose the common type of all variables to be the integers, rationals, reals or any other non-empty set we wish. The evaluation of a WFF is done in exactly the same way as the calculation of a Boolean expression on a computer. The definition will tell us to calculate the truth value of the innermost quantified formulae first and work outwards to larger formulae in the same way as the formulae were built up by successive application of the rules in the definition of a WFF. We can see the processes involved by keeping the example of computing expressions in mind.

For simplicity, let us assume that in our intended interpretation all variables will take integer values. This is the *universe*. The functions we have in predicate calculus are used to build up terms which are used as actual parameters just as variables are. So, when a term or function is evaluated an integer must again be obtained. Thus a function identifier like Add in a formula of the predicate language has a corresponding actual function + which operates on the universe of integers. The universe is therefore the universal type in which all terms have their values; the arguments of functions and the results of functions, as well as constants, belong to this common type. So, the interpretation we choose has to supply at least a type called the universe, which is the set of values which terms are allowed to take and, for each function symbol in the language, an associated function operating on the universe.

We must also decide what to do with predicate symbols such as Gt (greater than) in the language. When the operands of Gt have been evaluated as integers we require a relation on the integers to say whether the particular instance of Gt is true or not. If we interpret Gt as the usual relation $>$ on integers then Gt will be associated with the set of pairs (x, y) of integers with $x > y$. This is the set on which we intend that Gt be true. Therefore, if in the formula Gt(Term1, Term2) we find that Term1 and Term2 have values 4 and 3 respectively then the formula is evaluated as True since $4 > 3$. Thus, in an interpretation we also need a relation on the universe for each predicate symbol. The interpretation will then provide two types. One is the universe, which may vary, and the other is fixed, namely the Booleans. Another view of predicates in the language is that in the interpretation there are corresponding functions with arguments which have the type of the universe and results which are of type Boolean.

To sum up, all the function and predicate symbols of a predicate language have actions defined in an interpretation in terms of the universe in exactly the same way as a programming language specifies its types like integer and its operators like $+$, succ, $<$ etc. which act on them.

In the formal definition of an interpretation which follows U^n is the set of vectors $(u_1, u_2, \ldots, u_n)$ with n entries each of which is an element of U, i.e. the set on which an n-ary function operates.

An *interpretation* I of a predicate language $\mathscr{L}$ consists of the following:
(i) a non-empty set U called the *universe* or *domain* of I, which is the set of values which the variables may take;
(ii) for each predicate symbol P of n variables an n-ary subset P_I of n-tuples in U^n which is the set of points or vectors at which P is to be true;
(iii) for each function symbol f of n variables a function f_I from U^n to U.
(iv) for each constant symbol c an element c_I of U, which will be the value of c.

In reality, on a computer a universe of integers is not possible because an infinite amount of space is not available; the universe is therefore, rather, the finite set of values which a word of memory may take. Then operators of a given programming language require certain processes to be performed on these words of memory in terms of the most primitive functions such as $+$, $*$, Abs, and relational operators such as And, $=$, $<$. The universe and these processes can and do vary between implementations and each corresponds to a different interpretation. Some programming languages attempt to describe the specific implementation interpretation, e.g. by defining the type Integer as the interval $-\text{MaxInt} .. \text{MaxInt}$, but others do not. However, usually in computer applications the universe U will be a suitable subset of Real $\cup$ Integer $\cup$ Boolean $\cup$ Text $\cup \ldots$ which includes all defined types in the program of interest and, for concrete implementations, restricts infinite types like Real and Integer to prescribed finite subsets.

We shall consider first an example in which the universe is $U = \text{Nat}$, the set of natural numbers (including 0). This is the set of integers with the negative numbers deleted. One of the ways of generating Nat is to start with the constant 0 and successively add 1 to obtain every natural number. A predicate language in which this can be done has a constant symbol Zero and a unary successor function symbol Succ. The way of writing 4, for example, is then as Succ(Succ(Succ(Succ(0)))). The standard interpretation has universe Nat, $\text{Zero}_1 = 0$ and Succ_1 defined by $\text{Succ}_1(n) = n + 1$. Note that constants behave just like functions of no variables. If Zero were regarded as a function of no variables then, as it has no parameters which could change, the function into U associated with Zero would have to be constant, taking the value Zero_1. The same applies to predicates of no variables, i.e. propositions.

In the subset of Pascal which we could use to form a predicate language we have the 0-ary predicate True and the unary predicate Odd. With Odd we have to specify the set Odd_1 on which we wish Odd to be true, namely $\{1, 3, 5, \ldots\}$ in the current example (plus the negative odd numbers if we had not restricted the universe to Nat). This is a subset of $U^1 = U$. For the predicate True we want a subset of U^0, which is a set containing the single vector ( ) with no entries. If we take True_1, the set on which True is to be true, to be the whole of U^0 in every interpretation, then True will always be evaluated as T, as we wish. The only other subset of U^0 is the empty set $\{\}$ which we associate with the predicate False in every interpretation. When False is evaluated, it is always for the single vector ( ) in U^0 and this does not lie in $\text{False}_1 = \{\}$. Therefore False will take the value F.

Thus there are two special predicates of no variables, i.e. True and False, which evaluate to T and F respectively in every interpretation. Other constant predicates, i.e. propositions, may be true in some interpretations and false in others. If we restrict our attention to propositions, then choosing an interpretation is the same as assigning truth values in propositional calculus.

As a second example, let us take a procedure which calculates completion days for jobs from information about the starting day, the work involved and the manpower available. The **ForAll** statement has the expected semantics.

```
type        WeekDay              = (M, Tu, W, Th, F);
            Nat                  = 0 .. MaxInt;
var         MenAvailable         : array[WeekDay] of Nat;
            CompletionDay        : array[WeekDay] of WeekDay;

procedure   ComputeCompletionDay(ManDaysReqd:Nat);
var         Day, DaySoFar    : WeekDay;
            Effort           : Nat;
begin       {ComputeCompletionDay}
            ForAll Day in WeekDay do
            begin
                Effort := 0;
                DaySoFar := Day;
                while Effort < ManDaysReqd do
                begin
                        DaySoFar := Succ(DaySoFar);
                        Effort := Effort + MenAvailable[DaySoFar]
                end;
                CompletionDay[Day] := DaySoFar
            end {*}
end; {ComputeCompletionDay}
```

The intended universe for this procedure is $Nat \cup WeekDay \cup \{Undefined\}$ where Undefined will be the value of unassigned variables. The constants to which we have access are $0, 1, 2, \ldots$, MaxInt, M, Tu, W, Th, F. These identifiers have corresponding constant values in the implemented universe in which, typically, Tu would be represented by its ordinal value in the type WeekDay. So perhaps $Tu_I = ord(Tu)$ if I is the interpretation specified for the programming language.

The function Succ in this programming language is interpreted so that

$$Succ_I(M_I) = Tu_I$$
$$Succ_I(Tu_I) = W_I$$
$$\ldots$$
$$Succ_I(F_I) = M_I$$
$$Succ_I(0_I) = 1_I$$
$$\ldots$$
$$Succ_I(MaxInt_I) = 0_I$$
$$Succ_I(Undefined_I) = Undefined_I$$

With a strongly typed language there are checks performed at compile time using predicates such as InWeekDay defined by

$InWeekDay_I(M_I) = T$

. . .

$InWeekDay_I(F_I) = T$
$InWeekDay_I(0_I) = F$

. . .

$InWeekDay_I(MaxInt_I) = F$
$InWeekDay_I(Undefined_I) = F$

With this predicate we can insert at $\{*\}$ the assertion

$\forall Day\ (InWeekDay(Day) \Rightarrow CompletionDay[Day] \neq Undefined)$

and at other points in the text assertions that should also be checked at compile time. Arrays like CompletionDay are just partial functions, i.e. they are not defined for all values. One way to treat them in this language is to insist that the intended interpretation I satisfies

$CompletionDay_I[0_I] \qquad\qquad = Undefined_I$

. . .

$CompletionDay_I[MaxInt_I] \quad = Undefined_I$
$CompletionDay_I[Undefined_I] = Undefined_I$

However, an assignment statement will change the interpretation during program execution. Thus, if $CompletionDay_I[M_I] = Tu_I$ and Completion-day$[M] := W$ is executed then the function CompletionDay[ ] has a different interpretation before and after the statement because $CompletionDay_I$ has been redefined. What needs to be done is to view CompletionDay as a variable, just as it is declared in the program, and not as a function. This entails defining a function _ [_] of two variables, the first argument of which is intended to be an expression with value in the type Array[Weekday] of Weekday, and the second an expression in the type Weekday. With this way of treating arrays, the universe has to be extended from the above to include values of such arrays, e.g. the 5-tuple vector (Tu, W, F, Th, W).

Valuations

As yet we have not decided what values to ascribe to the variables, just that we wish them to be in some universe, e.g. the integers. This is a problem which is not resolved in the definition of an interpretation, which is really a description of the environment in which computations are performed and which is more or less constant throughout the duration of a program execution. Variable values are the result of whatever initialization and computational procedures were encountered to give each variable its current value. This process is separated from an interpretation because it varies during computation, whereas the universe, its functions and relations are fixed throughout.

The introduction of variables to the language involves greater subtlety in assigning truth values than was the case in the propositional calculus. Within the same interpretation I we have already observed that we wish formulae to be either true or false depending on the values of their (free) variables. When the value of each variable is chosen in the universe, the value can be calculated for every term in the obvious way (i.e. following the recursive way in which the term is constructed) using the functions $f_i: U^n \to U$. Then each predicate P is evaluated at the defined point in U^n and assigned T or F according as the point is in the set P_I of the interpretation or not. Two maps (i.e. functions) are involved here corresponding to the two cases of us requiring values for the maps which lie in the target 'types' of the universe U and the Booleans. The first evaluates each term giving a value in U from a chosen assignment of values for each variable. The other is a truth valuation in the sense of propositional calculus but with additional properties. These two maps constitute an I-valuation.

A truth valuation assigns truth values to compound WFFs constructed with the logical connectives $\wedge$, $\vee$ and $\sim$ in exactly the same way as defined in the truth tables of Chapter 1 for propositional calculus.

A *truth valuation* for a predicate language $\mathscr{L}$ is a function σ: $\mathscr{L} \to \text{Booleans} = \{T, F\}$ satisfying

$$\sigma(\sim U) \ = T \text{ if and only if } \sigma(U) = F$$
$$\sigma(U \vee V) = T \text{ if and only if } \sigma(U) = T \text{ or } \sigma(V) = T \text{ or both}$$
$$\sigma(U \wedge V) = T \text{ if and only if both } \sigma(U) = T \text{ and } \sigma(V) = T.$$

The truth valuation required for predicate calculus assigns values to single predicates—the atomic formulae—as described above, but must also act on quantifiers in the way implied by the English phrase 'for all . . .' or 'there is a . . .'. Then $\forall x (W)$ will be true if W is true for every possible choice $a \in U$ of value for x, and false otherwise. For a given interpretation such a truth valuation combined with a list of the values of each variable will enable the value of each term, and hence of each predicate and formula, to be deduced.

The valuation σ of interest at a particular point during the execution of a program is the one that associates to each variable the value in its assigned memory location. Suppose the Boolean expression Eq(Sqr(z), Add(Sqr(x), Sqr(y))) is to be evaluated at that point. Call this formula W. If 3, 4 and 5 are in the memory locations for variables x, y and z, and Eq, Add and Sqr are interpreted as equality, addition and squaring respectively, then $\sigma(\text{Sqr}(z)) = (\sigma z) * (\sigma z) = 5 * 5 = 25$ and similarly $\sigma(\text{Add}(\text{Sqr}(x), \text{Sqr}(y))) = \sigma(\text{Sqr}(x)) + \sigma(\text{Sqr}(y)) = (\sigma x) * (\sigma x) + (\sigma y) * (\sigma y) = 9 + 16 = 25$. There is an axiom for equality which states that $\sigma(t_1 = t_2) = T$ for terms t_1, t_2 if and only if $\sigma(t_1) = \sigma(t_2)$. In this case $\sigma(W) = T$ since both terms evaluate to 25.

The formal definition of an I-valuation requires a little extra notation. Suppose σ is a map that assigns a value to each variable. So $\sigma: \text{VAR} \rightarrow U$ is a map from the set of variables into the universe of values. Then we let $\sigma_{x \rightarrow a}$ be the map $\text{VAR} \rightarrow U$ which is identical with σ except that $\sigma_{x \rightarrow a}(x) = a$ instead of $\sigma(x)$, i.e. x has the value a under $\sigma_{x \rightarrow a}$ and all other variables retain the same values as under σ. We may think of the subscript $x \rightarrow a$ as an update function, changing the values of the variables from that given by σ to that given by $\sigma_{x \rightarrow a}$ in exactly the way that they would be changed as control passed the assignment statement $x := a$ in a program. Also in the following definition and in future we shall often write $\sigma(x)$ more simply as σx.

Let I be an interpretation for a predicate language $\mathscr{L}$. An *I-valuation* σ is determined by I and a map $\sigma: \text{VAR} \rightarrow U$ and generates two maps. There is an evaluation map $\sigma: \text{TERMS} \rightarrow U$ and a truth valuation $\sigma: \mathscr{L} \rightarrow \text{Booleans} = \{T, F\}$ which are defined recursively as follows.

(i) $\sigma: \text{VAR} \rightarrow U$ is extended to a map $\sigma: \text{TERMS} \rightarrow U$ by defining $\sigma f(t_1, t_2, \ldots, t_n) = f_1(\sigma t_1, \sigma t_2, \ldots, \sigma t_n)$ for terms $t_1, t_2, \ldots, t_n$ and any n-ary function f.

(ii) The truth values of atomic formulae are obtained by defining $\sigma P(t_1, t_2, \ldots, t_n) = T$ if and only if $(\sigma t_1, \sigma t_2, \ldots, \sigma t_n) \in P_1$ where P is any n-ary predicate and $t_1, t_2, \ldots, t_n$ are any terms.

(iii) Quantified formulae have truth values determined by $\sigma(\forall x(W)) = T$ if and only if $\sigma_{x \rightarrow a}(W) = T$ for all $a \in U$, where x is any variable and W any formula of $\mathscr{L}$.

Note specifically that the valuation map from WFFs to Booleans must be a truth valuation in the sense of the previous definition.

Let us consider the expression $\forall x(W)$ where W is again the formula Eq(Sqr(z), Add(Sqr(x), Sqr(y))). Suppose the interpretation is the same as before, namely Nat with the same meanings for Eq etc., and σ maps x, y and z to 3, 4 and 5 respectively. Then $\sigma_{z \rightarrow a}$ maps x, y and z to 3, 4 and a respectively. We find $\sigma(W) = T$ but $\sigma_{z \rightarrow a}(W) = F$ if $a \neq 5$. Hence $\sigma(\forall x(W)) = F$.

This example should help to explain rule (iii) in the definition. This rule gives the truth values of quantified formulae in terms of the truth values of formulae with fewer quantifiers and so ultimately in terms of quantifier-free formulae. Hence this recursive aspect of the definition does lead eventually to cases that we know about by virtue of the earlier rules.

The same name has been used for convenience for both maps in a valuation. No confusion should arise because one operates on formulae giving Boolean values and the other operates on terms giving values in the universe. Remember that when formulae and terms were defined it was observed that these two sets of terms and formulae do not intersect.

It was decided earlier that to simplify definitions, theorems and proofs we would restrict the alphabet to a minimum. As a consequence we have no rule giving us the truth value of, say, existentially quantified formulae. In extending the alphabet it is necessary to define the valuation σ on all new formulae. This is done by using our semantic rules to rewrite the given formula W as a formula W' within the existing language. We have called these 'semantic' rules because we are not changing the meaning of the formula, just the way it is written. Therefore the truth value of W should be the same as W', whence we obtain the additional rule for valuations:

(iv) $\sigma W = \sigma W'$ where W' is obtained from W by application of the semantic transformation rules.

For example, in the case of the existential quantifier, $\exists x(W)$ means $\sim \forall x(\sim W)$. Thus both are true if and only if $\forall x(\sim W)$ is false, i.e. if $\sim W$ is false for some value of x. Hence $\sigma \exists x(W) = T$ if and only if $\sigma_{x \to a} W = T$ for some value a of x. This is clearly what we intended.

The rule above enables us not only to increase the alphabet to encompass all desirable symbols but also to delete redundant features. If we know, for example, that $Sqr(z) = Sqr(x) + Sqr(y)$ and $P(x, y, z)$ are always simultaneously true or false for any valuation then we can decide to define $P(x, y, z)$ as shorthand for $Sqr(z) = Sqr(x) + Sqr(y)$ and so delete P from the basic alphabet. Therefore we can increase and decrease the alphabet at will. With a larger alphabet the language should become clearer and more concise, but with a smaller alphabet it is easier to see what universes, interpretations and valuations are possible and to work with them.

In rule (iii) no use is made of the value $\sigma(x)$ of x when evaluating a quantified formula $\forall x(W)$. The choice of image, i.e. value, for x is forgotten in the valuations $\sigma_{x \to a}$ and the underlying subformula W is evaluated for every possible choice instead. The same must be true for any variable with no free occurrences. In general the truth of a formula can only then depend on the values of the free variables. In a sentence there are no free variables and so the truth is independent of the valuation. We thus have the following result.

Theorem 3.1

(i) The truth σW of a formula W for some valuation σ depends only on the images of the assignment map σ for the free variables of W.

In particular,

(ii) the truth of a sentence depends only on the interpretation and not on the valuation chosen.

Consider again the formula

$$\forall i \forall j ((\text{Matrix}(i, j) = i + 3j) \wedge \forall i (\text{Vector}(i) = 2j))$$

Suppose that the interpretation I for this sentence has as universe U the integers modulo 4, i.e. the remainders 0, 1, 2, 3 on division by 4. Also suppose that the universe function Matrix_1 is defined by $\text{Matrix}_1(a, b) = 2(a + b)$ where multiplication and addition on the right-hand side of this equation are on U × U, the 2 is that of U, and a and b are elements of U. To evaluate the subformula $\text{Matrix}(i, j) = i + 3j$ there are 16 different valuations σ of interest, one for each possible assignment of the free variables i and j. We can easily find the value of the subformula for each valuation:

σi	σj	$\sigma(\text{Matrix}(i, j))$	$\sigma(i + 3j)$	$\sigma(\text{Matrix}(i, j) = i + 3j)$
0	0	0	0	T
0	1	2	3	F
0	2	0	2	F
0	3	2	1	F
1	0	2	1	F
. . .				

This shows that for the valuation $\tau = \sigma_{i \to 0, j \to 1}$ we have $\tau(\text{Matrix}(i, j) = i + 3j) = F$, so that $\tau((\text{Matrix}(i, j) = i + 3j) \wedge \forall i (\text{Vector}(i) = 2j)) = F$, $\sigma_{i \to 0} \forall j ((\text{Matrix}(i, j) = i + 3j) \wedge \forall i (\text{Vector}(i) = 2j)) = F$ and $\sigma \forall i \forall j ((\text{Matrix}(i, j) = i + 3j) \wedge \forall i (\text{Vector}(i) = 2j)) = F$.

Theorem 3.1 shows how the truth of a formula depends on the values of only a few variables. We can also ask how much it depends on the names of the variables. This is just the same problem as that of changing identifiers for program variables, which was encountered when AcNo was changed to CurrentAcNo in an earlier example. If we replace x by y in a formula, what is the effect on its truth? In changing variables we must rename all occurrences which take the same value at one time to preserve any connection between the truth values. Thus we will be replacing all free occurrences of a variable at once, or all those bound to a particular quantifier at once.

Let us consider free variables first. The two ways in which problems may arise when x is changed to y are that either a new occurrence of y becomes bound or there are other free occurrences of y. In both cases some new occurrences of y become confused with other variables. It is like having two variables with the same name y in a program and expecting to be able to tell them apart at every use. These problems arise in the formulae $\forall y\,(x > y)$ and $(x > z) \wedge (y > z)$ where changing x to y can clearly change the truth value.

However, suppose that every free occurrence of x in a formula W is replaced by y to give a new formula W' in which the free occurrences of y are precisely those new instances just introduced. The new formula W' is written $W[x\,|\,y]$ and is said to be obtained by *alphabetic substitution*. The restricted choice for the variable y ensures that the process is reversible: just replace every free occurrence of y by x to obtain W again. If y does not occur in W at all, then certainly it must be suitable for replacing any free variable. In the formula

$$\forall t\,(\forall x(y > x*z) \Rightarrow P(z,\ z,\ t)) \wedge \forall x\,((x > t) \wedge \forall x(u * x > 0))$$

all occurrences of y, z and u and the last occurrence of t are free. Therefore none of these can be renamed yet using the name of one of the other free variables. Except for these, and possibly also the quantified variables x and t, any other choice is legitimate. Neither x nor t is possible because t is already present with a free occurrence and changing any free occurrence of a variable to x makes it bound. However, we are free to replace, for example, all free occurrences of x by an unused variable, say newx.

When we evaluate W and $W[x\,|\,y]$ using σ, the only differences to arise are over the values of x and y for the changed instances since the formulae are otherwise identical. If both x and y are given the same value a then the truth values must be the same, i.e. the following theorem holds.

Theorem 3.2

$$\sigma_{x \to a}(W) = \sigma_{y \to a}(W[x\,|\,y])$$

The truth of $W[x\,|\,y]$ is thus essentially the same as that of W.

In the above we only changed the identifiers and values of free variables. Now let us consider changing the names of bound variables in a formula W. Suppose that $\forall x\,(U)$ is a subformula of W and we wish to change its quantified variable x. If $U[x\mid y]$ is obtained by alphabetic substitution then $\sigma_{x\to a}U = \sigma_{y\to a}U[x\mid y]$ for each a in the universe. Either these are true for all a, or for some a both are false. In the first case both $\forall x\,(U)$ and $\forall y\,U[x\mid y]$ are true, and in the other case both are false. Thus

$$\sigma(\forall x\,U) = \sigma(\forall y\,U[x\mid y])$$

Let W' be the formula obtained from W by this change of variable in the subformula. Since W and W' are otherwise identical, when we evaluate them we find $\sigma W = \sigma W'$. Therefore this particular change of variable does not affect the truth of the whole formula.

The condition we required of y was in terms of the subformula U. In terms of the whole WFF W containing the subformula $\forall x\,(U)$, when x is replaced by y we have to change every occurrence of x governed by the chosen quantifier and, in order to preserve the truth value, we need the new occurrences of y to be precisely those that are governed in the new formula W' by this quantifier.

This process may be iterated. In the new WFF W' we may change another bound variable to obtain a further formula W'', again with the same truth value as W. Repeating the process as many times as desired gives a formula which is called a *variant* of W, and the process is called a *change of variables*. It is clearly reversible. Such changes are useful when trying to disentangle the actions of different variables which happen to have the same name. In this way all quantifiers can be given differently named variables. Note that only bound variables are renamed in this process.

The property of preservation of truth is given by the following theorem.

Theorem 3.3

If W and W' are variants then $\sigma W = \sigma W'$ for every valuation σ.

Consider again the example

$$\forall y\,(y < 3 \Rightarrow \forall x\,(z = Sqr(x) + Sqr(y)))$$

When each x is changed to y to obtain

$$\forall y\,(y < 3 \Rightarrow \forall y\,(z = Sqr(y) + Sqr(y)))$$

the last y then comes within the scope of the second quantifier and is bound by it, instead of being associated with the first quantifier which previously governed that occurrence of y. Therefore this change of variable is illegitimate. Either we should change each x to an unused variable, say t, obtaining the variant

$$\forall y\,(y<3 \Rightarrow \forall t\,(z=Sqr(t)+Sqr(y)))$$

or, if we still wish to change each x to y, we must first choose a variant in which y is already renamed, such as

$$\forall t\,(t<3 \Rightarrow \forall x\,(z=Sqr(x)+Sqr(t)))$$

and the formula

$$\forall t\,(t<3 \Rightarrow \forall y\,(z=Sqr(y)+Sqr(t)))$$

is then clearly a variant of the initial formula. They have the same truth values.

Boolean expressions in a program are examples of formulae which we want in our predicate language. We require to instantiate them with general value parameters in any constituent function calls. Therefore in our use of predicate calculus to make statements about programs we can expect to want to substitute terms for free variables in a formula.

If a term t is to be substituted for the free occurrences in W of a variable x then the necessary restrictions are just those that ensure that the correct values are assigned to the variables within t. Therefore for every variable y of t we require the free occurrences of y to include all those arising from the substitutions of t for x in W. Alternatively, we wish no further bound instances of variables to occur in the new formula $W[x\,|\,t]$ thus obtained. For such terms t we say that t is *free to be substituted* for x in W. Under a valuation σ, the values of the new occurrences of t are then just σt. Hence, by building up the values of the subformulae of W and $W[x\,|\,t]$ and at the same time using $\sigma_{x\to\sigma t}$ and σ respectively to obtain $\sigma_{x\to\sigma t}W$ and $\sigma W[x\,|\,t]$, we find that the truth values are identical. For example, if W is $\forall x\,(x*y=z)$ then $t=x+y$ is not free to be substituted for either y or z but $t=y+z$ is free to be so substituted. Then $W[y\,|\,y+z]$ is $\forall x\,(x*(y+z)=z)$. There are no new occurrences of the variables y and z which are bound in $W[y\,|\,y+z]$ but not in W.

Suppose that t is not free to be substituted for x in W. Then there are some occurrences of variables from t which become bound in W. However, by choosing a suitable variant W' we can avoid any clash between the quantified variables of W and those of t so that t is free to be substituted for x in W. In particular, we might choose a variant in which the quantified variables were all distinct from the variables of t. Then $\sigma_{x\to\sigma t}W = \sigma_{x\to\sigma t}W' = \sigma W'[x\,|\,t]$, the first equality by virtue of Theorem 3.3 and the second by the last paragraph. In the last example, if we choose the variant $\forall i\,(i*y=z)$ of W then $t = x + y$ is now free to be substituted for y.

Let us denote by $W[x\,|\,t]$ any formula obtained by choosing a variant W' of W in which t is free to be substituted for x and then making the substitution of t for each free occurrence of x in W'. Then, from the above, we have the following theorem.

Theorem 3.4

$\sigma W[x\,|\,t] = \sigma_{x\to\sigma t}W$ for any valuation σ, formula W, variable x and term t.

Since we are really only interested in the truth of the formulae, it does not matter which particular variant of W is chosen in $W[x\,|\,t]$ because all yield the same truth value.

Example 3.1

A computer provides an interpretation for the predicate language ARITH of arithmetic. Let us assume that single-precision arithmetic is employed, and that each word of memory has just 3 bits. The universe is the set of eight values which can be placed in a word of memory. The function symbols of arithmetic are written $+, -, *, /$ in the language ARITH and realized as the binary functions Add, Sbt, Mlt, Div respectively on the universe. These could be implemented in various ways, each corresponding to a different interpretation.

The constant symbols $0, 1, -1, 2, -2, 3, \ldots$ of ARITH must each be mapped by the interpretation to a unique element of the universe. Any choice is permissible, but in practice one of three ways is standard if we neglect additional parity check bits and other error-correcting features. These are the sign-magnitude, one's complement and two's complement methods of representing integers. Each yields a different interpretation although the universe is the same. In fact, -1 is mapped to the words 101, 110, 111 respectively in them.

In two's complement numbers are represented by the binary form of their remainder mod 2^k where k is the number of bits in the word of memory, and arithmetic is performed on these binary strings mod 2^k. Thus Add(101, 011) = 000, Mlt(101, 011) = 111, etc. These functions are generally hard-wired logic circuits.

A valuation states the values of each variable at a given point during the execution of a program. To evaluate a formula at that point, say $x * y - z$ in ARITH, the computer observes that the appropriate valuation is $x \mapsto 010$, $y \mapsto 011$, $z \mapsto 101$ because these three strings are currently in the associated memory locations, and the value of $x * y - z$ is Sbt(Mlt(010, 011), 101) which is Sbt(110, 101), i.e. 001. The machine looks for a constant in ARITH whose value is 001 and returns the answer 1.

The set on which the equality predicate = holds is Eq = {(000, 000), (001, 001), . . .}. Indeed the equality predicate = always is defined to be true on the *diagonal* set $\{(u, u) \,|\, u \in U\}$ and false otherwise. Therefore $x = y$ is true precisely if (010, 011) is in Eq, which is plainly not so. Thus $x = y$ has truth value F. However, $x < y$ is true if (010, 011) is in the subset LT of $U \times U$ corresponding to $<$. Assuming that the implementation is correct, we then find $x < y$ holds at this point in the program.

In general, life is more complicated than this because overflow, underflow, rounding errors and undefined values may occur. These are difficult problems beyond the scope of this book although we touched on them by having an element 'undefined' in the universe of the main example in the previous section on interpretations.

Models and Induction

In the previous sections of this chapter the motivation for looking at formulae and valuations was to write down and evaluate assertions which were supposed to hold at certain points during program execution. If required, procedures can be written to check the truth of such assertions at run time. The assertions provide documentation for maintenance during the life cycle of the program and also form the basis of program verification, which we come to in Chapter 5.

Some assertions hold not only when control passes a certain point in the program but also over a whole section of code, or even during the entire program execution. These are generally connected with restricting values that variables can take or describing properties preserved when certain groups of procedures are called. Such properties are called *data invariants*.

Consider the natural numbers defined by Nat = 0 . . in the obvious notation with the usual arithmetic operators. Peano listed a number of properties which the operators should satisfy in order to characterize the universe of Nat:

(i) $\mathrm{succ}(n) \neq 0$;

(ii) $\mathrm{succ}(n) = \mathrm{succ}(m) \Rightarrow n = m$;

(iii) $n + 0 = n$;

(iv) $n + \mathrm{succ}(m) = \mathrm{succ}(n + m)$;

(v) $n * 0 = 0$;

(vi) $n * \mathrm{succ}(m) = (n * m) + n$.

These, together with

(vii) (the induction principle) for any subset S of Nat, if $0 \in S$ and $(n \in S \Rightarrow \mathrm{succ}(n) \in S)$ then $S = \mathrm{Nat}$,

form *Peano's axioms* for the natural numbers. Of these, the last cannot be written as a formula of a (first-order) predicate language. (In (vii) the set S can be thought of as the subset P_{Nat} of Nat on which a unary predicate P is true. Then (vii) can be rewritten as

$$\forall P \,((P(0) \wedge \forall n\,(P(n) \Rightarrow P(\mathrm{Succ}(n)))) \Rightarrow \forall x\,(P(x)))$$

in a predicate language that allows quantification over predicates, i.e. in a second-order predicate language.) Let S be the set of numbers which have the form $\mathrm{succ}^n(0)$, i.e. are generated by a finite but unbounded number of applications of succ to 0. Then $0 \in S$ and $n \in S \Rightarrow \mathrm{succ}(n) \in S$. So $S = \mathrm{Nat}$ by the induction principle and every number therefore has this form. Using axioms (i) and (ii) we can deduce that none of the terms 0, succ(0), succ(succ(0)), ..., is equal to another. This means that the universe of the interpretation in which all these axioms hold is necessarily the same as the set Nat which we know.

The second and third pair of axioms define addition and multiplication in terms of succ and addition respectively. Thus, $4 + 3 = 4 + \mathrm{succ}(2) = \mathrm{succ}(4 + 2) = \mathrm{succ}(4 + \mathrm{succ}(1)) = \mathrm{succ}(\mathrm{succ}(4 + 1)) = \mathrm{succ}(\mathrm{succ}(4 + \mathrm{succ}(0))) = \mathrm{succ}(\mathrm{succ}(\mathrm{succ}(4 + 0))) = \mathrm{succ}(\mathrm{succ}(\mathrm{succ}(4)))$ shows how to rewrite $4 + 3$ as a term not using $+$. We have replaced the term $4 + 3$ successively by terms which have the same value in any interpretation for which the appropriate axioms, namely (iii) and (iv), hold. Thus the equality symbol above really denotes equality of values under a valuation σ such that formulae (iii) and (iv) are true. We should write $\sigma(4 + 3) = \ldots = \sigma(\mathrm{succ}(\mathrm{succ}(\mathrm{succ}(4))))$. Similarly, $4 * 3 = 4 * \mathrm{succ}(2) = (4 * 2) + 4 = (4 * \mathrm{succ}(1)) + 4 = ((4 * 1) + 4) + 4 = (((4 * 0) + 4) + 4) + 4 = ((0 + 4) + 4) + 4 = (4 + 4) + 4$ shows how to rewrite $4 * 3$ as an equivalent term not involving $*$.

The order predicate $<$ can also be defined by additional formulae; this is left as an exercise.

The above describes Nat as an abstract data type. In general, an *abstract data type* consists of one or more sets of elements together with functions operating on these sets. These are realized in programming languages by type declarations and by functions and procedures which use those declarations. They can be realized in a predicate language by writing down formulae which specify the properties of the types and functions involved. We are interested in the interpretations for which these formulae are true. Our hope is to have sufficient formulae in the predicate language to make only the intended interpretation possible, for then the formulae give a complete specification of the data type.

In this section we look at relationships between a set of formulae and its models, i.e. interpretations for which the formulae defining the abstract data type are all true. For example, we want to know about the WFFs that are true in a model, i.e. properties of the abstract data type.

For a given set of formulae, we can ask what concrete universes, functions and predicates form interpretations in which each formula is always true. More generally, we are interested in what other predicates hold when we demand that those of our abstract data type hold. They will give more information about the possible interpretations or models for the initial premises. This applies to all aspects of computing, and not just when we are actively creating a data type, because all the fundamental types used in programming such as Boolean, Integer, Real etc. are examples of them. For example, in Nat we might deduce

$$\forall n\,(m_1 + n = m_2 + n \Rightarrow m_1 = m_2)$$

holds for all terms m_1 and m_2.

Let us define the notation needed for such discussions. It is identical with that for propositional calculus when the appropriate simplifications are made.

A set of formulae which we wish to hold true in every interpretation of interest is called a set of *hypotheses* or *axioms*. An interpretation I is a *model* for a set of hypotheses **H** if every *H* in **H** is true for every I-valuation.

For example, let **H** be the set of formulae (i)–(vi) above. Then the natural numbers with the usual definitions of 0, succ, $+$ and $*$ form a model of **H**. Also, however, we could take the polynomials in one variable with coefficients in Nat, i.e. the set of elements $a_0 + a_1 x + \ldots + a_n x^n$, where $a_i \in$ Nat for each *i*. This universe with the usual addition and multiplication of polynomials and succ as $+1$ defines another model of **H**.

We are interested in properties that hold in models of the hypotheses **H**. The logical consequences of **H** are the formulae which are true when all the WFFs in **H** are true. This definition applies to all interpretations, not only to those which are models of **H**. We can state this more precisely as follows.

For an interpretation I the formula W is a *logical consequence* of **H** in I if $\sigma W = T$ whenever σ is an I-valuation such that $\sigma H = T$ for every hypothesis H in **H**. This is written $\mathbf{H} \models_I W$.

Clearly, for example, every hypothesis in **H** is a logical consequence of **H** in I, i.e. $\mathbf{H} \models_I H$ if H is in **H**. Again with **H** as the set of formulae (i)–(vi) we can deduce that

$$n + 1 = \text{succ}(n)$$

where 1 means succ(0) because $\sigma(n + 1) = \sigma(n + \text{succ}(0)) = \sigma(\text{succ}(n + 0)) = \sigma(\text{succ}(n))$ by applying (iii) and (iv) and the property

$$\sigma(t_1 = t_2) = (\sigma(t_1) = \sigma(t_2))$$

of equality for terms t_1 and t_2. Therefore, for any interpretation I we have

$$\mathbf{H} \models_I n + 1 = \text{succ}(n)$$

As usual, if there are no hypotheses so that **H** is the empty set then we just write $\models_I W$ and W is said to be *logically true* in I. Such a formula is always true for that interpretation. Therefore I is a model for **H** if and only if $\models_I H$ for all H in **H**.

Two formulae V, W are *logically equivalent* in I if the truth of either implies the truth of the other, i.e. if $\{V\} \models_I W$ and $\{W\} \models_I V$. These mean, respectively, that for every I-valuation σ, $\sigma(V) = T$ implies $\sigma(W) = T$ and $\sigma(W) = T$ implies $\sigma(V) = T$ or, equivalently, $\sigma(V) = \sigma(W)$ for all I-valuations. Thus V and W are either both true or both false for any given valuation. Hence $\models_I(V \Leftrightarrow W)$ for logically equivalent formulae. Conversely, if $V \Leftrightarrow W$ is logically true in I then V, W are logically equivalent in I. An easy example of this is to observe that W and W are logically equivalent since $(W \Leftrightarrow W)$ is logically true in I. Of course this formula must be true for all valuations in every interpretation. It is an example of a *valid* formula: a WFF W is *valid* if $\models_I W$ for every interpretation I.

Slightly less trivial examples of this are that $U \Leftrightarrow \sim \sim U$ and $U \vee \sim U$ are valid formulae. In the context of arithmetic with model I of formulae (i)–(vi) above we have that $m = \text{succ}(n * 2)$ and $m = n + n + 1$ are logically equivalent in I, when 2 means succ(1).

To show that $\mathbf{H} \models_I W$ may depend on I, we take the universe of I to be $U = \{0, 1\}$ with unary predicates P and Q having associated sets $P_I = \{0\}$

and $Q_1 = \{1\}$. Therefore P is true for 0 and false for 1 whereas Q is false for 0 but true for 1. Then $\sigma(P(x) \vee Q(x)) = T$ for any valuation σ because precisely one of P(x) and Q(x) is true whichever value x takes: if $\sigma x = 0$ then P(x) is true and otherwise $\sigma x = 1$ so that Q(x) is true. Thus $\models_I P(x) \vee Q(x)$. However, let J be the interpretation with the same universe but $P_J = Q_J = \{1\}$. Then $\sigma(P(x) \vee Q(x)) = F$ for any J-valuation σ such that $\sigma x = 0$. Therefore $\models_J P(x) \vee Q(x)$ does not hold for this interpretation. Since there are valuations for which $P(x) \vee Q(x)$ is false, it cannot be a valid formula in the sense just defined.

The definitions above all have equivalents which hold for all interpretations I. They are obtained by omitting the 'in I' and deleting the subscript I from $\models_I$. Thus, we have the following.

(i) *V* is a *logical consequence of* **H**, written $\mathbf{H} \models V$, if and only if $\mathbf{H} \models_I V$ for all interpretations I.

(ii) When **H** is empty $\mathbf{H} \models V$ is abbreviated to $\models V$ and *V* is called a *logical truth* or a *valid* formula.

$\mathbf{H} \models V$ is read as '**H** logically implies *V*'. This means that *V* holds for any valuation for which every formula of **H** is true, irrespective of the interpretation. If **H** is the set of formulae as above for natural numbers then

$$\mathbf{H} \models n + 1 = \mathrm{succ}(n)$$

Thus $n + 1 = \mathrm{succ}(n)$ is a logical consequence of **H**. However, $m * n = n * m$ is not a logical consequence of **H**. (To see this we could take a model of **H** in which the elements of the universe are 2×2 matrices, $+$ and $*$ are the usual addition and multiplication of matrices, 0 is the matrix of all zeros and $\mathrm{succ}(x) = x + I$ for the identity matrix I.)

Using this notation we can rewrite Theorem 3.3 from the last section as follows.

Theorem 3.5

If *W* and *W'* are variants then they are logically equivalent, i.e. $\models (W \Leftrightarrow W')$.

Theorem 3.4 stated that $\sigma W[x \mid t] = \sigma_{x \to \sigma t} W$ for any term t. From this we obtain the following theorem.

Theorem 3.6

For any formula *W*, variable x and term t we have

(i) $\mathbf{H} \models W$ implies $\mathbf{H} \models W[x\,|\,t]$
(ii) $\mathbf{H} \models (\forall x(W) \Rightarrow W[x\,|\,t])$.

An example of this with the usual arithmetic hypotheses $\mathbf{H}$ is that from $\mathbf{H} \models n + 0 = n$ we can deduce $\mathbf{H} \models m * n + 0 = m * n$ and $\models (\forall m(m \geqslant 0) \Rightarrow (m * n \geqslant 0))$.

Theorem 3.7

If $\mathbf{H} = \{H_1, H_2, \ldots, H_n\}$ is a finite set then V is a logical consequence of $\mathbf{H}$ if and only if

$$(H_1 \wedge H_2 \wedge \ldots \wedge H_n) \Rightarrow V$$

is a valid formula.

Proof. To see this, let W be the given implication. Observe that if $\models W$ then for any valuation either V is true or some H in $\mathbf{H}$ is false. Hence $\mathbf{H} \models V$. Conversely, if $\mathbf{H} \models V$ then V can only be false for valuations for which some H in $\mathbf{H}$ is also false. Hence W is true for such valuations as well as for those for which V is true. Thus $\models W$. It follows that $\mathbf{H} \models V$ and $\models W$ are equivalent.

The set of hypotheses $\mathbf{H}$ are the initial conditions we wish to impose to restrict attention to interpretations which have universes with the desired properties. For example, $\mathbf{H}$ could be a set of formulae describing properties of the addition of integers, such as the defining property of zero $(x + 0 = x)$, the existence of the negative of a number, and the commutative and associative laws. These are actually the axioms for a structure called an Abelian group. As well as the integers themselves there are infinitely many examples including the integers mod n under addition. In the earlier example with 3 bit strings the arithmetic was that of the integers mod 8, which is the arithmetic of remainders after division by 8. The language needed to write down these hypotheses contains

+   a function of two variables
=   the equality predicate
0   a constant

Then the axioms mentioned above which define Abelian groups are the four formulae

$$\forall x \exists y \, (x + y = 0)$$
$$\forall x \, (x + 0 = x)$$
$$\forall x \forall y \, (x + y = y + x)$$
$$\forall x \forall y \forall z \, ((x + y) + z = x + (y + z))$$

Any model of this set **H** of hypotheses is therefore an Abelian group and vice versa. If we desired to have just the integers Int as the model then certainly more initial hypotheses must be added to **H**. Indeed, too many more for convenience are necessary.

We can obtain cardinality conditions on the universe, i.e. bounds on the number $|U|$ of elements in the universe U, in, for example, the following manner. Let ThreeOrMore be the formula

$$\exists x \exists y \exists z \, ((x \neq y) \wedge (y \neq z) \wedge (z \neq x))$$

where $(t_1 \neq t_2)$ means $\sim (t_1 = t_2)$. It is easy to rewrite this with only universal quantifiers, from which it is apparent that ThreeOrMore is a sentence. It has no free variables, and so for a given interpretation I it is true for all valuations or false for all valuations by Theorem 3.1. In fact the truth can only depend on the choice of universe U because there are no predicates, functions or constants appearing in ThreeOrMore except for the equality predicate for which the set $\models_1$ is always fixed as $\{(u, u) \, | \, u \text{ in } U\}$. If I has a universe with at least three different elements, say a, b and c, then for the valuation $\sigma: x \mapsto a, \, v \mapsto b, \, z \mapsto c$ we have $\sigma((x \neq y) \wedge (y \neq z) \wedge (z \neq x)) = T$. Hence $\sigma(\text{ThreeOrMore}) = T$ for all I-valuations σ, i.e. $\models_1 \text{ThreeOrMore}$ if the number of elements $|U|$ in U satisfies $|U| \geqslant 3$. However, if $|U| < 3$ for the universe U then for any valuation $\sigma: x \mapsto a, \, y \mapsto b, \, z \mapsto c$ at least one pair of elements from a, b and c are identical, ensuring that at least one of $x \neq y$, $y \neq z$, $z \neq x$ is false under σ. Thus $\sigma((x \neq y) \wedge (y \neq z) \wedge (z \neq x)) = F$ and so $\sigma(\text{ThreeOrMore}) = F$ also. Therefore $\models_1 \text{ThreeOrMore}$ does not hold if $|U| < 3$. Indeed, $\models_1 \sim \text{ThreeOrMore}$ if $|U| < 3$.

In a similar way we can obtain much more general restrictions on the cardinality $|U|$ of the universe. (The cardinality of a model is just the number of elements in the universe of the model.) For example, a model of the formula $\sim \text{SixtyOrMore} \wedge \text{FiftyOrMore}$ (with analogous meanings for SixtyOrMore and FiftyOrMore) would satisfy $50 \leqslant |U| < 60$. However, one major disadvantage is that it is not possible to write down a formula for which an interpretation is a model if and only if its universe is countable. (Countable means that there is a one-to-one correspondence between the elements and a subset of Nat. In particular, finite sets are countable.) In the case of Nat, generating the natural numbers from a constant Zero in the language and a function Succ, meaning add 1, the formula

$$\forall n\,(Succ(n) \neq 0) \wedge \forall n \forall m\,(succ(m) = succ(n) \Rightarrow m = n)$$

ensures that any model has an infinite universe. Having forced this number to be infinite, there is no further cardinality restriction we can impose because of one of the fundamental theorems of model theory due to Löwenheim and Skolem.

Theorem 3.8 (Löwenheim and Skolem)

Suppose that a (countable) set **H** of sentences has a model of infinite cardinality. Then **H** has a model of every infinite cardinality.

The proof of this is not of much interest to us, but the result is. It shows that there may be many more models of the structure we are trying to model than just those that are intended. Suppose, for example, that we were to write down some axioms for the natural numbers Nat. As in the case of Abelian groups, by scattering a few quantifiers around as necessary we can ensure that a set of sentences is obtained. As in that example, the universe of a model of these axioms will be just the sort of object we are looking for, i.e. one in which all our axioms hold. Nat itself is an infinite model of the axioms and so the Löwenheim–Skolem result says that there are other models. In particular, there is one with the same cardinality as the real numbers. This was certainly not intended when we wrote down the axioms for Nat, but it is unavoidable unless we allow formulae which are not part of first-order predicate calculus. Even if we continue to add a countable number of extra formulae which hold in our intended interpretation in order to restrict the number of models, there are probably still models that we do not want.

One important aspect of this theorem is that it makes life difficult. There are many formulae which are true for the standard model Nat but false for some valuations in other interpretations. This is Gödel's incompleteness theorem. In the next chapter we shall see that, as in Chapter 1, proof rules only allow us to deduce logical consequences of our hypotheses, i.e. formulae which hold in all models of the hypotheses (this is the soundness theorem). Therefore we cannot hope to prove such formulae within first-order predicate calculus using the deduction principles we shall describe there, even though they may be true for every valuation on Nat. If they are false in some model then they are not provable in general using these principles. We must use structural induction on the elements of the intended universe, and apply an induction principle in a higher-order language like that above in Peano's axiom (vii).

Structural induction, as defined in Chapter 1, works on the principle that every element in the universe of interest must be one that can eventually be reached in some computation and is therefore constructible as a term from the constants and functions of the language. A *ground* term is a term constructed solely from constant and function symbols. Every element in the intended universe is then the value of a ground term in the language. (Therefore the universe is an image of the *Herbrand* universe defined in Chapter 6.) If S is the subset of elements with some property then we can prove that S is the whole universe if we can prove that every ground term has the property. This means showing that every constant has property S and, if terms $t_1, \ldots, t_n$ lie in S then so does $f(t_1, \ldots, t_n)$ for every n-ary function symbol f. Since every ground term is constructed from a finite number of constants and applications of functions, we can deduce step by step that every ground term is in S and then the whole universe will have the desired property. Thus, if in the intended model every element is the value of a ground term we have an induction principle to obtain properties for all elements in the model even if they are not true in more general models. In the natural numbers, the unique constant and function required to generate every element of the standard interpretation are 0 and succ. Hence only they are necessary in Peano's induction principle (vii) which is used for this sort of induction on Nat.

Recursively defined functions, i.e. functions defined in terms of themselves, abound in computing. They usually require a universe given by values of ground terms in order to be fully defined. They make use of the recursive definition of a term being constructed from a function application to a list of terms. The function is often defined for each term $f(t_1, \ldots, t_n)$ by describing how to construct its value from the values of the function for $t_1, t_2, \ldots, t_n$. After using this recursive definition a number of times the 'base' cases are reached when the function must be defined on every constant of the language. A couple of standard examples are Factorial(succ(n)) = succ(n) * Factorial(n) with Factorial(0) = 1 and $a ** succ(b) = a ** b * a$ with $a ** 0 = 1$. Both these have a simplifying step for removing succ and a base case for the constant 0. Different recursion schemata result from the use of alternative constant and function symbols for generating representative terms for the elements of the standard model of Nat. An example appears in the exercises.

Exercises

1 List the predefined constants, functions and predicates of
(a) integer arithmetic
(b) real arithmetic
(c) character strings
(d) Booleans
in a programming language of your own choice. Give the arity of each function and predicate.

2 Using, if possible, only those constants, functions and predicates in the answer to Exercise 1, write down formulae with the following meanings.
(a) The (integer) variable x is the square of an even number.
(b) Max(x, y) is the larger of the (real) variables x, y.
(c) If the (string) variable x has length at least 2 then its second letter is 'e'.
(d) Every value in the (one-dimensional array) variable x is non-zero.

3 Describe the languages generated by the alphabets given in your answer to Exercise 1 by stating how to create terms and formulae as they are used in the programming language.

4 Give appropriate rules for enriching a predicate language to include a **case** operator on Boolean expressions with the meaning **if** . . . **then** . . . **else if** . . . **else if** . . . . What problems are there if the number of cases is not fixed?

5 Provide the semantic rules for describing $\forall$, $\vee$, $\Rightarrow$, $\Leftarrow$ and $\Leftrightarrow$ in terms of a language with only the logical operators $\wedge$ and $\sim$ and the quantifier $\exists$.

6 Show that the function Max(x, y) of Exercise 2(b) can be defined using a term involving only standard arithmetic functions.

7 Let a, b, . . . , h be variables or constants and assume the standard conventions for notation in arithmetic.
(a) Rewrite the following terms in the usual infix notation:
(i) $+(*(e, +(*(*(b, c), a), *(f, c))), d)$
(ii) $-(\text{div}((2, 4), 3), \text{mod}(14, \text{sqr}(-(6, 3))))$
(b) Remove as many brackets as possible from your answer to (a).

(c) Rewrite the following terms and WFF with all functions and predicates in prefix notation:

    (i) $g(a + (bc - e)f)/h$

    (ii) sqr$(-a - b - c$ div $3 * pi)$

    (iii) $a + 1 > bc \wedge a - 1 < bc \Rightarrow a = bc$

8 Insert brackets in the following expressions using the usual priority rules:

    (a) $a \wedge b \wedge c \Rightarrow d \wedge e \Rightarrow f$

    (b) $a \Rightarrow b \Rightarrow c \wedge d \Rightarrow e \wedge f$

    (c) $a \wedge b \wedge c \vee d \wedge e \vee f$

    (d) $a \vee b \vee c \wedge d \vee e \wedge f$

    (e) $a * b * c + d * e + f$

    (f) $a + b + c * d + e * f$

    (g) $a/b/c - d/e - f$

    (h) $a - b - c/d - e/f$

    (i) $a \Rightarrow b \Rightarrow c \Leftarrow d \Rightarrow e \Leftarrow f$

    (j) $a \Leftarrow b \Leftarrow c \Rightarrow d \Leftarrow e \Rightarrow f$

9 $\exists!x(W)$ means that there is exactly one value of x such that W holds. Give a semantic rule for translating this into a formula of the type defined in the text.

10 Describe the set P_1 in terms of the universe U of an interpretation I in which

    (a) $\forall x \forall y P(x, y)$ holds

    (b) $\forall x \forall y \sim P(x, y)$ holds

11 For the formulae

    (i) IsTerm$(y) \Leftrightarrow$ IsConst$(y) \vee \exists x(y = $Concat$($minus$, x) \vee \exists z(y = $Concat$(x, $Concat$($plus$, z))))$

    (ii) $\forall x (P(x) \wedge Q(y)) \Rightarrow \forall x P(x) \wedge \forall y Q(y) \wedge Q(x))$

do the following.

    (a) Identify the free occurrences and the quantifier governing each bound occurrence of each variable.

    (b) State the restrictions on variables which are free to be substituted for any free variable.

    (c) Find $W[y \mid t]$ where $t = x + y$ and W is the formula.

    (d) Give a variant in which no two quantifiers are over the same variable and no free variable is the same as a bound variable.

12 (a) Prove that the following hold:

$$\models \; \sim \forall x \forall y \, (x \neq y)$$
$$\forall x \, P(x) \models \exists y \, P(y)$$
$$\exists y \forall x \, Q(x, \, y) \models \forall x \exists y \, Q(x, \, y)$$

(b) Prove that the following do not hold:

$$\exists x \, P(x) \models \forall y \, P(y)$$
$$\forall y \exists x \, Q(x, \, y) \models \exists x \forall y \, Q(x, \, y)$$

13 A program has declarations as follows:

type	Response	$=(y, \, n)$;
var	Answer	: Response;
	Comment	: **array**[Response] **of** Response;

Assuming that the universe also requires an element $*$ for uninitialized variables and overflow, and interpreting $\_[\_]$ as a binary function for selecting an entry from an array, construct the intended interpretation explicitly.

For each marked point in the program below give the associated valuation when control reaches that point, first with input n and then with input y.

```
begin
{*1}        Read(Answer);
{*2}        Comment[y]:=n; Comment[n]:=y;
{*3}        if Answer=n then
            begin
                        Answer:=Comment[Answer]; {*4}
                        Comment[Answer]:=y
            end
            else
            begin
                        Answer:=Comment[n]; {*4}
                        Comment[n]:=n
            end
{*5}
end.
```

14 (a) A unary function f from U to U defines a subset P_U of $U \times U$, i.e. the set of pairs (a, b) such that $f(a) = b$. What formulae need to hold for the binary predicate P if its set P_U is to satisfy the conditions in every interpretation for the following:

(i) a function of one variable;

(ii) a surjective (or onto) unary function (i.e. every point in U is a value of the function);

(iii) an injective (or 1–1) unary function (i.e. no two distinct points in U have the same value under the function).

(b) Repeat part (a) for binary functions.

15 The predicate $<$ is called a *total* or *linear ordering* if it satisfies the law of trichotomy, i.e. that for all x, y precisely one of $x<y$, $x=y$ or $y<x$ is true and it is transitive, i.e. $x<y \wedge y<z \Rightarrow x<z$ for all x, y, z.

(a) Give a model of such a predicate using the set of character strings for the universe.

(b) Give a formula which ensures that a function Succ has the expected meaning of the next item on any such model.

(c) Give a formula which ensures that Pred, when it exists, also has the intended obvious meaning.

(d) If Pred(x) is defined for every element x except the empty string (the string with no characters) in the model you gave then give another typical model of the axioms for $<$ in which Pred is not always defined in other cases. To which strings does Pred then not apply?

(e) Describe also a model in which Pred exists for every element except the empty string, which you should represent in the language by a constant.

(For this question you may assume that strings are formed only from the alphabet of capital letters A to Z.)

16 Add to Peano's axioms by giving formulae that define

(a) Pred (when defined)

(b) $<$ (Hint: use Exercise 15)

(c) $\leqslant$, $\geqslant$ and $>$

(d) ** (raising to a power)

(e) div, mod (the definitions should not be recursive)

(f) any other predicate or function used in Boolean expressions of your favourite programming language.

17 Give a finite model of the subset of Peano's axioms in which the first axiom is excluded.

18 (a) Construct a sentence using one binary predicate and no function symbols or operators such that any model of it has exactly one element in its universe.

(b) Construct a sentence using one binary predicate and no function symbols such that every model has an infinite universe. (Hint: define a linear order by and-ing together formulae which express the required properties.)

19 (a) We can define a typed predicate language by declaring some unary predicates Type1, Type2, ..., with the semantics of Type1(x) true when term x is in the appropriate type. Functions, constants and predicates then have typed arguments and results (as appropriate) rather than just a fixed number of places. Quantifiers come also with a type constraint, giving formulae of the form

$$\forall(x \text{ in Type1})(W)$$

Define the syntax for such a language formally, and show how it might be translated into an untyped predicate language.

(b) The universe of an interpretation is the union of the various types. Give the obvious formal definitions of an interpretation and a valuation.

(c) Re-do Exercise 13 using a typed predicate language. (Remark: In practice typed predicate languages are much more suitable than untyped ones for describing strongly typed programming languages.)

20 Suppose that the alphabet of a predicate language is finite and $<$ is a total ordering of the symbols of the alphabet. The *weight* wt of a term is defined recursively by

wt(c) = 0 for constant symbols c,

wt(f(t$_1$, ..., t$_n$)) = 1 + max{wt(t$_1$), ..., wt(t$_n$)} for an n-ary function symbol f and terms t$_1$, ..., t$_n$.

The order $<$ can be extended to a total ordering of all ground terms as follows. Let Term1 be f(s$_1$, ..., s$_n$) and Term2 be g(t$_1$, ..., t$_m$). Then Term1 $<$ Term2 if and only if

wt(Term1) $<$ wt(Term2)

or

wt(Term1) = wt(Term2) and f $<$ g

or

wt(Term1) = wt(Term2) and f = g and s$_1$ = t$_1$ and s$_2$ = t$_2$ and ... but wt(s$_i$) $<$ wt(t$_i$).

(a) Write down the first few ground terms in this total ordering for the language of arithmetic with only constant 0 and functions succ and $+$.

(b) Write a program to generate all ground terms in order for the language of arithmetic with constant 0 and functions succ, $+$ and $*$.

21 A *stack* is an abstract data type with unary predicate IsEmpty, constant NullStack, unary functions Top and Pop, binary function Push, and two types given by predicates IsItem and IsStack. Records of type Item are added to the stack, a linear linked list, by Push and removed from the same end using Top for the end record and Pop for the remaining stack. The last item added is the first to be recovered.

Define IsStack by writing down axioms for the intended model so that any term which we expect to represent a stack satisfies IsStack. (Assume IsItem is already given for non-stack elements.) Also write down hypotheses which the various functions and IsEmpty should satisfy on all terms so that in the model every computable stack is dealt with correctly (e.g. ∀stack ∀item (Top(Push(item, stack)) = item)).

22   A *queue* is another abstract data type. It has unary predicate IsEmpty, constant NullQueue, unary functions Front and Remove, binary function Add, and two types given by unary predicates IsItem and IsQueue. Records of type Item are added to the tail of the queue, a linear linked list, by Add and removed from the other end using Front for the front record and Remove for the remaining queue. The oldest Item in the queue is the first to be removed.

As in Exercise 21, define IsQueue on terms by giving formulae it must satisfy so that it has the expected meaning on all ground terms. Do this also for the various other functions and predicates to characterize them on such terms.

23   Define unary functions One and Zero in the language of arithmetic by

$$\forall x\,(\mathrm{Zero}(x) = 2 * x)$$

and

$$\forall x\,(\mathrm{One}(x) = 2 * x + 1)$$

respectively.

(a) Show that every natural number can be written in terms of One, Zero and 0 alone by recursively defining a translation function from Nat as generated by the function Succ and constant 0 to the set of such terms. (In such a term, reading the function identifiers in reverse order gives the binary representation of the number.)

(b) Write down the appropriate induction principle for Nat constructed from One, Zero and 0 instead of Succ and 0.

(c) Define a ** b recursively in terms of a, *, 0 and Succ when b is written in the representation using One, Zero and 0.

Chapter 4

Deductions

Introduction

In the last chapter predicate languages were developed and interpretations and truth valuations were defined. These enable us to describe data structures on which programs operate and properties that hold at points in programs during execution. We considered models of a set of assumptions (for an abstract data type) and raised the problem of whether or not the hypotheses were sufficient to specify the desired structure. In this chapter we are concerned with deducing properties of whatever structure has been specified by the given formulae. This applies not just to deriving further data invariants that will hold throughout the execution of the program, but also to the deduction of assertions as the program is executing. In the final chapter we shall consider predicate calculus as a programming language in which these techniques for proving formulae are automated.

In Chapter 1 proofs were defined in the general context of a set of rules of inference in a formal theory. Both there and here we investigate *modus ponens* (MP) as our only rule of inference for proving formulae, but in the last two chapters we consider an alternative, SL resolution, which is more amenable to automated reasoning. The soundness theorem (4.1) shows that MP generates only valid formulae from our hypotheses and this is easy to see. However, the main requirement is to ensure that MP or any other choice of inference rule set produces all valid formulae. This is the so-called *completeness* property. We want to know that a formula which we suspect to be true can actually be deduced if it is true. As in Chapter 1 this property does indeed hold, provided that we start with a sufficiently large set of initial valid formulae called logical axioms. With this result (Gödel's completeness theorem) under our belt we have the equivalence of the truth-functional and deductive-theoretical approaches to predicate calculus.

There are pitfalls for the unwary. Gödel's theorem states that if a formula is always true then it is provable. However, it is possible that the property that requires proof is not always true. It may be true in the intended model of our hypotheses but not true in general. This has already been observed with the formula $m*n = n*m$ in models of Peano's first six axioms. In such cases it may be necessary to add further hypotheses because the specification of the intended model is then incomplete. In the case of mechanical theorem provers this might be achieved by inserting a model-dependent structural induction rule similar to that of the natural numbers (Peano's last axiom) to generate the required extra hypotheses. This is not an area that we shall look at in detail because it is outside first-order predicate calculus. Moreover, for (bounded) finite models the problems can be avoided. The infinite models likely to arise in practice can usually be restricted to only the integers, the reals and character strings, which can be considered specially. Nevertheless, it should always be borne in mind that the inability to prove a particular result which is believed to hold may be the result of a failure to make sufficiently many assumptions to tie down the model required rather than the fault of the strategy employed to generate a proof.

Axioms and Proofs

One of the main areas to which we shall apply the logic described in this and the previous chapters is in the verification of programs, i.e. in checking that they perform what is required by some specification. This is done by associating predicates with various points in the program and trying to prove that they hold upon execution. Alternative rules of inference are described in the final two chapters which are more suited to the derivation of properties of a static environment like an abstract data type.

The starting point for the proof of any formula is the set of hypotheses for the given problem, a set of self-evident truths called axioms and a set of inference rules. These define a formal theory in the sense given in Chapter 1. It may or may not be convenient to include the hypotheses of the chosen structure in the axioms of the theory. If we do so then we shall obtain, for example, the theory of arithmetic or the theory of Abelian groups or the theory of stacks. To these formulae we apply the rule of *modus porens*, (MP) as for propositional calculus, and deduce further formulae until the required formula has been proved.

In the formal theory we should like a set of axioms which is sufficiently large that all valid formulae can be deduced but also small enough that they can be easily written down. Fortunately it is possible to choose such a set of axioms. One such choice is described below. They are sometimes called *logical* axioms to distinguish them from hypotheses which are not logical truths. Recall that $U[x \mid t]$ is a variant of U in which the term t is free to be substituted for x and that substitution has been performed. Also, x is *free* in U if and only if U has a free occurrence of x.

Axioms for Predicate Languages

The axioms for deducing valid formulae in a predicate language without equality are the formulae which satisfy one of the following schemes:

(A1) $U \Rightarrow (V \Rightarrow U)$

(A2) $(U \Rightarrow (V \Rightarrow W)) \Rightarrow ((U \Rightarrow V) \Rightarrow (U \Rightarrow W))$

(A3) $(\sim U \Rightarrow \sim V) \Rightarrow ((\sim U \Rightarrow V) \Rightarrow U)$

(A4) $\forall x \, (U \Rightarrow V) \Rightarrow (\forall x U \Rightarrow \forall x V)$

(A5) $U \Rightarrow \forall x U$ if x is not free in U

(A6) $\forall x U \Rightarrow U[x \mid t]$ for any term t

(A7) $\forall x (Axiom)$ where *Axiom* follows one of the schemes (A1)–(A7)

These seven schemata for generating axioms yield an infinity of WFFs which are the axioms assumed in the predicate language. The first three of these are precisely those that were used in propositional calculus, and the remainder are needed to deal with quantifiers. The axioms produced in (A7) have the form $\forall x \forall y \ldots \forall z (Axiom)$ where *Axiom* is a formula following one of the previous schemes, namely (A1)–(A6). Such a formula is called a *generalization* of the formula *Axiom*. As in propositional calculus there is considerable freedom in choosing these axioms. A sufficient set, such as that above, is required for the completeness theorem (Theorem 4.2) and they should be chosen to use only the logical connectives provided.

The qualification to axiom (A5) is clearly essential. There are interpretations in which $x \neq y \Rightarrow \forall x (x \neq y)$ is false (take Nat with $x = 4$ and $y = 5$) but this formula follows the scheme (A5) except that x is free in $x \neq y$. However, as the axioms given by (A1)–(A6) are true for all choices of values for their free variables, generalizing them using (A7) does not affect their truth.

The definition of proof coincides with that introduced in Chapter 1 for a formal theory. Really we ought to qualify 'proof' by specifying the theory to which it applies, because the definition is always relative to the choice of axiom system and set of inference rules. However, we shall always work within the same theory in which the axiom set is a bare minimum for obtaining completeness and MP is the sole inference rule. The presence of quantifiers and variables in predicate languages leads to a basic axiom set that is larger than that required for propositional languages.

A *proof* from **H** is a finite sequence or list of formulae $W_1, W_2, \ldots, W_n$ such that for each formula W_i one of the following holds:

(i) W_i is an axiom in the system (A1)–(A7);

(ii) W_i is in **H**;

(iii) for some j, k with $j<i$ and $k<i$ we have W_j identical with $(W_k \Rightarrow W_i)$.

In (iii) MP is used to deduce W_i from W_j (i.e. $W_k \Rightarrow W_i$) and W_k. We write **H** $\vdash W$ if there is a proof from **H** which contains W and read it as 'W is *provable from, deducible from* or *a consequence of* **H**' or as 'W is a *theorem* of **H**'.

Observe that with this definition, every proof in the sense of propositional calculus is still a proof in this new sense. The meaning of 'proof' has been extended. Therefore the examples which were given for proofs in Chapter 1 also serve as examples here.

Example 4.1

The following is a proof that for all formulae V, W

$$\{W, \sim W\} \vdash V$$

(note how each formula in the list forming the proof is annotated with its derivation):

(1) W	hypothesis
(2) $\sim W$	hypothesis
(3) $(\sim V \Rightarrow \sim W) \Rightarrow ((\sim V \Rightarrow W) \Rightarrow V)$	by (A3)
(4) $W \Rightarrow (\sim V \Rightarrow W)$	by (A1)
(5) $\sim W \Rightarrow (\sim V \Rightarrow \sim W)$	by (A1)
(6) $\sim V \Rightarrow W$	MP on (1) and (4)
(7) $\sim V \Rightarrow \sim W$	MP on (2) and (5)
(8) $(\sim V \Rightarrow W) \Rightarrow V$	MP on (7) and (3)
(9) V	MP on (6) and (8)

Each axiom generated by the list (A1)–(A7) is clearly valid. As in propositional calculus, by considering truth valuations it is immediate that $\models U$ and $\models (U \Rightarrow V)$ yield $\models V$. Therefore MP preserves validity. Hence we have the following.

Theorem 4.1 (Soundness theorem)

H $\vdash W$ implies **H** $\models W$.

This just says that formulae deduced from **H** (using the given axiom scheme of the chosen formal theory) are true in every valuation in which the formulae of **H** are all true. One of the most fundamental properties of predicate languages is that the converse of this theorem holds, namely that anything which is always true can be proved to be true.

Theorem 4.2 (Gödel's completeness theorem)

$\mathbf{H} \vdash W$ if and only if $\mathbf{H} \models W$

for any set of hypotheses **H** and any formula W.

The interested reader is referred to Enderton (1970) for a proof of this and for a much more detailed discussion of the topics in this and the previous chapter. Another useful reference for this is Kleene (1967).

The following is a particularly important metatheorem (a theorem about theorems) which can be used to construct formal proofs. After its proof we give an example in which it is used.

Theorem 4.3 (Generalization theorem)

If x is not free in any $H \in \mathbf{H}$ then $\mathbf{H} \vdash W$ implies $\mathbf{H} \vdash \forall x W$.

Proof. The proof uses induction (a simple example of this is given in Chapter 5) on the length of a proof of the formula W. The induction starts with the observation that formulae with proofs containing a single formula must be either axioms or hypotheses since the use of MP forces any proof to contain at least three formulae. These initial cases are proved below in the induction step. The induction hypothesis is that we suppose $W_1, W_2, \ldots, W \equiv W_n$ is a proof of W and that the theorem holds for all formulae W' which have shorter proofs. In particular, each W_i ($1 \leqslant i < n$) has a shorter proof than W so that the induction hypothesis yields $\mathbf{H} \vdash \forall x W_i$. There are three cases for $W \equiv W_n$ to be considered, corresponding to the three classes in the definition of a proof.

(i) If W is an axiom then so is the generalization $\forall x W$ by (A7) and $\mathbf{H} \vdash \forall x W$ must hold.

(ii) If $W \in \mathbf{H}$ then the proof is the ordered list

(1) W	hypothesis
(2) $W \Rightarrow \forall x W$	by (A5)
(3) $\forall x W$	MP on (1) and (2)

(iii) The last possibility is that W is derived using MP from two previous formulae, say, W_i and W_j where W_j is identically $(W_i \Rightarrow W)$. Recalling the induction hypothesis and combining the proofs of $\forall x\, W_i$ and $\forall x\, W_j$ gives the following proof of $\forall x\, W$:

(1) $\forall x\, W_i$	induction hypothesis
(2) $\forall x\, (W_i \Rightarrow W)$	induction hypothesis
(3) $\forall x\, (W_i \Rightarrow W) \Rightarrow (\forall x\, W_i \Rightarrow \forall x\, W)$	by (A4)
(4) $\forall x\, W_i \Rightarrow \forall x\, W$	MP on (2) and (3)
(5) $\forall x\, W$	MP on (1) and (4)

The induction step is now complete as we have deduced $\mathbf{H} \vdash \forall x\, W$ for all formulae W with proofs containing n formulae. Hence the theorem holds by induction for all W.

As an example let $a \mid b$ mean $\exists x\, (a * x = b)$, i.e. a divides b. Let the set $\mathbf{H}$ of hypotheses include the Peano axioms (see Chapter 3) and any other suitable formulae of arithmetic deemed to be necessary. Suppose that we have already proved $(n-1)*(n+1) = n^2 - 1$. Our aim is to prove $\forall n\, (n^2 - 1 \mid n^4 - 1)$. Note that in the proof below it helps to number the successive formulae and include their derivations. In the case of results deduced previously, the proof has been condensed by omitting the intermediate steps and making the comment 'theorem of ...' in the margin. Also we have omitted the necessary restriction $n \neq 0$ at all points to simplify the formulae.

(1) $((n-1)*(n+1) = n^2 - 1)$	Theorem of $\mathbf{H}$
(2) $((n-1)*(n+1) = n^2 - 1) \Rightarrow \exists x\, ((n-1)*x = n^2 - 1)$	
	Theorem (Exercise 7(c))
(3) $\exists x\, ((n-1)*x = n^2 - 1)$	MP on (1) and (2)
i.e. $n-1 \mid n^2 - 1$	
(4) $\forall n\, (n-1 \mid n^2 - 1)$	Theorem 4.3 on (3)
(5) $\forall n\, (n-1 \mid n^2 - 1) \Rightarrow (n-1 \mid n^2 - 1)[n \mid n^2]$	by (A6)
(6) $(n-1 \mid n^2 - 1)[n \mid n^2]$	MP on (4) and (5)
i.e. $n^2 - 1 \mid n^4 - 1$	
(7) $\forall n\, (n^2 - 1 \mid n^4 - 1)$	Theorem 4.3 on (6)

(In (6) we cheated by assuming that $(n^2)^2$ and n^4 were identical. This should have been proved.)

In practice we rarely need to give a complete proof of some formula W direct from $\mathbf{H}$ and the logical axioms (A1)–(A7). It suffices to ascertain that a proof exists because our main interest is usually in the truth of the formula. If a collection $\mathbf{B}$ of results has already been obtained from some set $\mathbf{A}$ of hypotheses then we write $\mathbf{A} \vdash \mathbf{B}$. If these results are used to prove those in a set **C**, i.e. if **B** $\vdash$ **C**, then by concatenating the proofs of the formulae in **C** after the proofs of those in **B** we have proofs of all the formulae in **C** from those in **A**, i.e. the following theorem.

Theorem 4.4

For sets **A**, **B** and **C** of formulae, if **A** $\vdash$ **B** and **B** $\vdash$ **C** then **A** $\vdash$ **C**.

In our proofs of formulae in **C** from **A**, rather than repeat the proofs of formulae in **B** as required, we shall just remark that they are theorems from **A** as was done in the previous example. This metatheorem just restates, for predicate languages, something that we already knew for propositional languages. This is the concatenation of deductions result given in (4) of the final section in Chapter 1. The other results stated there hold automatically also, because proofs in propositional calculus carry over as proofs into predicate calculus.

Can we write the above theorem as $(\mathbf{A} \vdash \mathbf{B}) \wedge (\mathbf{B} \vdash \mathbf{C}) \Rightarrow (\mathbf{A} \vdash \mathbf{C})$? The answer is yes provided that the symbols are interpreted correctly. This statement says something about the predicate language in which the formulae of **A**, **B** and **C** lie. It is not in the predicate language itself, but is a formula in a language used to describe the predicate language. This language is the *meta-language* of predicate calculus. The symbols $\vdash$, $\wedge$ and $\Rightarrow$ used in the meta-language formula are just like the symbols $\Rightarrow$, $\wedge$ and $\Rightarrow$ in the predicate language. They are easy to confuse, particularly because two of them are written in the same way, but, as we stressed before, it is important to notice the difference between when a symbol is being used in the metatheory and when it is being used in the predicate language. Most of the book has been written in the meta-language: phrases such as 'is an alphabet', 'is a predicate', 'is a term' are all predicates of this language whilst 'for all formulae W' is clearly a quantifier over the variable W in the meta-language. We have tended to use English words rather than symbols for the meta-language and symbols instead of words for the predicate language. However, such a choice was free. (Within a program there is no such meta-language problem and keyboard restrictions then usually dictate that we actually use English words there, e.g. 'and', 'or' etc., for the subset of the programming language which forms a predicate language instead of the symbols $\wedge$, $\vee$ etc. which we have used here.)

The word 'proof' in the sense of a finite sequence of formulae with certain properties is yet another word of the meta-language. Our use of 'proof' in any other case has been in the meta-meta-language: the key words 'definition', 'theorem', 'proof' etc. have usually been applied to describe series of statements in the meta-language and so belong to that meta-meta-language. We can always ask what kind of language is being used in this paragraph to describe the different levels of meta-languages!

Let us continue with another theorem in the meta-language of the predicate language we were studying. The aim is to produce a battery of results which can transform a hard problem of finding a deduction of a formula from a set of hypotheses into a set of much easier problems to solve. In Theorem 3.7 it was observed that $\mathbf{H} \models V$ could be written as $\models W$ for $W \equiv (H_1 \wedge H_2 \wedge \ldots \wedge H_n) \Rightarrow V$ if $\mathbf{H} = \{H_1, H_2, \ldots, H_n\}$ were finite. The same proof shows that $\mathbf{H} \cup \{H\} \models V$ is equivalent to $\mathbf{H} \models (H \Rightarrow V)$. This result also holds for proofs, providing a recipe for simplifying formulae or reducing $\mathbf{H}$ as necessary.

Theorem 4.5 (Deduction theorem)

For a set $\mathbf{H}$ of formulae, if V and W are WFFs then $\mathbf{H} \cup \{W\} \vdash V$ if and only if $\mathbf{H} \vdash (W \Rightarrow V)$.

This was proved as Theorem 1.10 for propositional calculus. The proof there translates word for word into a proof for predicate calculus.

Satisfiability and Consistency

A set $\mathbf{H}$ of formulae is *satisfiable* if and only if for some interpretation I there is an I-valuation σ such that $\sigma H = \mathrm{T}$ for all $H \in \mathbf{H}$.

It is easy to see that unsatisfiable sets exist. If $\mathbf{H}$ contains a pair of formulae V and $\sim V$ then whenever one is true the other is false. Therefore $\mathbf{H}$ is unsatisfiable as it always contains at least one false formula. Next suppose that although our set $\mathbf{H}$ may not contain a pair of formulae V and $\sim V$ we can nevertheless deduce such a pair from $\mathbf{H}$ using proofs in the sense of $\vdash$. Then, by the soundness theorem, V and $\sim V$ would both have to be true for every valuation in every interpretation. As this is ridiculous the set $\mathbf{H}$ can never be satisfied by any valuation. The set is inherently inconsistent. This can be stated formally as follows.

A set $\mathbf{H}$ of formulae is *inconsistent* if there is a formula V such that $\mathbf{H} \vdash V$ and $\mathbf{H} \vdash \sim V$. Otherwise it is *consistent*.

We have noted that if $\mathbf{H}$ is inconsistent then it is not satisfiable. From such a self-contradictory set we are bound to be able to prove amazing results. Indeed, everything can be proved!

Theorem 4.6

H is inconsistent if and only if $H \vdash W$ for every formula W.

Proof. To see this let us choose a formula W that exhibits the inconsistency of H. Therefore $H \vdash W$ and $H \vdash \sim W$, i.e. $H \vdash H_1$ where $H_1 = \{W, \sim W\}$. It now suffices to deduce any formula V from H_1 and apply Theorem 4.4. This was done in Example 4.1. For the converse choose a pair W, $\sim W$ of formulae which can be proved from H. These show that H is inconsistent.

The concepts of consistency and satisfiability are closely related to those of provability and truth respectively. This relationship can be made very precise. Firstly, consistency can be defined in terms of provability by means of the following theorem.

Theorem 4.7

For any set of formulae H and formula W
(i) $H \cup \{\sim W\}$ is inconsistent if and only if $H \vdash W$,
(ii) $H \cup \{W\}$ is inconsistent if and only if $H \vdash \sim W$.

Proof. The backward implications are easy to prove. For example, with (i) if W can be proved from H then W and $\sim W$ can be proved from $H \cup \{\sim W\}$ so that $H \cup \{\sim W\}$ is inconsistent. For (ii) we require $\sim \sim W \vdash W$ from Chapter 1, Exercise 12, but the proof is otherwise identical.

For the forward implications suppose that $H \cup \{\sim W\}$ is inconsistent. By Theorem 4.6 for any formula V we have $H \cup \{\sim W\} \vdash V, \sim V$. By the deduction theorem (4.5) $H \vdash \sim W \Rightarrow V$ and $H \vdash \sim W \Rightarrow \sim V$. By axiom (A3), $(\sim W \Rightarrow \sim V) \Rightarrow ((\sim W \Rightarrow V) \Rightarrow W)$, from which W can be deduced after two applications of MP. When $H \cup \{W\}$ is inconsistent, then so is $H \cup \{\sim \sim W\}$, and by the same method as before $\sim W$ is a consequence of H.

Secondly, the concepts of truth and satisfiability are closely related by the following.

Theorem 4.8

For any set of formulae **H** and formula W
(i) $\mathbf{H} \cup \{\sim W\}$ is unsatisfiable if and only if $\mathbf{H} \models W$,
(ii) $\mathbf{H} \cup \{W\}$ is unsatisfiable if and only if $\mathbf{H} \models \sim W$.

The reverse implications are trivial since if $\mathbf{H} \cup \{\sim W\}$ or $\mathbf{H} \cup \{W\}$ were satisfiable then so would $\mathbf{H} \cup \{W, \sim W\}$ be, which is plainly absurd. However, suppose, for example, that $\mathbf{H} \cup \{\sim W\}$ were unsatisfiable. For any valuation σ either $\sigma H = \mathrm{T}$ for all $H \in \mathbf{H}$ and $\sigma(\sim W) = \mathrm{F}$, or $\sigma H = \mathrm{F}$ for some $H \in \mathbf{H}$. Thus $\sigma W = \mathrm{T}$ whenever $\sigma H = \mathrm{T}$ for all $H \in \mathbf{H}$. Hence $\mathbf{H} \models W$.
   Combining these two theorems yields the following theorem.

Theorem 4.9

For a given set **H** of formulae and any formula W the following are equivalent:
(i) $\mathbf{H} \models W$ if and only if $\mathbf{H} \vdash W$;
(ii) $\mathbf{H} \cup \{\sim W\}$ is unsatisfiable if and only if $\mathbf{H} \cup \{\sim W\}$ is inconsistent.

Since Gödel's completeness theorem (Theorem 4.2) states that the first of these statements is true, it follows that the second also holds. Hence the truth-functional and deductive-theoretical approaches to predicate calculus are equivalent. From now on we shall frequently translate the problem of showing that $\mathbf{H} \models W$ or $\mathbf{H} \vdash W$ into that of showing that $\mathbf{H} \cup \{\sim W\}$ is unsatisfiable.

Equality

The equality predicate $=$ has been used several times so far although no precise definition has been given. It is a binary predicate, usually written $=$, for which we require the property that, for any valuation σ, $\sigma(t_1 = t_2)$ is true if and only if the terms t_1 and t_2 are found to be equal when evaluated in the universe. Thus for an interpretation I with universe U the set $=_1$ on which $=$ is to be true must be the *diagonal* subset $\{(u, u) \mid u \in U\}$ of U^2.
   Similarly, the constant predicates *True* and *False* of no variables need to be incorporated. We have insisted that the appropriate sets for *True* and *False* in every interpretation were fixed, the whole of U^0 for *True* and the empty set $\{\}$ for *False*.
   We now extend the axiom set to include these three predicates. Generalizations of the new axioms using (A7) are allowed just as before.

Axioms for Equality, True and False

(A8) $t = t$ for any term t.

(A9) $(s_1 = t_1) \Rightarrow ((s_2 = t_2) \Rightarrow \ldots ((s_n = t_n)$
$$\Rightarrow f(s_1, s_2, \ldots, s_n) = f(t_1, t_2, \ldots, t_n)) \ldots)$$
for any n-ary function f and terms $s_1, t_1, s_2, t_2, \ldots, s_n, t_n$.

(A10) $(s_1 = t_1) \Rightarrow ((s_2 = t_2) \Rightarrow \ldots ((s_n = t_n)$
$$\Rightarrow (P(s_1, s_2, \ldots, s_n) \Rightarrow P(t_1, t_2, \ldots, t_n))) \ldots)$$
for any n-ary predicate P and terms $s_1, t_1, s_2, t_2, \ldots, s_n, t_n$.

(A11) $W \Rightarrow True$ for any formula W.

(A12) $False \Rightarrow W$ for any formula W.

We chose to use $\Rightarrow$ and $\sim$ as the fundamental connectives in the initial axiom system (A1)–(A7) because this fits in well with the usual form of MP. Had $\wedge$ been included, the axiom (A9) would have a more natural appearance as

$$(s_1 = t_1) \wedge (s_2 = t_2) \wedge \ldots \wedge (s_n = t_n) \Rightarrow f(s_1, s_2, \ldots, s_n) = f(t_1, t_2, \ldots, t_n)$$

Given these axioms, an inconsistent set could now be defined as one for which $\mathbf{H} \vdash False$ holds. Of course, we need only have defined *True*, say, and chosen *False* as a synonym for $\sim True$, just as $\exists$ was defined in terms of $\forall$. In fact, we need not make use of *True* and *False* at all: they are logically equivalent to $(W \vee \sim W)$ and $(W \wedge \sim W)$ respectively. But, following good programming practice, the use of the constant predicates *True* and *False* is to be preferred.

The following are left as exercises.

Theorem 4.10

Equality is an equivalence relation, i.e. for all terms r, s and t

(i) $\vdash r = r$

(ii) $\vdash (r = s) \Rightarrow (s = r)$

(iii) $\vdash (r = s) \wedge (s = t) \Rightarrow (r = t)$

Theorem 4.11

The equality predicate satisfies
$$\{ s_1 = t_1, s_2 = t_2, \ldots, s_n = t_n \} \vdash$$
$$U[x_1 | s_1][x_2 | s_2] \ldots [x_n | s_n] \Rightarrow U[x_1 | t_1][x_2 | t_2] \ldots [x_n | t_n]$$

for all terms $s_1, \ldots, s_n, t_1, \ldots, t_n$, variables $x_1, \ldots, x_n$ and formulae U.

As a further example of a proof, let us return to the problem raised in an earlier example of this chapter, i.e. $(n^2)^2 = n^4$. First, we present a trivial result.

Theorem 4.12

$\forall x_n \ldots \forall x_2 \forall x_1 (U) \vdash U[x_1 | t_1] [x_2 | t_2] \ldots [x_n | t_n]$ for any terms $t_1, t_2, \ldots, t_n$.

A few more axioms for natural numbers are required beyond the first six of Peano. The proof below therefore starts with the first three formulae already given.

(1) $\forall x \forall r \forall s ((x^r)^s = x^{(r*s)})$	hypothesis
(2) $(2*2) = 4$	Exercise 11
(3) $(n^2 - 1) \mid ((n^2)^2 - 1)$	earlier theorem
(4) $(n^2)^2 = n^{(2*2)}$	Theorem 4.12 with the substitution $[x|n][r|2][s|2]$ applied to the formula in (1)
(5) $(n^2)^2 = n^{(2*2)} \Rightarrow (n^2)^2 = n^4$	by Theorem 4.11 and (2) with U the formula $(n^2)^2 = n^{x_1}$
(6) $(n^2)^2 = n^4$	by MP on (4) and (5)
(7) $(n^2 - 1) \mid ((n^2)^2 - 1) \Rightarrow (n^2 - 1) \mid (n^4 - 1)$	by Theorem 4.11 and (6) with U the formula $(n^2 - 1) \mid (x_1 - 1)$
(8) $(n^2 - 1) \mid (n^4 - 1)$	by MP on (3) and (7)

This completes the proof of (8) from (3) which was previously lacking. Note that for clarity the theorems and axioms used need documenting with the choice of formulae, term or variable to give the explicit instance used. Note also that the proof of (1) uses the induction principle which does not lie in a first-order predicate language, and so we must assume this as a hypothesis to make use of it. It is possible, however, but tedious to derive the particular case used in (4).

From this example it must be apparent that formal deductions of even the simplest results are extremely long and the only way to shorten them is to have a number of simple but general theorems that can just be quoted in the same way that, for example, Theorem 4.11 is used above.

Decidability

An expert system is a program that interactively requests data about a given situation in order to draw conclusions in the same way that human experts do. Such systems exist, for example, in specialist areas of medicine, for diagnosing diseases in grain crops, in oil prospecting and in X-ray crystallography. The program contains various facts about its specialist field. These are frequently coded explicitly as rules in a database and would then form the set of hypotheses **H** that was presupposed in the work of Chapters 3 and 4. If complications such as the probability that the rule holds in a particular case are neglected, these facts often have the form $(U_1 \wedge U_2 \wedge \ldots \wedge U_n) \Rightarrow V$ and are called *production rules*. By asking questions to obtain any additional required information, i.e. hypotheses, the machine hopes to establish the truth of $U_1, U_2, \ldots, U_n$ to conclude V. When a number of these rules have been successfully applied to reach a conclusion W, the steps via intermediate conclusions V form a proof in some formal theory. The algorithm by which the deduction steps are made makes use of a built-in axiom system and inference rule set.

An important practical problem is to establish whether the chosen algorithm will indeed establish the truth or falsehood of some formula W presented to the expert system under a given set of hypotheses **H**. More simply, is there an algorithm for establishing just the truth of $\mathbf{H} \models W$ when it does in fact hold? An affirmative answer is obtained by taking any algorithm which tries all proofs starting with the shortest and then considering larger proofs in the hope of eventually finding one that proves W. This can be done as follows. Since the alphabet of our predicate language is countable the number of formulae with a fixed total number of symbols is finite. This results in the number of proofs containing a fixed total of symbols being finite. Therefore the set of all proofs is countable by taking them in order according to the number of symbols they contain. If $\mathbf{H} \models W$ then $\mathbf{H} \vdash W$, and so this algorithm will sooner or later find a proof of W. However, if the formula W is not provable then the algorithm continues for ever, looking unsuccessfully for a proof.

In general, if after a long time no answer is obtained from the algorithm, it just means that a proof of W has not yet been found—the algorithm might find one at the next step. This is a problem with every such algorithm. In fact, no algorithm is possible which will always answer the question $\mathbf{H} \vdash W$? positively or negatively whatever **H** and W.

A set is called *decidable* if there is an algorithm which will always produce a 'yes' or 'no' answer for membership.

Therefore the sets of valid predicate formulae and the set of consequences of **H** are both undecidable. For this reason first-order predicate calculus is called *undecidable*. Propositional calculus, however, is decidable. To see this it is sufficient to note that truth tables will always show whether or not $H \models W$ holds. A general reference which includes a more detailed discussion of decidability, definable sets and related topics is *Computability and Logic* by Boolos and Jeffrey (1980).

Finally, observe that the undecidability of predicate calculus is quite far reaching. Any automatic theorem prover has the same problem whether it is at the heart of an expert system or is involved in the execution of a declarative language program. However, in general the problems tend to arise from insufficient hypotheses being made to restrict the model adequately. We have learned how to provide sufficient data for procedural language programs, but it may be in the nature of things that applications for which a theorem prover is needed contain so many data that it is no longer apparent whether enough information is present to draw the expected conclusion. If this is the case, then the undecidability problem ensures that non-procedural programs will always suffer the risk of occasional non-termination. Nevertheless, good techniques are available for theorem provers, and some of these are discussed in Chapter 6.

Exercises

1   Show that equality is an equivalence relation by obtaining deductions of the following defining properties of an equivalence relation P:

    (a) $\forall x P(x, x)$ (reflection)

    (b) $\forall x \forall y \, (P(x, y) \Rightarrow P(y, x))$ (symmetry)

    (c) $\forall x \forall y \forall z \, (P(x, y) \Rightarrow (P(y, z) \Rightarrow P(x, z)))$ (transitivity)

2   Show that none of the formulae in Exercise 1 is logically implied by the other two by constructing models of each pair in which the third sentence fails.

3   Suppose that **S** is a set of sentences such that if $S \in \mathbf{S}$ then $\models S$ or $\models \sim S$. Show that in any model I of **S** each sentence T satisfies $\models_I T$ if and only if $\mathbf{S} \models T$.

4   Prove Theorem 4.12 by supplying a deduction and also by giving a formal proof by induction.

5   Provide proofs of the following metatheorems:

    (a) $\mathbf{H} \vdash U_1$, $\mathbf{H} \vdash U_2$, ..., $\mathbf{H} \vdash U_n$ and $\{U_1, U_2, ..., U_n\} \vdash V$ imply $\mathbf{H} \vdash V$.

    (b) $U \vdash \sim V$ if and only if $V \vdash \sim U$.

    (c) $\vdash U \Rightarrow V$ implies $\vdash \forall x U \Rightarrow \forall x V$.

6 Provide deductions of the following theorems:
(a) $\vdash \forall x \forall y\, (x = y \Rightarrow y = x)$
(b) $\vdash (x = y) \Rightarrow (\forall z P(x, z) \Rightarrow \forall z P(y, z))$
(c) $\forall x W \vdash \exists x W$
(d) $\vdash \exists x\, (U \Rightarrow \forall x U)$

7 Show that deductions exist for the following theorems:
(a) $\forall x U \vee \forall x V \Rightarrow \forall x\, (U \vee V)$
(b) $\exists x\, (U \vee V) \Leftrightarrow \exists x U \vee \exists x V$
(c) $U[x \mid t] \Rightarrow \exists x U$ for any term t

8 Prove the following theorems:
(a) $\forall x U \wedge V \Leftrightarrow \forall x\, (U \wedge V)$ where x is not free in V
(b) $\exists x\, (U \vee V) \Leftrightarrow \exists x U \vee V$ where x is not free in V
(c) $\forall x \forall y\, (x = y) \Leftrightarrow \exists x \forall y\, (x = y)$
(d) $\forall x\, (U \Rightarrow V) \Rightarrow (\exists x U \Rightarrow \exists x V)$

9 Is the set $\mathbf{H} = \{\exists x_1 P(x_1),\ \sim P(x_1),\ \sim P(x_2),\ \sim P(x_3),\ \ldots\}$ consistent or satisfiable when $\mathrm{VAR} = \{x_1, x_2, x_3, \ldots\}$?

10 Use induction to prove Theorem 4.11. (Hint: Provide a formal deduction for the inductive step first. Then use the recursive definitions of terms and WFFs to prove the existence of a deduction in the base case.)

11 Add the hypotheses $1 = \mathrm{succ}(0)$, $2 = \mathrm{succ}(1)$, $3 = \mathrm{succ}(2)$, $4 = \mathrm{succ}(3)$, and $\forall x\, (1 * x = x)$ to Peano's axioms (i)–(vi) and hence prove that in any model of these hypotheses
(a) $\forall x\, (x * 1 = x)$
(b) $2 + 2 = 4$
(c) $2 * 2 = 4$

Chapter 5

Correctness Proofs

Introduction

It is perhaps no exaggeration to say that one of the greatest dangers facing mankind is that of the careless programmer. With the increasing reliance placed upon computer systems controlling our current frightening arsenal of nuclear weaponry, errors in code can be a threat to the world's very survival. There is a great urgency for a programming methodology which ensures accurate and correct code. With the advent of this, not only would we be surer of avoiding an accidental nuclear holocaust but we might also expect to be free of the more day-to-day horror stories caused by programmers' errors—such 'accidents' as collapsing bridges and buildings, massive financial mismanagement, totally ineffective long-range planning etc.

The computer scientist must take the task of proving the correctness of his or her programs very seriously. In this chapter we describe how predicate calculus can be used to reason about simple Pascal programs. We choose Pascal because of its wide use in teaching, its general applicability and its suitability for structured programming; the ideas we propose will apply to other similar languages. We shall concentrate on proving the correctness of programs that have already been designed. Of course, it would be hoped and expected that a correctness proof of a program would go hand-in-hand with its development. Indeed, it can be argued that the correctness proof should be of such overriding importance that it must surely influence the development itself. Such an approach is advocated by a number of leading computer scientists, but unfortunately is all too rare in practice. A good overview of this general approach to Pascal programming is given by Alagić and Arbib (1978). In their text the ideas introduced in this chapter are fully developed and it is shown how the correctness of large-scale programs can be proved. In this chapter we aim to convince the reader of the validity of the approach, and we keep to relatively simple examples. In particular, we avoid detailed discussion of topics such as typed variables, complex data structures and file processing. Our examples will involve just integers or reals or possibly arrays of these types—these are sufficient to

146

illustrate all the key concepts we wish to present. However, the reader can rest assured that the incorporation of more complex data structures can be handled using the techniques we describe. We shall thus largely be ignoring declarations but, nevertheless, shall be assuming that any variables used satisfy the normal axioms of arithmetic. In the general case whenever a declaration of a variable x of type T is encountered, it can be assumed that x satisfies a number of axioms specific to the type T. These axioms can can then be used in any subsequent argument about x.

Many of the ideas discussed in this chapter arise from the pioneering work of Floyd (1967) on proving the correctness of flowchart programs. This was later developed by Hoare in a series of research papers in the late 1960s and early 1970s.

Another approach towards securing correct code is the design of new programming languages which make correctness proofs much easier. In this chapter we shall see that there is a strong connection between mathematical induction and recursion. A style of programming based on recursion enables correctness proofs to be presented in terms of induction. The assignment (:=) can be avoided altogether if this style is used, and this considerably simplifies the situation. Functional programming uses this approach: a good introduction to this topic has been given by Glaser *et al.* (1984) and Henderson (1980).

If we use predicate calculus to reason about our programs and hence develop correctness proofs, it seems natural to develop languages that themselves are very close to predicate calculus. In such a case, the program and its correctness proof might be virtually the same. In Chapter 7 we shall be exploring the use of predicate calculus as a programming language and logic programming in general. For now, however, we return to traditional programming techniques and to Pascal in particular.

The first step in the design of any program is to determine exactly what is required of the program rather than immediately embarking upon details of how it is to perform. A *program specification* is developed by a *specifications engineer*. He or she will determine what is to be achieved by the program, i.e. its *functional specification*, as well as any attributes the program must have, i.e. its *property specification*. A functional specification comprises (i) constraints placed upon the input to the program and (ii) the relationship(s) between the desired output and the input. A property specification details program attributes such as efficiency (time and space constraints), portability and security.

Once these two parts of a program specification are determined, the next step is the development and implementation of a program to meet these requirements. This is generally achieved in two distinct phases. Firstly, during *algorithm design*, algorithms are developed which provide the details of how the program specification is to be achieved. These algorithms are presented in some form of pseudo-code, e.g. structured English. Secondly, the algorithms are developed into executable (e.g. Pascal) programs during the *implementation phase*. Finally the developed programs are tested and verified to confirm that they meet the specification laid down by the specifications engineer.

The task of the requirements engineer in designing a program specification should not be underestimated. If the job is not well performed, much of the effort of the algorithm designer and implementer can be wasted. If queries arise concerning specification during algorithm design and implementation, these queries should be referred back to the specifications engineer. It is not the task of the algorithm designer or implementer to decide details of specification.

Even with simple examples, however, program specification is often not as precise as we would wish. For example, a student programmer might be given the task of finding the roots of the quadratic equation $ax^2 + bx + c = 0$ given the values of the real numbers a, b, c. A full functional specification would either limit the input to ensure that real roots existed (by constraining $b^2 - 4ac \geqslant 0$) or specify the output required in the case where roots were complex. Similarly, problems arising in the case where $a = 0$ or where $b^2 - 4ac = 0$ should be handled by the specification. In more complex situations program specifications are often incomplete; the task of the specifications engineer is all too often taken too lightly. The programmer may be tempted to decide unilaterally what to do. This may have serious consequences if his or her code is part of a larger suite of programs and decisions made are not adequately recorded and reported.

In this chapter we shall be primarily concerned with functional specification and in techniques for proving that a given Pascal program is a correct implementation to meet a given functional specification. Functional specifications should be given formally to avoid any ambiguity. In fact, much research has been concerned with the design of *specification languages* for providing the means of formally stating specifications. Once a specification is given in one of these languages, it can be automatically checked for syntactic correctness. Further tests (usually manual) are then undertaken to confirm that such a formal specification does indeed describe the properties of the intended system. Once the specification is confirmed, it is used to guide the programmer in algorithm design and implementation. Notable specification languages include Affirm, Special, Ina Jo, VDMDM, Clear, OBJ and Z. Predicate calculus can be used as a specification specification language, and this is how we shall proceed in this text. We shall assume that our (functional) specification is in the form of two formulae. Firstly we have an input formula *I* which specifies the *pre-condition*, i.e. restrictions placed upon any input (global) variables. Secondly we have an output formula *O* which specifies the *post-condition*, i.e. how the output should be related to the input. Thus, for our quadratic equation example we might have the following specification.

Input variables: a, b, c: real;
Input formula: $a \neq 0 \wedge b^2 > 4ac$
Output variables: $x1$, $x2$: real;
Output formula: $x1 \neq x2 \wedge a(x1)^2 + b(x1) + c = 0$
$\wedge a(x2)^2 + b(x2) + c = 0$

It should be remembered that when we say that x is real we then mean that x satisfies all the axioms of real arithmetic (or, to be more precise, the axioms which describe real arithmetic as it is performed on our computer). In the proof techniques which we develop, we shall use the normal algebraic manipulation with which we are all familiar and neglect imprecision arising from the inexactitude of machine arithmetic. We know that these manipulations can be justified from the basic axioms of arithmetic, but to include such justification in each case would make our proofs long and extremely tedious.

As a second example of a specification, we consider the problem of sorting the elements of an array a of n distinct real numbers. Such a specification can be described as follows.

Input variables: n: integer; $a[1]$, $a[2]$, ..., $a[n]$: real;
Input formula: $n > 0 \wedge \forall i \forall j (1 \leq i \leq n \wedge 1 \leq j \leq n \wedge a[i] = a[j] \Rightarrow i = j)$
Output variables: $b[1]$, $b[2]$, ..., $b[n]$: real;
Output formula: $\{a[1], a[2], ..., a[n]\} = \{b[1], b[2], ...,$
$b[n]\} \wedge \forall k (1 \leq k < n \Rightarrow b[k] \leq b[k+1])$

In this example, we have again extended predicate calculus notation with mathematical notation knowing that we could formalize this if necessary.

If we wish to ensure that a program or procedure which we write has no side effects when used in a larger suite of programs, we shall generally have to insist that the values of input variables must *not* be changed by the

execution of any code. Thus in the sorting example above, the values of
$a[1], a[2], \ldots, a[n]$ remain unchanged.

A good Pascal programmer will usually include some or all of the
specification within the textual body of the program in the form of
comments. This alerts any user to the restrictions placed upon the use of the
code and also provides a description of the purpose of the code. A
specification should always be kept with the code to assist future
maintenance. Pascal code for the first specification above might be as
follows.

$$\{a \neq 0 \wedge b^2 > 4ac\}$$
var d: real;
begin
$\quad d := \text{sqrt } (b * b - 4 * a * c);$
$\quad x1 := (-b + d)/(2 * a);$
$\quad x2 := (-b - d)/(2 * a)$
end
$$\{x1 \neq x2 \wedge a(x1)^2 + b(x1) + c = 0 \wedge a(x2)^2 + b(x2) + c = 0\}$$

The correctness of this code can easily be verified. We must check that if
the input formula is satisfied and the program is executed then the output
predicate is satisfied. Since $b^2 > 4ac$, we must have $d \neq 0$. Then $a \neq 0$ ensures
that $x1, x2$ are both defined and $d \neq 0$ ensures that $x1 \neq x2$. To check that
$x1, x2$ both satisfy $ax^2 + bx + c = 0$ is then a matter of routine algebra.

In general then our task is to prove that a given sequence S of (Pascal)
instructions meets some specification defined by an input formula I and an
output formula O. We write this as

$$\{I\}S\{O\}$$

Thus if I is satisfied immediately prior to the execution of S and S is executed
then, provided that S halts, we expect O to be satisfied immediately after.
(Satisfaction of the formulae is defined in terms of the truth valuation given
by the current values of program variables.) Proving this result is called the
partial verification of $\{I\}S\{O\}$. If $\{I\}S\{O\}$ is partially verified, then we say
that S is *partially correct* with respect to the input formula I and the output
formula O. To (totally) verify $\{I\}S\{O\}$ we also have to show that S will
always halt given that the input formula I is satisfied. Once this has also
been achieved we say that S is *(totally) correct* with respect to the input
formula I and the output formula O.

An alternative way of representing $\{I\}S\{O\}$ is in terms of flowcharts (see

Fig. 5.1). Although flowcharts are rather an old-fashioned notation, they can be useful in this work as an aid to understanding. We thus use them in this text since it helps us to develop the results we need.

The braces surrounding I and O in $\{I\}S\{O\}$ correspond to their use as comments in Pascal programs. This is why we have adopted this particular notation—some authors use $I\{S\}O$.

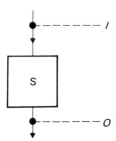

Fig. 5.1.

S will generally be a complex piece of structured code, and to verify $\{I\}S\{O\}$ we shall need to use various *proof rules*. The proof rules which we shall be developing provide ways of handling each of the various program structures met in Pascal. When applied and combined they provide a technique for partially verifying correct code. We shall then generally also be able to produce an argument for the termination of the code.

Basic Proof Rules

The partial verification of $\{I\}S\{O\}$ when S is a simple assignment statement is very straightforward. Consider the partial verification of

$$\{I\}x:=t\{O\}$$

If we denote by $O[x\,|\,t]$ the formula obtained by replacing each free occurrence of x by t in a suitable variant of O, then to partially verify $\{I\}x:=t\{O\}$ we merely have to prove that $I\Rightarrow O[x\,|\,t]$ is logically true in the interpreted implementation.

We want to be able to verify $\{I\}S\{O\}$ where S is a complex statement constructed from simple statements using the various Pascal programming structures. In this section, we take a top-down approach and develop rules which allow us to verify $\{I\}S\{O\}$ provided that we can verify certain subprograms. In a later section of this chapter we shall discuss functions and procedures and the verification of larger programs involving such structures once they themselves have been verified. Firstly, however, we state an obvious metatheorem which we shall use frequently.

Theorem 5.1

For the implemented interpretation
(i) If $\vdash_M I \Rightarrow J$ and $\{J\}S\{O\}$ is partially verified, then $\{I\}S\{O\}$ is partially verified.
(ii) If $\{I\}S\{J\}$ is partially verified and $\vdash_M J \Rightarrow O$, then $\{I\}S\{O\}$ is partially verified.

In this chapter we shall use a widely adopted notation for proof rules which takes the following form:

$$\frac{\{I_1\}S_1\{O_1\}, \{I_2\}S_2\{O_2\}, \ldots, \{I_n\}S_n\{O_n\}, R_1, R_2, \ldots, R_m}{\{I\}S\{O\}}$$

This is shorthand for 'if $\{I_1\}S_1\{O_1\}$, $\{I_2\}S_2\{O_2\}$, ..., $\{I_n\}S_n\{O_n\}$ are partially verified and the formulae $R_1, R_2, \ldots, R_m$ are all provable in the interpreted implementation, then $\{I\}S\{O\}$ is partially verified'. Theorem 5.1 provides us with the following two proof rules expressed in this notation:

$$\frac{\{J\}S\{O\}, I \Rightarrow J}{\{I\}S\{O\}}$$

and

$$\frac{\{I\}S\{J\}, J \Rightarrow O}{\{I\}S\{O\}}$$

A similar proof rule, which is left for the reader to establish as an exercise, is the *combining rule*

$$\frac{\{I_1\}S\{O_1\}, \{I_2\}S\{O_2\}, I \Rightarrow I_1 \wedge I_2, O_1 \wedge O_2 \Rightarrow O}{\{I\}S\{O\}}$$

The proof rule associated with the assignment $x := t$ is the *assignment rule*

$$\frac{I \Rightarrow O[x \mid t]}{\{I\}x := t\{O\}}$$

Assuming a is an integer, we can use this assignment rule to deduce from $a>0 \Rightarrow a-1 \geqslant 0$ that $\{a>0\}\ x:=a-1\ \{x \geqslant 0\}$. Also, since $a-1=a-1$ trivially holds, we have $true \Rightarrow a-1=a-1$ and hence the assignment rule allows us to partially verify $\{true\}\ x:=a-1\ \{x=a-1\}$. Then we can use the combining rule to partially verify $\{a>0\}\ x:=a-1\ \{x \geqslant 0 \wedge x=a-1\}$. Now, we consider the various ways in which Pascal enables us to construct complex statements from simpler components.

(1) The serial statement

If $S_1, S_2, \ldots, S_n\ (n \geqslant 1)$ are statements, then so is their serial composition

   begin $S_1; S_2; \ldots; S_n$ **end**

To partially verify

   $\{I\}$ **begin** $S_1; S_2; \ldots; S_n$ **end** $\{O\}$

we need formulae $J_1, J_2, \ldots, J_{n-1}$ and partial verifications of $\{I\}S_1\{J_1\}$, $\{J_1\}S_2\{J_2\}, \ldots, \{J_{n-1}\}S_n\{O\}$. The flowchart describing this is given in Fig. 5.2.

The proof rule for serial statements is

$$\frac{\{I\}S_1\{J_1\}, \{J_1\}S_2\{J_2\}, \ldots, \{J_{n-1}\}S_n\{O\}}{\{I\}\ \textbf{begin}\ S_1; S_2; \ldots; S_n\ \textbf{end}\ \{O\}}$$

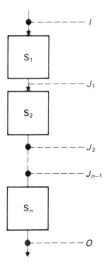

Fig. 5.2.

As an example of the use of this rule, consider the following code concerning integers:

> **begin**
> $x := a - 1;$
> $y := x * x + 2 * x + 1;$
> $y := y \textbf{ div } (x + 1)$
> **end**

From

$$\{a > 0\}x := a - 1\{x \geqslant 0 \wedge x = a - 1\}$$
$$\{x \geqslant 0 \wedge x = a - 1\}y := x * x + 2 * x + 1\{y = a^2 \wedge x \geqslant 0 \wedge x = a - 1\}$$
$$\{y = a^2 \wedge x \geqslant 0 \wedge x = a - 1\}y := y \textbf{ div } (x + 1)\{y = a \wedge x \geqslant 0 \wedge x = a - 1\}$$

we are able to partially verify

> $\{a > 0\}$
> **begin**
> $x := a - 1;$
> $y := x * x + 2 * x + 1;$
> $y := y \textbf{ div } (x + 1)$
> **end**
> $\{y = a \wedge x \geqslant 0 \wedge x = a - 1\}$

Thus, from Theorem 5.1, this simple three line program will meet any functional specification comprising input formula I and output formula O, provided that the following hold:

(i) $I \Rightarrow a > 0$

(ii) $y = a \wedge x \geqslant 0 \wedge x = a - 1 \Rightarrow O$

Thus, for example, since termination is obvious, we are able to totally verify

> $\{a > 0\}$
> **begin**
> $x := a - 1;$
> $y := x * x + 2 * x + 1;$
> $y := y \textbf{ div } (x + 1)$
> **end**
> $\{y = x + 1 \wedge x = a - 1\}$

(2) The conditional statement

If B is a Boolean expression and S_1, S_2 are two statements, then

> **if** B **then** S_1 **else** S_2

is also a statement.

This statement causes the evaluation of B and, if it is true, the actions defined by S_1 are performed; otherwise, the actions defined by S_2 are performed. The conditional statement is described by the flow chart of Fig. 5.3.

The proof rule associated with **if** statements is thus

$$\frac{\{I \wedge B\}S_1\{O\}, \{I \wedge \sim B\}S_2\{O\}}{\{I\} \text{ if } B \text{ then } S_1 \text{ else } S_2\{O\}}$$

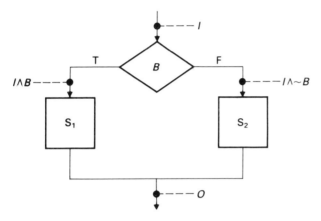

Fig. 5.3.

This proof rule holds under the assumption that the evaluation of B has no side effects. As an example of the use of the proof rule, consider the following: given the (trivial) verification of

$$\{x > 0\} \ y := x\{y > 0\}$$

and

$$\{x \leqslant 0\}y := -x\{y \geqslant 0\}$$

we can use Theorem 5.1 to deduce the partial verification of

$$\{x > 0\}y := x\{y \geqslant 0\}$$

and then use the above proof rule to obtain the partial verification of

$$\{\} \text{ if } x > 0 \text{ then } y := x \text{ else } y := -x\{y \geqslant 0\}$$

Note that in this example $\{\}$ represents no input restrictions and thus is equivalent to the formula which always evaluates to true.

The **else** clause is optional in Pascal and we can write

$$\text{if } B \text{ then } S_1$$

In this case, to verify $\{I\}$ **if** B **then** $S_1\{O\}$ we have to show that (a) if B holds and we perform the actions defined by S_1 then O will hold and (b) if B does not hold and we do nothing then O will hold. Thus the associated proof rule is

$$\frac{\{I \wedge B\}S_1\{O\},\ I \wedge \sim B \Rightarrow O}{\{I\}\ \textbf{if}\ B\ \textbf{then}\ S_1\{O\}}$$

Again, this holds under the assumption that B has no side effects. As an example of its use, we can verify

$$\{x<0\}x := -x\{x>0\}$$

using the proof rule for assignments and hence verify

$$\{x<0\}x := -x\{x \geqslant 0\}$$

using Theorem 5.1. Thus, since $\sim(x<0) \Rightarrow x \geqslant 0$ is always true in our model, we can use the above proof rule to verify

$$\{\}\ \textbf{if}\ x<0\ \textbf{then}\ x := -x\{x \geqslant 0\}$$

by setting I to true, B to $x<0$ and O to $x \geqslant 0$.

(3) The case statement

The conditional statement **if** B **then** S_1 **else** S_2 allows the selection of one of two possible actions. This is generalized in the **case** statement to allow a choice of any one of a finite number of actions. A **case** statement has the form

> **case** e **of**
> $\ell_1:S_1;$
> $\ell_2:S_2;$
> $\vdots$
> $\ell_n:S_n$
> **end**

If the value of the selector expression e is evaluated and if it equals the label ℓ_j for some j, $1 \leqslant j \leqslant n$, the statement S_j is executed. If no such value is found, we have a run time error. The proof rule for a case statement of the above form is clearly

$$\frac{\{I \wedge (e=\ell_j)\}S_j\{O\}\text{for } j=1, 2, \ldots, n}{\{I \wedge (e=\ell_1 \vee e=\ell_2 \vee \ldots \vee e=\ell_n)\}\ \textbf{case}\ e\ \textbf{of}\ \ell_1:S_1;\ \ell_2:S_2;\ \ldots \ell_n:S_n\ \textbf{end}\ \{O\}}$$

For this rule to apply, we assume that the evaluation of e should have no side effects.

The flowchart for the above **case** statement is given in Fig. 5.4. Note that the input condition $e = \ell_1 \vee e = \ell_2 \vee \ldots \vee e = \ell_n$ ensures that e must evaluate to one of the label values $\ell_1, \ell_2, \ldots, \ell_n$, and if this is not the case we do not specify what will happen.

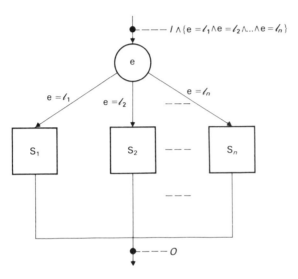

Fig. 5.4.

In Pascal we also have the possibility of multiple labels appearing before some S_i, so that instead of

$\quad \ell_i : S_i$

we might have

$\quad \ell_i 1, \ell_i 2, \ldots, \ell_i n : S_i$

This is to be regarded as a shorthand notation for

$\quad \ell_i 1 : S_i;$
$\quad \ell_i 2 : S_i;$
$\quad \quad \vdots$
$\quad \ell_i n : S_i$

and hence the proof rule we have constructed for **case** statements applies also to multiple labels.

(4) The while statement

If *B* is a Boolean expression and S is a statement then

    while *B* **do** S

is also a statement. Its effect is to evaluate the Boolean expression *B* and, provided that it is true, to execute the statement S; this process of evaluating *B* and, if true, of executing S is then continually repeated. Either (i) *B* eventually evaluates to false, in which case S is not executed again and we exit from the **while** statement, or (ii) *B* always evaluates to true and we stay in the **while** statement forever—in such a case we say that the statement does not terminate. From the above discussion it is clear that the programs

       $\{I\}$ **while** *B* **do** S$\{O\}$

and

       $\{I\}$ **if** *B* **then begin**

                    S; **while** *B* **do** S

         end$\{O\}$

are equivalent.

    We say that a formula *L* is an *invariant* of the **while** loop if, after each execution of S, *L* remains true. Since the Boolean expression *B* must necessarily be true for S to be evaluated, we can deduce that *L* is an invariant of the **while** loop if we can partially verify $\{L \wedge B\}$S$\{L\}$. If eventually the expression *B* is false, we exit from the **while** statement and provided that $\vdash L \wedge \sim B \Rightarrow O$ we can deduce the partial verification of $\{L\}$ **while** *B* **do** S$\{O\}$. Hence, the proof rule associated with **while** statements is

$$\frac{\{L \wedge B\}\text{S}\{L\}, \; I \Rightarrow L, \; L \wedge \sim B \Rightarrow O}{\{I\} \text{ \textbf{while} } B \text{ \textbf{do} S}\{O\}}$$

Again, the evaluation of *B* is assumed to have no side effects. This is represented in terms of flowcharts in Fig. 5.5.

    As a special case, obtained by setting *I* to be equal to *L* and *O* equal to $I \wedge \sim B$, we have

$$\frac{\{I \wedge B\}\text{S}\{I\}}{\{I\} \text{ \textbf{while} } B \text{ \textbf{do} S}\{I \wedge \sim B\}}$$

A loop invariant *L* is generally a formula which in some way expresses what has been achieved by previous iterations of the loop. For example,

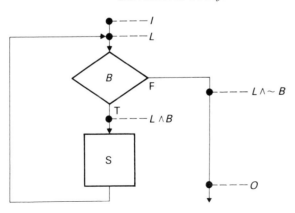

Fig. 5.5.

consider the following code designed to find the integer max equal to the largest integer of $A[1], A[2], \ldots, A[n]$:

$$\{n \geqslant 1\}$$
var i: integer;
$i := 1$;
$\max := A[1]$;
while $i < n$ **do**
begin
    $i := i + 1$;
    if $\max < A[i]$ **then** $\max := A[i]$
end
$$\{\forall k(1 \leqslant k \leqslant n \Rightarrow A[k] \leqslant \max) \wedge \exists j(1 \leqslant j \leqslant n \wedge A[j] = \max)\}$$

To partially verify this code we need to partially verify

$$\{n \geqslant 1 \wedge i = 1 \wedge \max = A[1]\}$$
while $i < n$ **do**
begin
    $i := i + 1$;
    if $\max < A[i]$ **then** $\max := A[i]$
end
$$\{\forall k(1 \leqslant k \leqslant n \Rightarrow A[k] \leqslant \max) \wedge \exists j(1 \leqslant j \leqslant n \wedge A[j] = \max)\}$$

In this case the loop invariant L is

$$\forall k(1 \leqslant k \leqslant i \Rightarrow A[k] \leqslant \max) \wedge \exists j(1 \leqslant j \leqslant i \wedge A[j] = \max) \wedge i \leqslant n$$

i.e. max is the maximum of the values of A so far considered. Upon entry to the loop, it is clear that

$$n \geqslant 1 \wedge i = 1 \wedge \max = A[1] \Rightarrow L$$

is true. Moreover, using techniques previously described, we can partially verify

$\{L \wedge i < n\}$
begin
    $i := i + 1$
    if $\max < A[i]$ **then** $\max := A[i]$
end
$\{L\}$

To complete the partial verification of the above code, all we need do is to prove that

$$L \wedge \sim (i < n) \Rightarrow [\forall k (1 \leqslant k \leqslant n \Rightarrow A[k] \leqslant \max) \wedge \exists j (1 \leqslant j \leqslant n \wedge A[j] = \max)]$$

is true.

Note that we have *not* proved that the above code is totally correct, i.e. we have not shown that it halts. To do this we need the pre-condition that $n \geqslant 1$ and the observation that i is initialized to 1 and with each iteration of the loop is incremented by 1. Thus, eventually, we must satisfy the condition that $\sim (i < n)$, i.e. the **while** statement cannot loop indefinitely.

If it is not immediately apparent to a reader what a particular **while** statement achieves, it is a good idea for a (Pascal) programmer to specify loop invariants as comments within the code. This can considerably simplify formal verification as well as clarifying the purpose of the code.

Usually the loop invariant is written immediately after the **do**. As an example, consider the following implementation of Euclid's algorithm for finding the highest common factor (hcf) or greatest common divisor (gcd) of two positive integers a, b.

$\{a > 0 \wedge b > 0\}$
var x, y, z: integer;
begin
    $x := a; y := b;$
    while $y < > 0$ **do** $\{\text{hcf}(x, y) = \text{hcf}(a, b) \wedge x \geqslant 0 \wedge y \geqslant 0\}$
        if $x \geqslant y$ **then** $x := x - y$
        else begin $z := x; x := y; y := z$ **end**
end
$\{x = \text{hcf}(a, b)\}$

The programmer has told us that the loop invariant is $\text{hcf}(x, y) = \text{hcf}(a, b)$ $\wedge x \geqslant 0 \wedge y \geqslant 0$. To partially verify the program, we have to partially verify

$\{a > 0 \wedge b > 0\} x := a \{x = a \wedge x > 0 \wedge b > 0\}$
$\{x = a \wedge x > 0 \wedge b > 0\} y := b \{\text{hcf}(x, y) = \text{hcf}(a, b) \wedge x \geqslant 0 \wedge y \geqslant 0\}$
$\{\text{hcf}(x, y) = \text{hcf}(a, b) \wedge x \geqslant 0 \wedge y \geqslant 0 \wedge y \neq 0\}$
    if $x \geqslant y$ **then** $x := x - y$
       else begin $z := x; \ x := y; \ y := z$ **end**
$\{\text{hcf}(x, y) = \text{hcf}(a, b) \wedge x \geqslant 0 \wedge y \geqslant 0\}$

and finally check the general truth of

$$\text{hcf}(x, y) = \text{hcf}(a, b) \wedge x \geqslant 0 \wedge y \geqslant 0 \wedge y = 0 \Rightarrow x = \text{hcf}(a, b)$$

All this is left as an exercise for the reader—it is very straightforward. However, if the programmer had not specified the loop invariant, a partial verification would have been made much harder. We would have had to recognize that the underlying principle of his program is that if $x \geqslant y > 0$ then

$$\text{hcf}(x, y) = \text{hcf}(x - y, y)$$

The invariant was easy for the programmer to specify since it arose naturally out of the program design.

To show that the above program is totally correct we need to observe that in every execution of the **while** loop the value $x + 2y$ is reduced by a positive quantity. However, $x \geqslant 0 \wedge y \geqslant 0$ is part of the loop invariant and hence we cannot continue reducing $x + 2y$ indefinitely, i.e. the **while** statement, and hence the whole program, must terminate.

(5) The repeat statement

The **repeat** statement is similar to the **while** statement. If B is a Boolean expression and S is a statement, the statement

    repeat S **until** B

executes S and then tests whether B is true; if it is not the process is repeated. Either B eventually evaluates to true and we exit from the **repeat** statement or B always evaluates to false and we are stuck in an infinite loop. Note that whereas **while** B **do** S may not execute S at all (i.e. in the case where B

immediately evaluates to false), there is always at least one execution of S in **repeat** S **until** *B*.

Upon exiting from **repeat** S **until** *B*, the formula *B* must hold. A partial verification will be concerned with programs of the form

$$\{I\} \text{ repeat } S \text{ until } B\{O\}$$

The flowchart for this is given in Fig. 5.6. From this, it is easy to deduce the proof rule

$$\frac{\{L\}S\{J\}, \ I \Rightarrow L, \ J \wedge \sim B \Rightarrow L, \ J \wedge B \Rightarrow O}{\{I\} \text{ repeat } S \text{ until } B\{O\}}$$

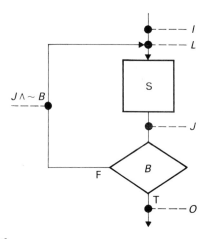

Fig. 5.6.

Again, this holds under the assumption that the evaluation of *B* has no side effects.

An alternative way of deducing the proof rule for **repeat** statements is to observe the equivalence of

> **repeat** S **until** *B*

and

> **begin** S; **while** $\sim B$ **do** S **end**

Now, as an exercise, we can deduce the proof rule for **repeat** statements from our earlier work on serial and **while** statements. Firstly we note

$$\frac{\{I\}S\{J\}, \ \{J\} \text{ while } \sim B \text{ do } S \ \{O\}}{\{I\} \text{ begin } S; \text{ while } \sim B \text{ do } S \text{ end } \{O\}}$$

is an application of the proof rule for serial statements. The proof rule for
while statements gives as a special case

$$\frac{\{J \wedge \sim B\}S\{J\}, \; J \wedge B \Rightarrow O}{\{J\} \; \textbf{while} \; \sim B \; \textbf{do} \; \text{S} \; \textbf{end} \; \{O\}}$$

Hence, combining these two, we obtain

$$\frac{\{I\}S\{J\}, \; \{J \wedge \sim B\}S\{J\}, \; J \wedge B \Rightarrow O}{\{I\} \; \textbf{repeat} \; \text{S} \; \textbf{until} \; B\{O\}}$$

The proof rule for **repeat** statements is thus obtained by a simple
application of Theorem 5.1.

(6) The for statement

Let x be a variable of ordinal type and let m, n be expressions of the same
type. Then, if S is a statement, we can construct a new statement of the form

for $x := m$ **to** n **do** S

Since we have specified that x is of ordinal type (e.g. integer), we can assume
that elements of that type can be well ordered (using $\leqslant$). Then, for every x,
either (i) $y \leqslant x$ for all y of that type (i.e. x is the *maximum* element of that type)
or (ii) there is a unique *successor* to x, denoted by $\text{succ}(x)$, such that
$x < \text{succ}(x) \wedge (x < y \Rightarrow \text{succ}(x) \leqslant y)$.

The effect of executing the above **for** statement is identical with that of
executing

```
begin x := m; finished := false;
      while x ⩽ n and not finished do
      begin
          S;
          if x = n then finished := true
          else x := succ(x)
      end
end
```

Hence, we could use the proof rules developed for conditional and **while**
statements to handle **for** statements. However, it is usually easier to exploit
the particular properties of **for** statements and to develop and use a
specifically designed proof rule. The simple proof rule we develop here
assumes that the programmer adheres to accepted good programming

practice by ensuring that the value of the control variable x is not altered during execution of the statement S. Then, to formulate the proof rule we introduce the following notation:

$[m..n]$ denotes the interval $\{i \mid m \leqslant i \leqslant n\}$

and

$[m..n[$ denotes the interval $\{i \mid m \leqslant i < n\}$

Hence, by definition, $[m..m[$ denotes the empty set $\{\}$ and $[m..n] = [m..\mathrm{succ}(n)[$ provided that $\mathrm{succ}(n)$ is defined, i.e. provided that n is not a maximum element.

Let $P(\mathrm{I})$ be some formula asserting a property of the interval I. Assume $m \leqslant n$ and say that we can partially verify $\{P[m..x[\}S\{P[m..x]\}$ for any x such that $m \leqslant x \leqslant n$. This then implies that each application of S suitably extends the interval over which the assertion P holds. Then, provided that we can additionally prove that (i) $I \Rightarrow P[m..m[$ and (ii) $P[m..n] \Rightarrow O$, we shall have achieved a partial verification of $\{I\}$ **for** $x := m$ **to** n **do** $S\{O\}$. Of course, in the case where $m > n$, we need only check that $I \Rightarrow O$ since the **for** statement will have no effect. Summarizing the above discussion, we have the following proof rule for **for** statements:

$$\frac{\{m \leqslant x \leqslant n \wedge P[m..x[\}S\{P[m..x]\},\ I \Rightarrow P[m..m[,\ P[m..n] \Rightarrow O}{\{I\}\ \textbf{for}\ x := m\ \textbf{to}\ n\ \textbf{do}\ S\{O\}} \quad \text{if } m \leqslant n$$

and

$$\frac{I \Rightarrow O}{\{I\}\ \textbf{for}\ x := m\ \textbf{to}\ n\ \textbf{do}\ S\{O\}} \quad \text{if } m > n$$

provided that S does not alter the value of the control variable x.

As an example of the application of this proof rule, consider the following code designed to find the largest element of an array A of positive integers with index range $1..10$.

```
{∀i(1 ≤ i ≤ 10 ⇒ A[i] > 0)}
begin
        max := 0;
        for k := 1 to 10 do
        if A[k] > max then max := A[k]
end
{∀i(1 ≤ i ≤ 10 ⇒ A[i] ≤ max) ∧ ∃i(1 ≤ i ≤ 10 ∧ A[i] = max)}
```

To partially verify this code, we define the formula $P[1..k[$ to be

$$\forall i(1 \leqslant i < k \Rightarrow A[i] \leqslant \max)$$
$$\wedge (k = 1 \Rightarrow \max = 0)$$
$$\wedge (k \neq 1 \Rightarrow \exists i(1 \leqslant i < k \wedge A[i] = \max))$$

Now, we can assert after $\max := 0$ that

$$\forall i(1 \leqslant i \leqslant 10 \Rightarrow A[i] > 0) \wedge \max = 0$$

holds. Hence, since $10 \geqslant 1$, to complete the partial verification we need only prove

$$(\forall i(1 \leqslant i \leqslant 10 \Rightarrow A[i] > 0) \wedge \max = 0) \Rightarrow P[1..1[$$

and

$$P[1..10] \Rightarrow (\forall i(1 \leqslant i \leqslant 10 \Rightarrow A[i] \leqslant \max)$$
$$\wedge \exists i(1 \leqslant i \leqslant 10 \wedge A[i] = \max))$$

as well as partially verifying

$$\{1 \leqslant k \leqslant 10 \wedge P[1..k[\} \text{ if } A[k] > \max \text{ then } \max := A[k] \{P[1..k]\}$$

These are all straightforward. Note how the assertion $P[1..k[$ has to handle the special case $k = 1$—this correctly highlights a rather special feature of the program.

Procedures

Structured programming practice is essentially a top-down approach to program design in which complex tasks are refined into simpler tasks. Pascal is a suitable language for structured programming in which any step of an algorithm which requires further refinement can be implemented as a call to a procedure. For example, we might have a program in which we want to interchange the values of the variables i, j. This may even be done several times. Rather than include the code

```
temp := i;
i := j;
j := temp
```

on each such occasion, we might have simply called

    Swap

and later defined Swap once and for all by the procedure declaration

    procedure Swap;
    var temp: integer;
    begin
        temp := i;
        i := j;
        j := temp
    end

Note that since the only use of the integer variable temp is in this interchanging process, we have declared this variable local to the procedure Swap. It cannot then be accessed outside Swap. This is another example of good programming practice: if the value of an identifier is not referenced outside a procedure it should be declared local to that procedure. We shall assume that our readers adhere to this rule.

Now, if

    procedure p; S

is a declaration of a parameterless procedure p with procedure body S, then any call of p results in the execution of S. The proof rule for such procedures is thus

$$\frac{\{I\}S\{O\}}{\{I\}p\{O\}}$$

The procedure Swap defined above can only interchange the values of variables i and j. This is very restrictive; a more general interchange procedure is often required which will enable the interchange of any two arbitrary integer variables. To achieve this we introduce parameters and define

    procedure Swapvars (**var** x, y: integer);
    var temp: integer;
    begin
        temp := x;
        x := y;
        y := temp
    end

Then Swapvars(i, j) would result in the interchange of the values of variables i and j. We could also use Swapvars to interchange other values such as in Swapvars($A[1]$, $A[2]$). The parameters x, y used in the procedure declaration of Swapvars are called *formal parameters*. Any parameters used in a call of the procedure, e.g. i, j or $A[1]$, $A[2]$ above, are called *actual parameters*.

Consider then the declaration of a procedure p with a parameter list L defining the n ($\geqslant 1$) formal parameters $x_1, x_2, \ldots, x_n$ and with procedure body S:

procedure p(L);S

The formal parameters $x_1, x_2, \ldots, x_n$ occurring in L either specify that the corresponding actual parameters are to be *called by value substitution* or *called by reference substitution*. In the declaration of p, the variables which will correspond to parameters to be called by reference substitution must appear in a list headed by **var**.

For example, in

procedure Example (**var** i: integer; j, k: integer);
begin
    $j := i + k; i := j + k$
end

the formal parameters are i, j and k. If we now write

var a, b, c; integer;
begin
    $a := 1; b := 2; c := 3;$
    Example (a, b, c)
end

then we execute Example with actual parameters a, b, c. The formal parameter i is associated with the actual parameter a by reference substitution (sometimes called *variable substitution*), i.e. every time we use i in the procedure it refers to the same location in the memory as a. Any assignment to i will update the value of the variable a. The actual parameters b, c are associated with the formal parameters j, k by value substitution. At the time of the call the current values of b, c (i.e. 2, 3) are assigned to new variables j, k used in the procedure. Assignments to j or k will not then affect the values of the variables b, c. Hence, after execution of Example (a, b, c), the values of b, c are unaltered but a is assigned the new value of 7.

One of Pascal's strengths is the way it makes very clear when parameters are to be called by reference and when they are to be called by value. If a programming language does not make its parameter-passing mechanism clear, the programmer must make sure that he understands exactly what is going on. Here is a (bad) piece of code written in an invented Pascal-like language which we shall call LULU:

```
procedure Report (j);
begin
      A[2]:= 1; i:= 3; print (j)
end
```

The parameter j is assumed to be integer but no parameter-passing mechanism for LULU has been stated. Now, consider the following code:

```
for k:= 1 to 3 do A[k]:= k;
{A[1] = 1 ∧ A[2] = 2 ∧ A[3] = 3}
i:= 2;
Report (A[i])
```

What output would you expect? Our LULU code might print any of 1, 2 or 3 depending upon the parameters-passing mechanism it exploits! If LULU uses call by reference, the parameter j refers to the same location as $A[2]$ and thus, since we assign 1 to $A[2]$ within Report, our output will be 1. If, however, LULU uses call by value, the parameter j is the value of $A[2]$ at the time of the call, i.e. 2, and thus print (j) gives an output of 2. There is also another possibility—*call by name*. By this we mean a textual replacement. Whatever expression is given as the actual parameter that expression is used as a textual replacement for the corresponding formal parameter in the code. Thus, if LULU uses call by name, Report ($A[i]$) will result in the execution of the code specified by Report but with each occurrence of j textually replaced by the expression $A[i]$. Hence, since $i = 3$ when we call print (j), we print $A[3]$, i.e. 3. Pascal does not offer call by name but it is this concept which represents variable substitution used in predicate calculus.

To ensure that we do not make errors in verifications concerning procedures we must be particularly careful. Without such care, it is very easy to come seriously unstuck! For example, consider the following simple procedure declaration:

```
procedure Addone(var i: integer; j: integer);
begin
      i:= j+1
end
```

If we call

Addone(a, a)

then a is associated with i by reference substitution and also with j by value substitution. Even though we can trivially verify

$$\{\} \; i := j+1 \{i=j+1\}$$

we cannot simply substitute both i and j by a to deduce

$$\{\} \; \text{Addone}(a, a) \{a=a+1\}$$

which would after all be patent nonsense!

Suppose that we have a procedure p with body S and parameters $x_1, x_2,$ $\ldots, x_n$. If we have a partial verification of $\{I\}S\{O\}$, when can we infer a partial derivation of $\{I[x_1 \mid a_1, \ldots, x_n \mid a_n]\} \; \text{p}(a_1, \ldots, a_n) \{O[x_1 \mid a_1, \ldots, x_n \mid a_n \mid a_n]\}$?

Provided that we restrict the procedure p to obeying certain rules this sort of textual replacement will be a valid technique. The formal parameters $x_1, \ldots, x_n$ can be divided into two subsets—those whose value may change, i.e. to which there is some assignment in S, and those whose value remains the same throughout S. We call elements of the first set *dynamic formal parameters* and those of the second set *static formal parameters*. Then in a call p($a_1, \ldots, a_n$) some of the actual parameters are associated with dynamic formal parameters, some with static formal parameters and (possibly) some with both. Let D_A denote the subset of $\{a_1, \ldots, a_n\}$ associated with dynamic formal parameters and S_A the subset associated with static formal parameters. The proof rule

$$\frac{\{I\}S\{O\}}{\{I[x_1 \mid a_1, \ldots, x_n \mid a_n]\} \text{p}(a_1, \ldots, a_n) \{O[x_1 \mid a_1, \ldots, x_n \mid a_n]\}}$$

is applicable to a call p($a_1, \ldots, a_n$) of the procedure p if the following hold:

(i)   every element of D_A must itself be a variable;
(ii) no element of D_A can be called by value substitution;
(iii) no element of D_A can occur more than once (even as a subterm) in the parameter list $a_1, a_2, \ldots, a_n$;
(iv) none of the global variables which may occur in S and which can be reassigned during the execution of S occurs within S_A (even as subterms).

Applying this proof rule to the procedure Addone, we achieve a partial verification of

$$\{\} \; \text{Addone}(a, b) \{b=a+1\}$$

provided that a, b are distinct variable identifiers. Note that this proviso is essential since without it we would violate condition (ii) above.

As a further example of the application of this simple proof rule for procedures consider the following procedure designed to compute $k = i^j$ for integers $i \geqslant 0$, $j > 0$:

```
procedure Power (i, j: integer; var k: integer);
var i1, j1: integer;
begin
        {i≥0∧j>0}
        i1 := i; j1 := j; k := 1;
        {i1 = i ≥ 0 ∧ j1 = j > 0 ∧ k = 1}
        while j1 < >0 do {k * i1^{j1} = i^j}
            if odd(j1) then
              begin
                  j1 := j1 − 1; k := k * i1
              end
            else
              begin
                  i1 := i1 * i1;
                  j1 := j1 div 2
              end
        {k = i^j ∧ j1 = 0}
end
```

Since the programmer has (quite correctly) specified the loop invariant and provided other annotation, the partial correctness of the body of this procedure follows easily. The reader should check the details.

Now, let us call

Power(a, b, x)

where a, b are distinct from x and x is a variable. Then $D_A = \{x\}$ and $S_A = \{a, b\}$. Our four restrictions are all satisfied, so we can deduce the partial correctness of

$\{a \geqslant 0 \wedge b > 0\}$ Power(a, b, x) $\{x = a^b\}$

Note that our restrictions would prevent us from applying our proof rule directly to calls

Power(a, x, x)

or

> Power(x, b, x)

but we could use it for

> Power(a, a, x)

The actual parameters in a procedure call are terms. Thus, we might call

> Power($2+a$, $a*b$, x)

In this case $S_A = \{2+a, a*b\}$ and $D_A = \{x\}$. Our proof rule is still applicable and enables us to deduce

$$\{2+a \geqslant 0 \wedge a*b > 0\} \text{Power}(2+a, a*b, x)\{x = (2+a)^{a*b}\}$$

However, we would not be able to apply our proof rule if the third argument was not a simple variable or if it occurred as a subterm of the first two parameters.

If a call of a procedure does not satisfy our restrictions so that the simple proof rule for procedures does not apply, we can still provide a partial verification. However, we have to take extreme care to represent the parameter-passing mechanism correctly. This can make formal correctness proofs difficult to construct and to understand. The fact that it is difficult to apply logical reasoning to Pascal programs is considered by many computer scientists to be a fierce indictment of the language. The same criticism can be levelled at most traditional languages, and hence we have one of the motivations for developing completely different (functional or logic) programming languages.

As an example of a partial verification of a procedure which does not satisfy our restrictions, consider the following:

```
procedure Multiply(i, j: integer; var k: integer);
begin
        {i ⩾ 0 ∧ j = j0 > 0}
        k := 0;
        repeat  {k + j * i = j0 * i}
                k := k + i; j := j − 1
        until j = 0
        {k = j0 * i ∧ j = 0}
end
```

In this example we have used $j0$ to denote the initial value of j.

With the loop invariant specified, the deduction of the partial correctness of the body of the code is easy. The parameters j, k are both dynamic and, since j is called by value substitution, we know that the simple proof rule for procedures cannot be applied, i.e. we cannot deduce a partial verification of

$$\{a \geqslant 0 \wedge b = j0 > 0\} \text{ Multiply}(a, b, c) \{c = j0 * a \wedge b = 0\}$$

This is just as well because $b = 0$ cannot be true after calling the procedure since $b = j0 > 0$ and b was called by value. However, we can argue that, since b was called by value, if $b = j0$ before calling the procedure, $b = j0$ after calling the procedure. The parameters c, a have not violated our conditions on procedure calls so it is possible to deduce the partial verification of

$$\{a \geqslant 0 \wedge b = j0 > 0\} \text{ Multiply}(a, b, c) \{c = j0 * a\}$$

and hence of

$$\{a \geqslant 0 \wedge b > 0\} \text{ Multiply}(a, b, c) \{c = b * a\}$$

Functions

Unlike procedures, functions deliver values and thus a call to a function in Pascal is an expression whilst a call to a procedure is a statement. Functions should simply compute and deliver their desired result. They should be regarded completely differently from procedures. A procedure may reassign values of global variables or of its parameters. This is not the purpose of a function: such side effects are dangerous as they make for obscure code and difficult verifications. One of the criticisms we level at Pascal (and at most other programming languages) is that the language allows the blatant misuse of functions. Functions should not be allowed to reassign global variables nor should they be allowed to reassign values to parameters. We assume that our programmers will adopt a programming style which accepts these restrictions. Under these assumptions, we shall develop some techniques for the partial verification of programs involving such functions.

The general form of a Pascal function declaration is

function f(L): T; S

where f is the function name, L is the parameter specification defining parameters $x_1, x_2, \ldots, x_n$ (say), T is the type of the result (let us assume integer) and S is the function body. Within S the value of the function is specified by assigning it to the function name f. As an example, the following function evaluates $n^0 + n^1 + n^2 + \ldots + n^k$ for integers n, k

```
function sumpowers(n, k: integer): integer;
var partsum, counter, nextel: integer;
begin
        {    }
        partsum := 0;
        nextel := 1;
        for counter := 0 to k do
                begin
                        partsum := partsum + nextel;
                        nextel := n * nextel
                end;
        sumpowers := partsum
        {[k < 0 ⇒ sumpowers = 0]
         ∧ [k ⩾ 0 ⇒ sumpowers = Σᵏᵢ₌₀ nⁱ]}

end
```

The partial verification of the program body is left as an exercise for the reader but from this result we can infer $\forall n \forall k([k<0 \Rightarrow \text{sumpowers}(n,k)=0] \wedge [k \geqslant 0 \Rightarrow \text{sumpowers}(n,k)=\Sigma_{i=0}^{k} n^i])$. This can then be used in the verification of any program involving expressions of the form sumpowers(a, b).

In general, the proof rule for the function

function f(L): T; S

as described above is

$$\frac{\{I\}S\{O\}}{\forall x_1 \ldots \forall x_n (I \Rightarrow O[\text{f} \mid \text{f}(x_1, \ldots, x_n)])}$$

but remember that this proof rule can only be used when the use of the function has been suitably (and sensibly) restricted as described at the beginning of this section.

Induction and Recursion

Induction is a powerful technique used extensively in mathematics whenever it is required to prove that a countable number of formulae A_1,

A_2, A_3, ... are true. Denoting the set of natural numbers by $N = \{1, 2, 3, \ldots\}$ we can represent a countably infinite set of such formulae by $\{A_n : n \in N\}$. For example, we might be asked to prove that $8^n - 3^n$ is divisible by 5 for $n = 1, 2, 3, \ldots$ Then A_n is the proposition that 5 divides $8^n - 3^n$.

To prove that all the formulae in $\{A_n : n \in N\}$ are true, we proceed as follows.

(i) We show that A_1 is true.

(ii) We show that, for any $k \in N$, if A_n is true for all $n \leqslant k$ then it follows that A_{k+1} is true.

Now, if A_1 is true, result (ii) with $k = 1$ proves that A_2 is true; then, result (ii) with $k = 2$ proves that A_3 is true. Continuing to apply this argument, we find that A_4, A_5, ... are all true. An argument supporting this proof technique can be presented as follows. Suppose that A_n was not true for some $n \in N$ but that (i) and (ii) above hold. There must exist a least $j > 0$ such that A_j is false but A_n is true for all $n < j$. Now, $j \neq 1$ since this would contradict (i) but then we have a contradiction of (ii) for the case $k = j - 1$. Hence every A_n must be true.

Induction is used extensively in validations of recursive procedures and functions. When giving a proof using an induction argument, it is important that it is correctly presented. A suitable layout of a proof by induction of the truth of all the formulae in $\{A_n : n \in N\}$ is described below.

The proof is by mathematical induction.	the first line
The result holds for $n = 1$ because	} proof that A_1 is true
...	
Assume the result holds for all $n \leqslant k$,	} called the *induction hypothesis*
i.e. that ...	
Then	} proof that A_{k+1} is true follows
...	from the induction hypothesis
Hence the result holds for $n = k + 1$.	
Hence the result holds for all $n \in N$	
by induction.	the last line

As an example we shall prove that $8^n - 3^n$ is divisible by 5 for all $n \in N$. The proof is by mathematical induction. The result holds for $n = 1$ since $8^1 - 3^1 = 5$ is divisible by 5. Assume that the result holds for all $n \leqslant k$, i.e. that $8^n - 3^n$ is divisible by 5 if $n \leqslant k$. Then

$$8^{k+1} - 3^{k+1} = 8 \times 8^k - 3 \times 3^k$$
$$= 5 \times 8^k + 3 \times (8^k - 3^k)$$

Now, by the induction hypothesis, $8^k - 3^k$ is divisible by 5 and since 5×8^k is also clearly divisible by 5 it follows that so is $8^{k+1} - 3^{k+1}$. Hence the result holds for $n = k + 1$. Hence the result holds for all $n \in N$ by induction.

There is a close link between mathematical induction and recursion. Recursion is a technique whereby procedures and functions are allowed to call themselves within their procedure (function) bodies. For example, the following is a recursive definition given in Pascal of the function which computes the factorial of a positive integer.

```
function fact(n: integer): integer;
begin
        {n > 0}
        if n = 1 then fact := 1
        else fact := n * fact(n − 1)
        {fact = n!}
end
```

Thus, to evaluate fact(3), the function computes

$$\begin{aligned} \text{fact}(3) &= 3 * \text{fact}(2) \\ &= 3 * 2 * \text{fact}(1) \\ &= 3 * 2 * 1 = 3! \end{aligned}$$

To verify this function we would need to prove the result that for all inputs $n \in N$ the function fact halts and computes $\text{fact}(n) = n!$ We proceed by induction. Certainly, the function halts for $n = 1$ and correctly computes $\text{fact}(1) = 1 = 1!$ Hence the result holds for $n = 1$. If we assume that the function halts and computes $\text{fact}(n) = n!$ for all $n \leqslant k$ then, ignoring problems of arithmetic overflows, it must also halt for $n = k + 1$ and compute $\text{fact}(k + 1) = (k + 1) * \text{fact}(k) = (k + 1) * k! = (k + 1)!$ Hence the result holds for $n = k + 1$. Hence, by induction, the result holds for all $n \in N$.

As another example of a recursive definition, consider the following (rather contrived) definition of the function sum designed to add two natural numbers.

```
function sum(m, n: integer): integer;
begin
        {m > 0 ∧ n > 0}
        if m = 1 then
                if n = 1 then sum := 2
                else sum := sum(m, n − 1) + 1
        else sum := sum(m − 1, n) + 1
        {sum = m + n}
end
```

In this case we wish to prove that sum halts for positive inputs m, n and correctly computes $sum(m, n) = m + n$ for $m, n \in N$. The problem here is that there are two arguments and thus the countable number of formulae are indexed by $N \times N$. Our presentation of induction assumed that the formulae were indexed by N and hence ordered as $A_1, A_2, A_3, \ldots$. We thus need to define an ordering on $N \times N$ to obtain such an ordering of the formulae. One solution is to define $(m, n) \sqsubset (m', n')$ whenever $m + n < m' + n'$ or, if $m + n = m' + n'$, then when $m < m'$. This gives an ordering of $N \times N$ as illustrated in Fig. 5.7. Now, we can proceed to show by induction that sum

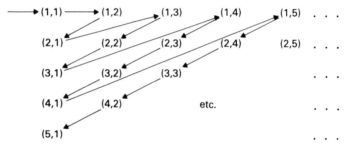

Fig. 5.7.

halts and computes $sum(m, n) = m + n$ for all input $m, n \in N$. The result holds for the first element in the ordering, i.e. $(1, 1)$, since sum halts for input $(1, 1)$ and computes $sum(1, 1) = 2 = 1 + 1$. Assume $(j, k) \neq (1, 1)$ and that the result holds for all $(m, n) \sqsubset (j, k)$. Then

$$sum(j, k) = \textbf{if } j = 1 \textbf{ then } sum(j, k - 1) + 1$$
$$\textbf{else } sum(j - 1, k) + 1$$

Now, both $(j, k - 1) \sqsubset (j, k)$ and $(j - 1, k) \sqsubset (j, k)$, so by the induction hypothesis sum halts on these inputs and computes $sum(j, k - 1) = sum(j - 1, k) = j + k - 1$. Hence sum halts on input (j, k) and hence for all $m, n \in N$ by induction with $sum(j, k) = j + k$.

The example induction proofs given above are proofs of total correctness—proving the halting of the functions was an easy addition to the proof of the relation between input and output. If we are only interested in a partial verification, the rigorous induction technique we have used is not really necessary. In particular, the ordering of the indexing of the formulae can be overlooked.

The proof rule for a procedure of the form **procedure** p(L); S has been previously stated as

$$\frac{\{I\}S\{O\}}{\{I[x_1|a_1,\ldots,x_n|a_n]\}\mathrm{p}(a_1,\ldots,a_n)\ \{O[x_1|a_1,\ldots,x_n|a_n]\}}$$

(subject to rules restricting the parameters). We are now saying that if p is recursive then, during the proof of $\{I\}S\{O\}$, we can assume the property $\{I[x_1|a_1,\ldots,x_n|a_n]\}\mathrm{p}(a_1,\ldots,a_n)\{O[x_1|a_1,\ldots,x_n|a_n]\}$ for every call $\mathrm{p}(a_1,\ldots,a_n)$ which occurs in S (provided that $a_1,\ldots,a_n$ obey the rules restricting the parameters). This will only give us a partial verification though and a formal induction argument based on an ordering will be necessary to obtain a total verification.

Similarly, with a recursive function of the form

function $f(x_1,x_2,\ldots x_n)$: T; S

a partial verification of $\{I\}S\{O\}$ can use the result that $I[x_1|a_1,x_2|a_2,\ldots,x_n|a_n]\Rightarrow O[x_1|a_1,x_2|a_2,\ldots,x_n|a_n,f|f(a_1,a_2,\ldots,a_n)]$ for all calls of the function $f(a_1,a_2,\ldots,a_n)$ which occur in S.

For example, consider the following Pascal function designed to search a sorted integer array A of n elements for a given value b:

```
type index = 0..n−1;
function binsearch(low, high:index):index;
var mid:index;
begin
    mid := (low + high) div 2;
    if b > A[mid] then binsearch := binsearch(mid + 1, high)
    else if b < A[mid] then binsearch := binsearch (low, mid − 1)
    else binsearch := mid
end
```

Let S denote the statements comprising the body of this function. Then, in a partial verification of

$$\{\forall i\,(\mathrm{low}\leqslant i\leqslant\mathrm{high}-1\Rightarrow A[i]\leqslant A[i+1])$$
$$\qquad \wedge\,\exists k(\mathrm{low}\leqslant k\leqslant\mathrm{high}\wedge A[k]=b)\}$$
$$\mathrm{S}$$
$$\{\mathrm{low}\leqslant\mathrm{binsearch}\leqslant\mathrm{high}\wedge A[\mathrm{binsearch}]=b\}$$

we can assume that both

$$\forall i\,(\mathrm{mid}+1\leqslant i\leqslant\mathrm{high}-1\Rightarrow A[i]\leqslant A[i+1])$$
$$\qquad \wedge\,\exists k(\mathrm{mid}+1\leqslant k\leqslant\mathrm{high}\wedge A[k]=b)$$
$$\qquad \Rightarrow\mathrm{mid}+1\leqslant\mathrm{binsearch}(\mathrm{mid}+1,\mathrm{high})\leqslant\mathrm{high}$$
$$\qquad \wedge\,A[\mathrm{binsearch}(\mathrm{mid}+1,\mathrm{high})]=b$$

and

$$\forall i\,(\text{low} \leqslant i \leqslant \text{mid} - 2 \Rightarrow A[i] \leqslant A[i+1])$$
$$\wedge\,\exists k(\text{low} \leqslant k \leqslant \text{mid} - 1 \wedge A[k] = b)$$
$$\Rightarrow \text{low} \leqslant \text{binsearch}(\text{low, mid} - 1) \leqslant \text{mid} - 1$$
$$\wedge\,A[\text{binsearch}(\text{low,mid} - 1)] = b$$

are true. Hence, we can partially verify both

$$\{\forall i\,(\text{mid} + 1 \leqslant i \leqslant \text{high} - 1 \Rightarrow A[i] \leqslant A[i+1])$$
$$\wedge\,\exists k\,(\text{mid} + 1 \leqslant k \leqslant \text{high} \wedge A[k] = b)\}$$
$$\text{binsearch} := \text{binsearch}(\text{mid} + 1, \text{high})$$
$$\{\text{mid} + 1 \leqslant \text{binsearch} \leqslant \text{high} \wedge A[\text{binsearch}] = b\}$$

and

$$\{\forall i\,(\text{low} \leqslant i \leqslant \text{mid} - 2 \Rightarrow A[i] \leqslant A[i+1])$$
$$\wedge\,\exists k(\text{low} \leqslant k \leqslant \text{mid} - 1 \wedge A[k] = b)\}$$
$$\text{binsearch} := \text{binsearch}(\text{low, mid} - 1)$$
$$\{\text{low} \leqslant \text{binsearch} \leqslant \text{mid} - 1 \wedge A[\text{binsearch}] = b\}$$

Completion of the partial verification of the function body is now a fairly straightforward task. If I denotes the original input formula

$$\forall i\,(\text{low} \leqslant i \leqslant \text{high} - 1 \Rightarrow A[i] \leqslant A[i+1])$$
$$\wedge\,\exists k\,(\text{low} \leqslant k \leqslant \text{high} \wedge A[k] = b)$$

Then after the assignment

$$\text{mid} := (\text{low} + \text{high})\ \textbf{div}\ 2$$

the formula $I \wedge \text{low} \leqslant \text{mid} \leqslant \text{high}$ must be true. Now,

$$I \wedge \text{low} \leqslant \text{mid} \leqslant \text{high} \wedge b > A[\text{mid}]$$
$$\Rightarrow \forall i\,(\text{mid} + 1 \leqslant i \leqslant \text{high} - 1 \Rightarrow A[i] \leqslant A[i+1])$$
$$\wedge\,\exists k(\text{mid} + 1 \leqslant k \leqslant \text{high} \wedge A[k] = b)$$

is true. Similarly,

$$I \wedge \text{low} \leqslant \text{mid} \leqslant \text{high} \wedge b < A[\text{mid}]$$
$$\Rightarrow \forall i\,(\text{low} \leqslant i \leqslant \text{mid} - 2 \Rightarrow A[i] \leqslant A[i+1])$$
$$\wedge\,\exists k(\text{low} \leqslant k \leqslant \text{mid} - 1 \wedge A[k] = b)$$

holds.

Also, $I \wedge \text{low} \leqslant \text{mid} \leqslant \text{high} \wedge \sim (b > A[\text{mid}]) \wedge \sim (b < A[\text{mid}])$
$$\Rightarrow \text{low} \leqslant \text{mid} \leqslant \text{high} \wedge b = A[\text{mid}]$$

is true. We can use these results with the proof rules that we have developed to deduce that if I holds before S is executed then after execution

$$(\text{mid} + 1 \leqslant \text{binsearch} \leqslant \text{high} \wedge A[\text{binsearch}] = b)$$
$$\vee (\text{low} \leqslant \text{binsearch} \leqslant \text{mid} - 1 \wedge A[\text{binsearch}] = b)$$
$$\vee (\text{binsearch} = \text{mid} \wedge A[\text{binsearch}] = b)$$
$$\wedge (\text{low} \leqslant \text{mid} \leqslant \text{high})$$

holds. Hence, $\text{low} \leqslant \text{binsearch} \leqslant \text{high} \wedge A[\text{binsearch}] = b$ holds and the function body is partially verified.

Programs with gotos

Anyone trained in structured programming will have been taught that **goto**s and labels should be avoided wherever possible. Their use causes program obscurity and makes program verification considerably harder. Essentially, the problem arises because the use of **goto**s destroys the principle that every statement S has just one entry and just one exit. This has been the fundamental assumption on which our notation $\{I\}S\{O\}$ was based. If we want to allow **goto**s in our program and still attempt verification we need to make some fundamental changes in our notation.

Suppose that a complex statement S contains one or more substatements of the form

goto ℓ

where ℓ is some label. We can then exit from S in one of two ways, either via the normal exit at the end of S or via the label ℓ. We thus need two output formulae, one for each of these possible exits. In such a case our program specification is written

$$\{I\}S\{O_o\}\{\ell:O_1\}$$

If S contains exits to several labels $\ell_1, \ell_2, \ldots, \ell_n$ (say) then we have an even more complicated specification of the form

$$\{I\}S\{O_0\}\{\ell_1:O_1\} \ldots \{\ell_n:O_n\}$$

This is interpreted to mean that if the input condition I is true then, on normal exit from S, O_0 will be true. However, if we exit to the label $\ell_i(1 \leqslant i \leqslant n)$ then O_i will be true.

The simplest example of such a specification is $\{I\}$ **goto** $\ell\{\text{false}\}\{\ell: I\}$ for every I. We can generalize the basic proof rules to cope with statements involving labels. For example, if S is a statement and ℓ is a label, we have the following.

(i)   If S does not contain **goto** ℓ then

$$\{I\}S\{O\} \text{ implies } \{I\}S\{O\}\,\{\ell: \text{false}\}$$

(ii)   If S is a serial statement of form **begin** $S_1; \ell: S_2$ **end** then the proof rule is

$$\frac{\{I\}S_1\{O_0\}\,\{\ell: O_1\},\ \{O_1\}S_2\{O\},\ O_0 \Rightarrow O_1}{\{I\} \text{ begin } S_1; \ell: S_2 \text{ end } \{O\}}$$

However, if S is a serial statement of the form **begin** $S_1; S_2$ **end** containing one or more occurrences of **goto** ℓ but the label ℓ is external to S, we use

$$\frac{\{I\}S_1\{J\}\,\{\ell: O_1\},\ \{J\}S_2\{O_0\}\,\{\ell: O_1\}}{\{I\} \text{ begin } S_1; S_2 \text{ end } \{O_0\}\,\{\ell: O_1\}}$$

(iii)   For conditional statements S of the form **if** B **then** S_1 **else** S_2 **end** where either or both of S_1, S_2 contain occurrences of **goto** ℓ but the label ℓ is external to S we have

$$\frac{\{I \wedge B\}S_1\{O_0\}\,\{\ell: O_1\},\ \{I \wedge \sim B\}S_2\{O_0\}\,\{\ell: O_1\}}{\{I\} \text{ if } B \text{ then } S_1 \text{ else } S_2\{O_0\}\,\{\ell: O_1\}}$$

(iv)   If the statement is of the form **while** B **do** S_1 and ℓ is external to S_1 we use

$$\frac{I \Rightarrow L,\ \{L \wedge B\}S_1\{L\}\,\{\ell: O_1\},\ L \wedge \sim B \Rightarrow O_0}{\{I\} \text{ while } B \text{ do } S_1\{O_0\}\,\{\ell: O_1\}}$$

The other proof rules that we have described earlier can be similarly modified but any program involving significant looping is going to be tiresome to verify. This is really no surprise—the reader will no doubt have already found understanding and debugging such programs a difficult chore. The best advice we can give is to advise readers to avoid using **goto**s if at all possible.

The Quicksort Algorithm

We now illustrate the proof rules that we have developed for procedures by verifying the correctness of a fairly complex program. The program we consider uses the Quicksort algorithm to sort the elements of an integer array A. This algorithm with an associated correctness proof was first given by Foley and Hoare (1971).

The program uses a procedure Partition. Partition (A, i, j, m, n) takes an integer array A of bounds $1..N$ (say) and two integers m, n such that

$1 \leqslant m < n \leqslant N$. The subarray of A between m and n, comprising elements $A[m], A[m+1], \ldots, A[n]$ can be denoted by $A[m..n]$. The procedure reorganizes these elements into two possibly overlapping subarrays $A[m..i-1]$ and $A[j+1..n]$ such that any element in the first subarray is less than or equal to any element in the second subarray. Suitable values of i, j must satisfy $i > j$ and are returned using the second and third parameters of the procedure. The situation is shown in Fig. 5.8. The output formula which Partition must satisfy is given by the formula ψ defined by

$$i > j \wedge \forall p \forall q(m \leqslant p < i \wedge j < q \leqslant n \Rightarrow A[p] \leqslant A[q]) \wedge \text{perm}(A)$$

where perm(A) is true iff the elements of the array A are a permutation of the elements of the original array. An annotated procedure for Partition is given below.

procedure Partition (**var** A: **array** $[1..N]$ **of** integer;
                          var i, j: integer;
                          m, n: integer);

var c: integer;
begin

```
    {1 ≤ m < n ≤ N}
    c := A[(m + n) div 2];
    i := m; j := n;
    while i ≤ j do
    {m ≤ i ∧ ∀p (m ≤ p < i ⇒ A[p] ≤ c) ∧ j ≤ n ∧ ∀q(j < q ≤ n ⇒ c ≤ A[q])
    ∧ perm(A)}
    begin{L ∧ i ≤ j}
        while A[i] < c do i := i + 1;
        {L ∧ A[i] ≥ c}
        while A[j] > c do j := j - 1;
        {L ∧ A[i] ≥ c ≥ A[j]}
        if i ≤ j then
        begin
            {L ∧ A[i] ≥ c ≥ A[j] ∧ i ≤ j}
            Swapvars(A[i], A[j]);
            {L ∧ A[j] ≥ c ≥ A[i] ∧ i ≤ j}
            i := i + 1; j := j - 1
            {L}
        end
    end
    {L ∧ i > j}
end
```

This loop invariant is denoted by L.

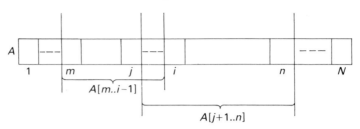

Fig. 5.8.

This procedure has been annotated to such an extent that a partial verification is relatively straightforward. Clearly $L \wedge i > j \Rightarrow \psi$ holds. The reader should now check through each detailed step of the verification of this procedure using the proof rules developed earlier in this chapter. The only non-standard feature he or she will encounter lies in the use of the procedure Swapvars to interchange the values of $A[i]$, $A[j]$. If $A[i]$, $A[j]$ are distinct we can use the proof rule

$$\frac{\{x = a \wedge y = b\} \ \text{temp} := x; \ x := y; \ y := \text{temp} \ \{x = b \wedge y = a\}}{\{A[i] = a \wedge A[j] = b\} \ \text{Swapvars} \ (A[i], A[j]) \ \{A[i] = b \wedge A[j] = a\}}$$

to partially verify

$$\{L \wedge A[i] \geqslant c \geqslant A[j] \wedge i < j\} \ \text{Swapvars} \ (A[i], A[j]) \{L \wedge$$
$$A[j] \geqslant c \geqslant A[i] \wedge i < j\}$$

However, we are not sure that $A[i]$, $A[j]$ are distinct because $i = j$ is a possibility. Hence the partial verification of the special case

$$\{L \wedge A[i] \geqslant c \geqslant A[j] \wedge i = j\} \ \text{Swapvars} \ (A[i], A[j]) \ \{L \wedge$$
$$A[j] \geqslant c \geqslant A[i] \wedge i = j\}$$

cannot be achieved by a straightforward application of our proof rule for procedures. However, we can deduce the partial verification in this case by observing the truth of

$$A[i] \geqslant c \geqslant A[j] \wedge i = j \Leftrightarrow A[i] = c = A[j] \wedge i = j$$

and by deriving a partial verification of

$$\{A[i] = c = A[j] \wedge i = j\}$$
$$\text{temp} := A[i]; \ A[i] := A[j]; \ A[j] := \text{temp}$$
$$\{A[i] = c = A[j] \wedge i = j\}$$

Having shown the partial correctness of the procedure Partition, we must also check that it always halts if we wish to have a proof of total correctness. We have three **while** loops to consider. With every iteration of the outer **while** loop, the value of $j - i$ must decrease. Since we exit from this loop as soon as $j - i$ is negative, this outer **while** loop cannot loop infinitely. Neither is infinite looping a problem with the two inner **while** loops but perhaps we might, nevertheless, think that there is a possibility of them failing. For example, in

> **while** $A[i] < c$ **do** $i := i + 1$

it may be that every element in A with index greater than or equal to i is less than c. This statement would then fail because it would try to access an element of A out of bounds. Similarly,

> **while** $A[j] > c$ **do** $j := j - 1$

will fail if every element in A with index less than or equal to j is greater than c. To see that neither of these cases can occur, we can show that the following formula is always true before and after each execution of these **while** statements:

$$\exists r \,(i \leqslant r \leqslant n \wedge A[r] \geqslant c) \wedge \exists s \,(m \leqslant s \leqslant j \wedge A[s] \leqslant c)$$

Initially, assigning $r = (m + n)$ **div** 2 will establish the truth of this formula. This will remain the case until the first call of Swapvars which may involve $A[(m + n)$ **div** 2]. However, once Swapvars is called, we immediately increment i and decrement j. Hence, after this, $i > m$ and $j < n$. We know that

$$\forall p \,(m \leqslant p < i \Rightarrow A[p] \leqslant c)$$

and

$$\forall q \,(j < q \leqslant n \Rightarrow c \leqslant A[q])$$

hold. Hence if $i > m$ we can deduce $A[m] \leqslant c$ and if $j < n$, $c \leqslant A[n]$. Then our formula is true with the assignment $r = n$ and $s = m$.

Note that a corollary of the above reasoning is that $m \leqslant i \leqslant n$ and $m \leqslant j \leqslant n$.

Having verified Partition, we can now establish the correctness of the Quicksort algorithm given by the following recursive procedure:

> **procedure** Quicksort (**var** A: **array** $[1 .. N]$ **of** integer; m, n: integer);
> **var** i, j: integer;

begin

    if

        $m < n$ **then**

        begin

                Partition (A, i, j, m, n);

                Quicksort (A, m, j);

                Quicksort (A, i, n)

        end

    end

Quicksort is an algorithm designed to sort the elements of $A[m..n]$ into non-decreasing order. To establish the total correctness of Quicksort, we have to show that Quicksort (A, m, n) halts for all $1 \leqslant m \leqslant n \leqslant N$ and to partially verify

$$\{1 \leqslant m \leqslant n \leqslant N\} \text{ Quicksort } (A, m, n) \{\forall p \forall q (m \leqslant p \leqslant q \leqslant n \Rightarrow$$
$$A[p] \leqslant A[q]) \wedge \text{perm}(A)\}$$

We establish both these results simultaneously by induction on the number of elements $k = n - m + 1$ in $A[m..n]$.

If $k = 1$, i.e. $m = n$, then Quicksort (A, m, n) takes no action so that it trivially halts and $\forall p \forall q (m \leqslant p \leqslant q \leqslant n \Rightarrow A[p] \leqslant A[q]) \wedge \text{perm}(A)$ is also obviously a post-condition.

Now assume that $n - m \neq 0$ and that the result holds for all calls to the procedure where $k < n - m$. Consider Quicksort (A, m, n). In this case $m < n$ and so we execute

    Partition (A, i, j, m, n);
    Quicksort (A, m, j);
    Quicksort (A, i, n)

We have shown that Partition (A, i, j, m, n) will halt. Also, we know from our partial verification that the formula $\psi \equiv (i > j \wedge \forall p \forall q (m \leqslant p < i \wedge j < q \leqslant n \Rightarrow A[p] \leqslant A[q]) \wedge \text{perm}(A))$ holds after the call of Partition (A, i, j, m, n). We have also established that this is true for $m \leqslant i \leqslant n$ and $m \leqslant j \leqslant n$. Since $j < i$ and $i \leqslant n$ we know that $j < n$ and hence we can use our induction hypothesis to establish the total verification of

$$\{1 \leqslant m \leqslant j \leqslant N\} \text{ Quicksort } (A, m, j) \{\forall p \forall q (m \leqslant p \leqslant q \leqslant j \Rightarrow$$
$$A[p] \leqslant A[q]) \wedge \text{perm}(A)\}$$

Similarly, we can totally verify

$\{1 \leqslant i \leqslant n \leqslant N\}$ Quicksort (A, i, n) $\{\forall p \forall q\,(i \leqslant p \leqslant q \leqslant n \Rightarrow$
$A[p] \leqslant A[q]) \wedge \mathrm{perm}(A)\}$

Observe also that a call to Quicksort (A, m, n) does not alter the values of A outside the index range $[m \,.\, . \, n]$. Hence, if $1 \leqslant m \leqslant n \leqslant N$, after we have called Quicksort (A, m, n) the following must hold:

(1) $\mathrm{perm}(A)$
(2) $i > j$
(3) $\forall p \forall q\,(m \leqslant p < i \wedge j < q \leqslant n \Rightarrow A[p] \leqslant A[q])$
(4) $\forall p \forall q\,(m \leqslant p \leqslant q \leqslant j \Rightarrow A[p] \leqslant A[q])$
(5) $\forall p \forall q\,(i \leqslant p \leqslant q \leqslant n \Rightarrow A[p] \leqslant A[q])$

Now, since $1 \leqslant m \leqslant j < i \leqslant n \leqslant N$, the following holds:

$$\forall p \forall q\,(m \leqslant p \leqslant q \leqslant n \Rightarrow m \leqslant p \leqslant q \leqslant j$$
$$\vee\, i \leqslant p \leqslant q \leqslant n$$
$$\vee\, (m \leqslant p < i \wedge j < q \leqslant n)$$

Hence, from (4), (5) and (3) we deduce

$$\forall p \forall q\,(m \leqslant p \leqslant q \leqslant n \Rightarrow A[p] \leqslant A[q]) \wedge \mathrm{perm}(A)$$

i.e. that the subarray $A[m \,.\, . \, n]$ is sorted. Since Partition (A, i, j, m, n) will halt and, by the induction hypothesis, so will Quicksort (A, m, j) and Quicksort (A, i, n), it follows that Quicksort (A, m, n) halts.

Combining the above results, we have a total verification of $\{1 \leqslant m \leqslant n \leqslant N\}$ Quicksort (A, m, n) $\{\forall p \forall q\,(m \leqslant p \leqslant q \leqslant n \Rightarrow A[p] \leqslant A[q])$ $\wedge\, \mathrm{perm}(A)\}$ as expected. A simple application of the proof rules for procedures will then prove that Quicksort $(A, 1, N)$ will successfully sort the array A into non-decreasing order.

As the reader will have noted, most of the difficulty encountered with this proof comes from our insisting upon a total verification—a partial verification could be obtained fairly easily. The proof rules we have formulated were specifically for partial verification and so perhaps this is no surprise. It is in partial verification that predicate calculus has proved particularly successful. Proving that a correct program halts usually involves finding for each loop some value which is being increased (decreased) with each iteration of that loop but which is nevertheless bounded above (below). This ensures that the loop cannot be repeated infinitely. This idea has been formalized using a predicate calculus notation by Manna and Pnueli (1974). In practice, once a programmer has stated a measure under which the computation converges, proof of termination is not too difficult.

Future Developments

In this chapter we have shown how we can use predicate calculus to reason about simple Pascal programs and hence produce formal verifications. However, we have had to place very severe restrictions on the use of Pascal to enable us to develop and use proof rules of the level of simplicity which we have described. Without restrictions on the use of the language, proof rules become more involved and the resulting proofs are much more difficult. The tragedy is that many programmers, even though they claim to be competent at their craft, do not have the ability or mathematical sophistication to produce such proofs. We are in a position where even an apparently well-structured programming language such as Pascal can cause great difficulties for program verification. Other languages are much worse; certainly, any language heavily dependent on **goto**s is going to prove very difficult to handle.

There are several ways of overcoming this fundamental dilemma in computer science. The first is to develop new programming languages which are designed to enable the programmer to write accurate but powerful programs with simple verification proofs. Progress is being made in this direction. One possibility is the development of functional programming languages; another is the development of logic programming languages (see Chapter 7). Alternatively, we could keep to the traditional programming languages but insist that programmers should be more professional, mathematically oriented and better trained. Commercial constraints and manpower shortage make this rather unrealistic. A better solution is to design and produce sophisticated software development tools which enable a programmer to write a specification which can then be transformed into a correct program. The development of specification languages is an encouraging step along this road. The interested reader is referred to Jones (1980) and Berg *et al.* (1982).

In the absence of a solution to the problem of ensuring correct programs, we shall no doubt have to continue facing the consequences of program bugs. Moreover, in the immediate future the situation is likely to become worse rather than better. Parallelism offers enormous scope for quick and efficient code execution, but programs which exploit parallelism can entrap the unwary programmer into making subtle and convoluted errors. Proof techniques applicable to such programs have been developed but their application is not easy in practice; progress so far does not encourage the authors to think that the day of bug-free programs is getting nearer. Rather it seems to be vanishing quickly over the horizon. However, it is such an important goal that the computer scientist will be irresponsible if he or she does not strive for it. Predicate calculus has proved a useful tool and will no doubt underpin any future steps towards that goal.

Exercises

1   Given that the input predicate is $x = a \wedge y = (x-1)^2$, what is the output predicate for each of the following?

    (a) $y := x - 1$

    (b) $x := x + y$

    (c) **begin** $y := x - 1$; $x := x + y$ **end**

2   Verify

        $\{a \geqslant 0 \wedge b \geqslant 0\}$

        if $a > b$ **then** $a := a - b$

        else $a := b - a$

        $\{a \geqslant 0 \wedge b \geqslant 0\}$

3   Assuming a, b are integers, verify

        $\{x = a \wedge y = b \wedge a > 0 \wedge b > 0\}$

        $z := 0$;

        while $x < >0$ **do**

        begin

            if odd(x) **then** $z := z + y$;

            $y := y * 2$;

            $x := x$ **div** 2

        end

        $\{z = a * b\}$

Is this code still verifiable if the pre-condition is simply $\{x = a \wedge y = b\}$?

4   Specify the two loop invariants in the following code. Hence establish that this code computes the product p of the positive integers x and y.

        $p := 0$; $q := x$;

        while $q < >0$ **do**

        begin

            $t := 0$;

            while $t < >y$ **do**

            begin $p := p + 1$; $t := t + 1$ **end**;

            $q := q - 1$

        end

5 Verify the following code for integer division:

$\{i = a \land j = b \land a \geqslant 0 \land b > 0\}$
$k := 0;$

while $j \leqslant i$ **do begin**

$\qquad\qquad i := i - j;$
$\qquad\qquad k := k + 1$

$\qquad$ **end**
$\{0 \leqslant i < b \land a = k * b + i\}$

6 Specify all the loop invariants in the following program designed to compute the highest common factor (hcf) or greatest common divisor of positive integers a, b:

$\{a > 0 \land b > 0\}$
begin

$\qquad x := a;\ y := b;$
$\qquad$ **repeat**

$\qquad\qquad$ **while** $x > y$ **do** $x := x - y;$
$\qquad\qquad$ **while** $y > x$ **do** $y := y - x$
$\qquad$ **until** $x = y$

end
$\{x = y = \text{hcf}(a, b)\}$

Hence, partially verify the above. By considering the value of $x + y$, obtain a total verification of this program.

7 Partially verify the following code:

$\{\ \}$
begin

$\qquad \min := A[1];\ \text{sum} := A[1];$
$\qquad$ **for** $k := 2$ **to** 10 **do**

$\qquad\qquad$ **begin**

$\qquad\qquad\qquad \text{sum} := \text{sum} + A[i];$
$\qquad\qquad\qquad$ **if** $\min > A[i]$ **then** $\min := A[i]$

$\qquad\qquad$ **end**

end
$\{\forall i\,(1 \leqslant i \leqslant 10 \Rightarrow \min \leqslant A[i]) \land \text{sum} \geqslant 10 * \min\}$

8 Establish the total correctness of the binsearch function given in the text. (Hint: consider the value high $-$ low.)

9 Modify the proof rule given for **for** statements to obtain a proof rule applicable to Pascal statements of the form

for $x := m$ **downto** n **do** S

Use this proof rule to partially verify

$$\{\forall i\,(1 \leqslant i \leqslant 10 \Rightarrow A[i] > 0)\}$$

begin

    $\max := 0;$

    for $k := 10$ **downto** 1 **do**

        if $\max < A[k]$ **then** $\max := A[k]$

end

$$\{\forall i\,(1 \leqslant i \leqslant 10 \Rightarrow A[i] \leqslant \max) \wedge \exists\, i\,(1 \leqslant i \leqslant 10 \wedge A[i] = \max)\}$$

10 Consider the Pascal procedure

procedure Example2(i: integer; **var** j, k: integer);

begin

    $k := i + j;$

    $m := j + k;$

    $i := i + m;$

    $j := i + k$

end

What restrictions have to be placed on a, b, c if we are to deduce the truth of

$b = 3c$ after execution of Example2(a, b, c)? Is $3a = 2b$? Justify your answers.

11 What is the parameter-passing mechanism used in BASIC, FOR-TRAN etc.? (Consider all the languages with which you are familiar.)

12 Consider the following procedure which uses the sieve of Eratosthenes to find all the prime numbers between 2 and N:

procedure Sieve (**var** S: **array**[$2..N$] **of** integer);

var i, j: integer;

begin

    for $i := 2$ **to** N **do** $S[i] := 1$;

    $i := 2$;

    while $i * i \leqslant N$ **do**

    begin

        $j := i * i$;

        if $S[i] = 1$ **then**

            repeat $S[j] := 0$;

                $j := j + 1$

            until $j > N$;

        $i := i + 1$

    end

end

Assume that A is an array with index range $2..100$ and give a total verification of

$$\{\} \; \text{Sieve}(A) \; \{\forall k (2 \leqslant k \leqslant 100 \Rightarrow (A[k] = 1 \Rightarrow \text{prime}(k)))\}$$

where prime(k) is true iff k is a prime number.

13   Prove the total correctness of the following function to compute the factorial of a natural number:

```
function factorial2 (n: integer);
begin
    factorial2 := splitfact(1, n)
end;
```
where splitfact is defined by
```
function splitfact(i, j: integer);
var mid: integer;
begin
    if i = j then splitfact := i
    else begin
            mid := (i + j) div 2;
            splitfact := splitfact(i, mid) * splitfact(mid + 1, j)
         end
end
```


14   Show that the following function computes m^n for integers $m > 0, n \geqslant 0$:

```
function power(m, n: integer);
begin
    if n = 0 then power := 1
    else power := m * power(m, n - 1)
end
```
Hence, verify

$$\{x \geqslant 1 \wedge y > 0\} z := y * \text{power}(y, x - 1) \; \{z = y^x\}$$

15   The following (poor) code is the core of a proposed algorithm to sort an array A with index range $1..n$. Is this algorithm correct? If so prove it, and if not locate the error.

```
begin
    j := n;
```

```
1: if j = 1 then goto 3;
big := A[1]; loc := 1; i := 2;
2: if i > j then begin
                    A[loc] := A[j];
                    A[j] := big;
                    j := j − 1;
                    goto 1
              end;
   if A[i] > big then begin
                    big := A[i];
                    loc := i
                    end;
   i := i + 1;
   goto 2;
3: end
```

Chapter 6

Resolution Theorem Proving

Introduction

In Chapter 3 we formally defined predicate calculus. We have called a well-formed formula (WFF) A valid iff A evaluates to true for *all* possible valuations. These valid WFFs are precisely the theorems of predicate calculus. Unfortunately, validity in predicate calculus is *undecidable*, i.e. we cannot design an algorithm to determine whether or not a WFF is valid. In this chapter we shall consider how we can use a computer to perform logical reasoning and, in particular, to establish whether WFFs are theorems. From the above comments this appears a formidable task but, nevertheless, there has been considerable success in the construction of automatic theorem provers. This is because, although we cannot find a procedure to determine whether or not a WFF is valid, we can find a procedure which, given a valid WFF, will verify its validity. However, given a WFF which is not valid, such a procedure may not terminate. Because of the existence of such a 'checking' procedure, validity in the predicate calculus is sometimes called *semidecidable*.

An automatic theorem prover which uses such a checking procedure will be less than ideal. Not only may it not recognize when a WFF is invalid, but also it may take considerable time to construct a proof of a valid WFF. We may then abandon the procedure too early, assuming that the WFF is not valid and that the procedure is not going to halt. A good automatic theorem prover will ensure that such cases are exceptional and thus should perform very satisfactorily for the majority of inputs. This is the best that we can hope for—fortunately, it appears to be achievable!

Our theorem prover will be required to answer questions of the form: 'Given an arbitrary finite set of WFFs $H = \{H_1, H_2, \ldots, H_n\}$, does the WFF A follow from H, i.e. is $\{H_1, H_2, \ldots, H_n\} \vdash A$ correct? The WFF A is called the *goal* WFF and the set H the *hypothesis set*. If A does follow from H then every valuation satisfying all the WFFs in H also satisfies A. Hence, as we have observed in Chapter 4, there can be *no* valuation satisfying the WFFs in H and $\sim A$, i.e. the set $\{H_1, H_2, \ldots, H_n, \sim A\}$ is *unsatisfiable*. Conversely, if $\{H_1, H_2, \ldots, H_n, \sim A\}$ is unsatisfiable, then every valuation satisfying H_1,

$H_2, \ldots, H_n$ must also satisfy A and hence $\{H_1, H_2, \ldots, H_n\} \vdash A$. Summarizing, we obtain from Theorems 4.8 and 4.9 and Gödels theorem (Theorem 4.2) the following.

Theorem 6.1

$\{H_1, H_2, \ldots, H_n\} \vdash A$ iff $\{H_1, H_2, \ldots, H_n, \sim A\}$ is unsatisfiable.

This result is the key to the construction of automatic theorem provers. In this chapter, we develop further techniques which can be more easily implemented on a computer. In particular, we develop the powerful technique known as resolution which has proved particularly successful in practical automatic theorem proving. In all the techniques we discuss in this chapter it is assumed that the WFFs are sentences and are written in a particular normal form called the clausal form.

Clausal Form

Any sentence in predicate calculus can be written in clausal form by applying a sequence of eight simple steps. We shall illustrate the process using the WFF

$$\forall x [\sim P(x) \Rightarrow \exists y (D(y, x) \wedge \sim \{E(y, f(x)) \vee E(y, x)\})] \wedge \sim \forall x P(x)$$

Step (1): Replace all connectives except $\sim$, $\wedge$ and $\vee$. We have discussed how to do this in Chapters 1 and 3. For our example we replace the implication sign using the logical equivalence of $A \Rightarrow B$ and $\sim A \vee B$. Hence our WFF becomes

$$\forall x [\sim \sim P(x) \vee \exists y (D(y, x) \wedge \sim \{E(y, f(x)) \vee E(y, x)\})] \wedge \sim \forall x P(x)$$

Step (2): Reduce the scopes of the negation signs. Each negation sign must be made to apply to just one predicate. Essentially, we want to 'push $\sim$ symbols inwards' as much as possible. To achieve this, we repeatedly replace

$$
\begin{array}{rcl}
\sim (A \wedge B) & \text{by} & \sim A \vee \sim B \\
\sim (A \vee B) & \text{by} & \sim A \wedge \sim B \\
\sim \sim A & \text{by} & A \\
\sim \forall x A & \text{by} & \exists x \sim A \\
\sim \exists x A & \text{by} & \forall x \sim A
\end{array}
$$

Our example WFF thus becomes

$$\forall x[P(x) \lor \exists y(D(y, x) \land \sim E(y, f(x)) \land \sim E(y, x))] \land \exists x \sim P(x)$$

Step (3): Rename the variables to ensure each quantifier has its own unique variable associated with it. This is called *standardizing the variables apart.* Given a WFF of the form $\forall xA$ or $\exists xA$, the truth value of the WFF will be unaffected if every occurrence of x which occurs free in A is replaced by a new variable not occurring in A provided that we also similarly replace the x in $\forall x$ or $\exists x$. By adopting such a replacement strategy, we can ensure that each quantifier has its own unique associated variable.

In our example WFF, x is used twice as a quantified variable. We replace the second occurrence by a new variable z to obtain

$$\forall x[P(x) \lor \exists y(D(y, x) \land \sim E(y, f(x)) \land \sim E(y, x))] \land \exists z \sim P(z)$$

Step (4): Eliminate existential quantifiers (i.e. *Skolemize*). In our example we have two occurrences of $\exists$. In the first case $\exists y(D(y, x) \land \sim E(y, f(x)) \land \sim E(y, x))$ occurs within the scope of the universal quantifier $\forall x$. Thus the y which we claim exists might depend on the value taken by x. We can define this dependence explicitly using some function g (say) and write y as g(x)—this process is called Skolemization and g is called a *Skolem function.* We must, of course, ensure that whatever symbol we introduce to denote this Skolem function does not occur elsewhere in the WFF. Thus we could not have used the symbol f in this case.

In the second case of an occurrence of $\exists$ in our WFF, $\exists z \sim P(z)$ does not occur within the scope of any universal quantifier and so the z which we claim exists does not depend upon the value of any other variable. Hence we can replace $\exists z \sim P(z)$ by $\sim P(a)$, where a is some Skolem constant (i.e. a Skolem function of no variables) which does not occur elsewhere in the WFF. Our example WFF now contains no existential quantifier and is of the form

$$\forall x[P(x) \lor (D(g(x), x) \land \sim E(g(x), f(x)) \land \sim E(g(x), x))] \land \sim P(a)$$

In general, when Skolemizing, if a variable x is in the scope of an existential quantifier $\exists x$ then x is replaced by a Skolem function whose arguments are those universally quantified variables in whose scope lay the existential quantifier $\exists x$.

Step (5): Convert the WFF to *prenex normal form.* A WFF is in prenex normal form if it consists of a string of quantifiers (called a *prefix*) followed by a quantifier-free formula (called a *matrix*). After step (4), the WFF has no existential quantifiers and step (3) has ensured that each universal quantifier has its own unique associated variable. We can therefore simply move all the quantifiers to the front of the WFF and regard the scope of each such quantifier to be the whole of the WFF following it. In our example there is just one universal quantifier and so we obtain

$$\forall x\{[P(x) \vee (D(g(x), x) \wedge \sim E(g(x), f(x)) \wedge \sim E(g(x), x))] \wedge \sim P(a)\}$$

Step (6): Eliminate universal quantifiers. Since all variables remaining at this stage must be universally quantified and since the ordering of the quantifiers in the prefix is unimportant, the whole of the prefix can be dropped.

Our example thus becomes

$$[P(x) \vee (D(g(x), x) \wedge \sim E(g(x), f(x)) \wedge \sim E(g(x), x))] \wedge \sim P(a)$$

Step (7): Convert to *conjunctive normal form*. The matrix can be written as the conjunction of a finite number of disjunctions of atomic formulae and/or their negations. This is achieved, as in Chapter 1, by the repeated replacement of

$$A \vee (B \wedge C) \quad \text{by} \quad (A \vee B) \wedge (A \vee C)$$

and of

$$(A \wedge B) \vee C \quad \text{by} \quad (A \vee C) \wedge (B \vee C)$$

Our example becomes

$$(P(x) \vee D(g(x), x)) \wedge (P(x) \vee \sim E(g(x), f(x)))$$
$$\wedge (P(x) \vee \sim E(g(x), x)) \wedge \sim P(a)$$

Step (8): Construct clauses. The $\wedge$ connectives are eliminated and each disjunct is written as a separate *clause*. Each clause is surrounded by braces { and }, and the $\vee$ connectives are replaced by commas. A negated atomic formula is usually represented by writing a bar over it rather than preceding it by the negation symbol $\sim$.

The *clausal form* for our example WFF is thus

$$\{P(x), D(g(x), x))\}$$
$$\{P(x), \overline{E(g(x), f(x))}\}$$
$$\{P(x), \overline{E(g(x), x)}\}$$
$$\{\overline{P(a)}\}$$

Each clause consists of a finite set of *literals*, i.e. atomic formulae or their negations. Some literals may contain variables but these are always understood to be universally quantified. If *ground terms*, i.e. terms not involving variables, are uniformly substituted for each of the variables in a literal then we obtain a *ground* instance of the literal. Thus, for example, a ground instance of the literal D(g(x), x) is D(g(a), a).

We say a clause is satisfiable iff there exists an interpretation which satisfies the disjunction of its literals. A set of clauses is then satisfiable iff there exists some interpretation which satisfies every clause in the set. The set of clauses is unsatisfiable iff there is no such interpretation. For example,

$$\{G(x, y), G(y, x), E(x, y)\}$$
$$\{\overline{E(x, x)}\}$$
$$\{\overline{G(x, s(x))}\}$$

is a satisfiable set of clauses. (To be more precise, $\{\{G(x, y), G(y, x), E(x, y)\}$, $\{\overline{E(x, x)}\}$, $\{\overline{G(x, s(x))}\}\}$ is a satisfiable set of clauses. However, we shall generally avoid the use of the outer braces and commas between clauses to simplify presentation.) To show that the set is satisfiable, we can take the integers as the domain of interpretation, define s(x) to be x + 1, G(x, y) to be true iff x > y and E(x, y) to be true iff x = y.

The set of clauses

$$\{P(x), \overline{Q(x)}\}$$
$$\{\overline{P(f(x))}\}$$
$$\{Q(f(x))\}$$

is, however, not satisfiable. For any constant a, P(f(a)) must be false to satisfy $\{\overline{P(f(x))}\}$ and Q(f(a)) must be true to satisfy $\{Q(f(x))\}$. Thus P(f(a)) ∨ ~Q(f(a)) is false and so the first clause will not be satisfied.

If we are given a set of WFFs $S = \{A_1, A_2, \ldots, A_n\}$ which is unsatisfiable and we construct the clausal form of $A_1 \wedge A_2 \wedge \ldots \wedge A_n$ then we obtain a set of clauses c(S). It should be clear from the construction of the clausal form that S is unsatisfiable iff c(S) is unsatisfiable. Theorem 6.1 has motivated us to find techniques for checking sets of WFFs to be unsatisfiable. Now we see the need to find techniques which check that sets of clauses are unsatisfiable—such techniques are called *refutation techniques*.

Refutation by Semantic Tree

Let $C = c(S)$ be some set of clauses. The *Herbrand universe* H(C) of C is the set of ground terms defined recursively as follows.

(i)   Every constant appearing in **C** also occurs in H(**C**); if there are no such constants, then H(**C**) contains a specially introduced symbol ω.

(ii)   If f is a function symbol of arity n that occurs in **C** and $t_1, t_2, \ldots, t_n$ are terms in H(**C**) then $f(t_1, t_2, \ldots, t_n)$ is in H(**C**).

(iii)   No other terms save those defined in (i) and (ii) above occur in H(**C**).

For example, if $\mathbf{C}_1$ is the set of clauses

$\{\overline{P(a)}\}$
$\{P(x), D(y, x)\}$
$\{\overline{P(x)}, E(x, x)\}$

then $\mathbf{C}_1$ contains just one constant symbol a but no function symbols. Thus the Herbrand universe H($\mathbf{C}_1$) of $\mathbf{C}_1$, is simply the finite set of terms $\{a\}$.

For the set of clauses $\mathbf{C}_2$ given by

$\{P(x), \overline{Q(x)}\}$
$\{\overline{P(f(x))}\}$
$\{Q(f(x))\}$

the Herbrand universe is H($\mathbf{C}_2$) = $\{\omega, f(\omega), f(f(\omega)), \ldots\}$

If $\mathbf{C}_3$ is

$\{\overline{P(a)}, D(a, b)\}$
$\{P(x), D(f(x), g(x, y))\}$
$\{P(x), \overline{E(x, x)}\}$

then $\mathbf{C}_3$ contains two constant symbols a, b and two function symbols f, of arity 1, and g, of arity 2. Hence H($\mathbf{C}_3$) = $\{$a, b, f(a), f(b), g(a, a), g(a, b), g(b, a), g(b, b), f(g(a, a)), f(g(a, b)), \ldots\}$.

For any finite set **C** of clauses, H(**C**) will always be countable, i.e. we shall be able to devise some technique for listing all the elements.

When we wish to show a set of clauses **C** to be unsatisfiable, we have to show that there is no valuation satisfying every clause in **C**. Since every variable occurring in a clause is assumed to be universally quantified, a unique truth value for that clause is determined by any given interpretation independently of the choice of truth valuation. To define an interpretation, we must first specify a universe or domain. The importance of the Herbrand universe is given by the result that if **C** is unsatisfiable then there is no valuation with domain H(**C**) and with the expected action of functions on elements of the universe in which every clause in **C** is true. Thus, to show that **C** is unsatisfiable, we can restrict our attention to interpretations with domain H(**C**) and where the action of a function is defined in the following way. If $t_1, t_2, \ldots, t_n \in H(C)$ and f is an n-ary function then the image of f with arguments $t_1, t_2, \ldots, t_n$ is simply the element $f(t_1, t_2, \ldots, t_n) \in H(C)$. Thus, for example, if a, $f(a) \in H(C)$ and g is a 2-ary function symbol, the term $g(a, f(a))$ is interpreted to mean the element $g(a, f(a)) \in H(C)$.

Having specified a domain and an interpretation for functions, the next stage in defining an interpretation is to decide for each n-ary predicate P and for each ground instance $P(a_1, a_2, \ldots, a_n)$, $a_i \in H(C)$, $1 \leqslant i \leqslant n$, of P, whether $P(a_1, a_2, \ldots, a_n)$ is assigned true or false. We define the *Herbrand base* of C to be the set of all ground instances of all atomic formulae in C where the domain is $H(C)$. When and only when every element of the Herbrand base has been assigned a truth value is the interpretation complete.

The Herbrand base of any finite set of clauses can always be enumerated—it will either be finite or countably infinite. For example, the Herbrand base for C_1 is simply $\{P(a), D(a, a), E(a, a)\}$ whilst the Herbrand base for the (unsatisfiable) set C_2 can be enumerated as $P(\omega)$, $Q(\omega)$, $P(f(\omega))$, $Q(f(\omega))$, $P(f(f(\omega)))$, ... Assume that the Herbrand base for the finite set of clauses C is enumerated as $b_1, b_2, b_3, \ldots$. For an interpretation, we shall require an assignment of truth values to each element in this sequence. A convenient way of representing all such assignments is by a binary tree. At the root node, we branch left if we assign T to b_1 and right if we assign F to b_1. Each path from the root to a node at depth i will represent an assignment of truth values to $b_1, b_2, \ldots, b_i$ and thus denote a partially constructed interpretation. From each node at depth i there are two branches to nodes at depth $i+1$. The left branch is labelled b_{i+1} and represents an assignment of T to b_{i+1} and the right branch, labelled $\overline{b_{i+1}}$, represents an assignment of F to b_{i+1}. Such a binary tree constructed from the Herbrand base of C is called a *semantic tree*. In Fig. 6.1 the path indicated in the semantic tree defines an interpretation which assigns T to b_1, F to b_2, T to b_3. If the Herbrand base of C is infinite then, of course, to represent all possible interpretations, the corresponding semantic tree must also be infinite. However, if C is unsatisfiable, then it is always the case that we need only consider a finite part of the semantic tree to establish this fact. As an example, consider the unsatisfiable set of clauses C_2. If we enumerate the Herbrand base for C_2 as $P(\omega)$, $Q(\omega)$, $P(f(\omega))$, $Q(f(\omega))$, $P(f(f(\omega)))$, ..., then we obtain the semantic tree given to depth 4 in Fig. 6.2. Any path through the node labelled (a) must correspond to an interpretation which assigns F to $P(\omega)$ and T to $Q(\omega)$. Any such assignment will ensure that the clause $\{P(x), \overline{Q(x)}\}$ evaluates to F. Thus all interpretations corresponding to paths

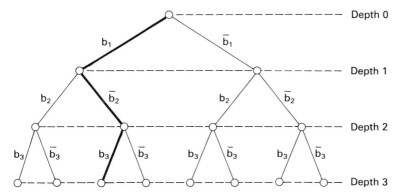

Fig. 6.1. A semantic tree.

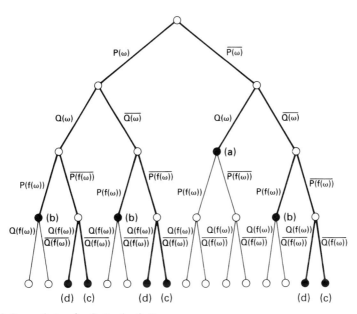

Fig. 6.2. Semantic tree for C_2 (to depth 4).

through node (a) will fail to satisfy C_2. We need not then expand the semantic tree below node (a). Node (a) is an example of a failure node.

Given a semantic tree for a set of clauses C, we say a node of the tree is a *failure node* iff

(i) there exists some clause $C \in C$ such that the partial valuation defined by the path from the root to the node in question ensures that C will be evaluated to F, and

(ii) there is no other node on the path from the root node to the node in question which satisfies (i).

Nodes labelled (b) in Fig. 6.2 are also failure nodes since all paths through them ensure that $\{\overline{P(f(x))}\}$ evaluates to F. Similarly, those nodes labelled (c) correspond to partial valuations failing to satisfy $\{Q(f(x))\}$. Finally, those nodes labelled (d) are also failure nodes since they correspond to partial valuations failing to satisfy $\{P(x), \overline{Q(x)}\}$. The semantic tree given in Fig. 6.2 is thus *closed*, i.e. all paths from the root must pass through a failure node.

Let **C** be an unsatisfiable set of clauses. We can construct a subtree of the semantic tree for **C** by deleting all the nodes which are descendants of failure nodes together with their associated arcs. The remaining tree is called the *primary semantic tree* for **C**. In Fig. 6.2, this primary semantic tree is shown by bold lines. All the leaf nodes of a primary semantic tree are necessarily failure nodes and we represent these by shading them in our diagrams. Moreover, the primary semantic tree for an unsatisfiable set will always be finite. If not, it would have to include an infinite path, i.e. a path not terminating in a failure node. If this were the case, then this path would correspond to a satisfying interpretation for **C**.

We now have a technique for establishing that a set **C** of clauses is unsatisfiable. We simply enumerate the Herbrand universe for **C** and hence the Herbrand base for **C**. We then construct, level by level, the primary semantic tree, checking whether any newly generated nodes are failure nodes. If not, they will be expanded further. Provided that **C** is unsatisfiable, we know that this process will terminate with a finite tree where all the leaves are failure nodes. However, the construction of the primary semantic tree could be a lengthy task and this refutation process is seldom used in practice. It is more usual to use a resolution technique (to be described below) but, as we shall see, the justification for the validity of such techniques relies on the principle of semantic trees which we have described. To appreciate the connection between semantic trees and resolution we need to make some further observations about semantic trees.

With each failure node f in a semantic tree for **C**, we can associate a ground instance of some clause in **C** which evaluates to F under the (partial) valuation defined by the path from the root to f. We call such a ground instance of a clause a *failing instance* associated with f. In the example of Fig. 6.2, the node labelled (a) has failing instance $\{P(\omega), \overline{Q(\omega)}\}$, those labelled (b) have failing instance $\{\overline{P(f(\omega))}\}$, those labelled (c) have failing instance $\{Q(f(\omega))\}$ and those labelled (d) have failing instance $\{P(f(\omega)), \overline{Q(f(\omega))}\}$.

Now, we know that the parent of a failure node cannot possibly also be a failure node. Hence, if the arc to a failure node f from its parent is labelled b_i (or $\overline{b_i}$), then the failing instance for f must necessarily contain $\overline{b_i}$ (or b_i). An *inference node* in the (primary) semantic tree for **C** is a node, both of whose children are failure nodes. Any primary semantic tree for an unsatisfiable set of clauses must have at least one inference node, e.g. the father of a failure node at the lowest level. In the example of Fig. 6.2 there are three inference nodes, all of which have one child labelled (c) and the other labelled (d).

We are going to develop ways of deducing new clauses from our original set of clauses **C**, such that the addition of these new clauses to **C** guarantees that the inference nodes (or their ancestors) will become failure nodes. By repeated use of such a procedure for any unsatisfiable set of clauses **C** we should be able to deduce an unsatisfiable set of clauses $\mathbf{C}' \supset \mathbf{C}$, where the primary semantic tree for $\mathbf{C}'$ is shrunk to the single root node. This is the key idea of resolution theorem proving.

Now, consider an inference node. Assume that the arcs from the node are labelled b_i and $\overline{b_i}$ as in Fig. 6.3(a). The failing instances associated with the two failing nodes which are the children of the inference node must be clauses of the form $\{\overline{b_i}\} \cup C'$ and $\{b_i\} \cup C''$ respectively. If there had been a clause in **C** which had a ground instance of $C' \cup C''$ then the inference node (or an ancestor of it) would itself have been a failure node.

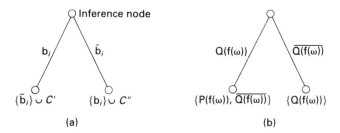

Fig. 6.3. (a) The general case; (b) example C_2.

If we consider the three inference nodes of Fig. 6.2, we see that they all have the form given in Fig. 6.3(b). If $\{P(f(x))\}$ had been a clause in C_2, then each inference node would have been a failure node. If $\{P(x)\}$ had been a clause in C_2 then, in one of our three cases, an ancestor of the inference node would have been a failure node and, in the other two, once again the inference node itself would have been a failure node. Let us consider the two clauses whose ground instances are the failing instances. These are $\{P(x), \overline{Q(x)}\}$ and

{Q(f(x))}. For any satisfying valuation, we know that both $P(x) \vee \sim Q(x)$ and $Q(f(x))$ must be true. Hence, $P(f(x)) \vee \sim Q(f(x))$ must also be true and, since $Q(f(x))$ is true, we can deduce that $P(f(x))$ is true. The clause $\{P(f(x))\}$ is called the resolvent of $\{P(x), \overline{Q(x)}\}$ and $\{Q(f(x))\}$. If only we had done this deduction earlier and added this resolvent to C_2, the primary semantic tree which we constructed would have been smaller.

In a resolution proof, we aim to add new clauses continually to an unsatisfiable set of clauses C until eventually we have one clause which is empty (and hence, trivially, unsatisfiable). In our example, once we have added $\{P(f(x))\}$ to our set of clauses, the corresponding primary semantic tree is reduced in size and we then have the set of clauses comprising

$$\{P(x), \overline{Q(x)}\}$$
$$\{Q(f(x))\}$$
$$\{\overline{P(f(x))}\}$$
$$\{P(f(x))\}$$

From the last two clauses we can immediately see that the set of clauses is unsatisfiable. A formal resolution proof would be completed by observing that the resolvent of $\{\overline{P(f(x))}\}$ and $\{P(f(x))\}$ is the empty clause $\{\}$. Once this empty clause is added to our set, unsatisfiability is immediately obvious. A proof by resolution that C_2 is unsatisfiable would normally be presented as a tree (Fig. 6.4). The leaf nodes are clauses in the original set C_2 and the internal nodes are resolvents. The root node is the empty clause $\{\}$.

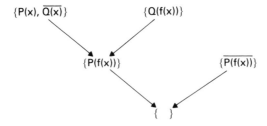

Fig. 6.4.

Unification

Before we can formally present the technique of refutation by resolution, we must first present the process known as unification.

Consider the two literals $P(b, x, y)$ and $P(z, g(z), b)$. If, in the first literal, we replace x by $g(b)$ and y by b, we obtain $P(b, g(b), b)$. This instance can also be obtained from the second literal by substituting b for z throughout. Finding substitutions of terms for variables to make literals identical is called *unification*. It is a key step in resolution and enables us to deduce, for example, that P(b, x, y) and $\sim$P(z, g(z), b) are not both satisfiable.

We represent a substitution σ of terms for variables by a set of ordered pairs $\sigma = \{x_1 \rightarrow t_1, x_2 \rightarrow t_2, \ldots, x_n \rightarrow t_n\}$. By this we mean the substitution where, simultaneously, every variable x_1 is replaced by t_1, every x_2 by $t_2, \ldots$, every x_n by t_n. Note that, since we are considering substitutions acting on literals, there are no quantifiers and hence all occurrences of any variable are free. The only constraint we need to impose on our sets of ordered pairs is that the variables $x_1, x_2, \ldots, x_n$ must be unique, i.e. $x_i = x_j \Rightarrow i = j$.

If σ_1, σ_2 are substitutions then their *composition* $\sigma_1 \circ \sigma_2$ is the substitution which has the effect of applying σ_2 and then σ_1. Thus, for any literal l, $(\sigma_1 \circ \sigma_2)l = \sigma_1(\sigma_2(l))$. The substitution $\sigma_1 \circ \sigma_2$ can be constructed from $\sigma_2 = \{x_1 \rightarrow t_1, x_2 \rightarrow t_2, \ldots, x_n \rightarrow t_n\}$ by applying σ_1 to each of the terms $t_1, t_2, \ldots, t_n$ of σ_2 and then adding any pairs of σ_1 having variables distinct from $x_1, x_2, \ldots, x_n$. Thus if $\sigma_2 = \{x \rightarrow f(y), y \rightarrow g(a, b), z \rightarrow x\}$ and $\sigma_1 = \{w \rightarrow x, x \rightarrow a, y \rightarrow b\}$, then $\sigma_1 \circ \sigma_2 = \{w \rightarrow x, x \rightarrow f(b), y \rightarrow g(a, b), z \rightarrow a\}$. Checking this on an example literal $l = P(f(w), x, g(f(y), z))$ we see that

$$\sigma_2(l) = P(f(w), f(y), g(f(g(a, b)), x))$$

and

$$\sigma_1(\sigma_2(l)) = P(f(x), f(b), g(f(g(a, b)), a))$$
$$= \sigma_1 \circ \sigma_2(l)$$

The task that we set ourselves is to take a set of literals $L = \{l_1, l_2, \ldots, l_n\}$ and find a substitution σ such that $\sigma(l_1) = \sigma(l_2) = \ldots = \sigma(l_n)$. Such a substitution is called a *unifier* and is said to *unify* L. Clearly, if such a unification is to be possible, all the literals must involve the same predicate. However, this is not a sufficient condition—consider $\{P(x, f(x)), P(f(y), y)\}$. If, as in this case, no unification is possible, we must be able to recognize this fact.

A *most general unifier* (mgu) μ of a set L of literals has the property that μ unifies L and, moreover, if θ is any other substitution that unifies L then $\theta = \varphi \circ \mu$ for some substitution φ. Thus μ is a 'simplest possible' unifier of L and, provided that L is unifiable, such an mgu will always exist. Furthermore, it is unique up to composition by alphabetic variations. For example, if $L = \{P(x, y, z), P(x, w, b), P(f(a), y, b)\}$ then a possible unifier is {x→f(a), y→a, w→a, z→b}, but this is not an mgu for L. Two mgus for L are {x→f(a), y→w, z→b} and {x→f(a), w→y, z→b}.

Finding an mgu (if it exists) for an arbitrary set of literals L is not difficult. There exists a simple algorithm called the *unification algorithm* which, given L, either reports that L is not unifiable or constructs an mgu μ for L. The algorithm works as follows. Each literal $l_i \in L$ is regarded as a string of symbols, with any overhead bars being replaced by preceding negations. We then detect the first symbol position k (say) where the literals differ. If the symbol at position k in any literal is a predicate symbol, parenthesis, connective or comma, L is not unifiable. Otherwise we consider the set of terms T containing the terms from each literal containing the symbol at position k. If T contains no variables then again L is not unifiable. Otherwise, we try to select a variable x from T and a term t in T which does not contain x as a subterm. Again, if this is not possible, we report that no unification is possible. Otherwise we apply the substitution {x→t} to all the literals in L. We then keep reapplying the whole procedure until all the literals are identical. The required mgu is the composition of the substitutions constructed in the successive iterations of the procedure.

For example, if L = {P(x, y, z), P(x, w, b), P(f(a), y, b)}, successive applications of the procedure result in the following.

First application: {P(x, y, z), P(x, w, b), P(f(a), y, b)}
                       $k = 3$; T = {x, f(a)} so apply {x→f(a)}

Second application: {P(f(a), y, z), P(f(a), w, b), P(f(a), y, b)}
                       $k = 8$; T = {y, w} so apply {y→w}
                       (or equally well, apply {w→y})

Third application: {P(f(a), w, z), P(f(a), w, b), P(f(a), w, b)}
                       $k = 10$; T = {z, b} so apply {z→b}

All literals will now be identical and the required mgu is

$$\{z{\to}b\} \circ \{w{\to}y\} \circ \{x{\to}f(a)\} = \{z{\to}b,\ w{\to}y,\ x{\to}f(a)\}$$

As a further example, consider the non-unifiable set {P(x, f(x)), P(f(y), y)}. After the first iteration $k = 3$, T = {x, f(y)} and we apply the substitution {x→f(y)} to obtain {P(f(y), f(f(y))), P(f(y), y)}. Then on the second iteration $k = 8$ and T = {y, f(f(y))}. There is only one variable in T, i.e. y, but unfortunately the only other term in T contains y as a subterm. At this stage the algorithm correctly reports that this set of literals is not unifiable.

An induction argument on the structure of the literals occurring in L can be used to verify the correctness of the unification algorithm. The details have been given by Robinson (1979). The skeleton of a LISP-like implementation of the algorithm has been given by Nilsson (1980). Any reader with access to LISP or to a language such as SNOBOL or ICON which supports sophisticated string processing and pattern matching should find it relatively easy to implement this unification algorithm.

Refutation by Resolution

In any set of clauses **C** we can rename the variables in any two clauses so that they do not share any variables. Since all the variables are effectively universally quantified, such a renaming of variables will not affect the satisfiability (or otherwise) of the set (see Chapter 4, Exercise 7(a)).

More formally, let C, C' be two clauses in **C**. A substitution τ is a *renaming substitution* for C, C' iff τ is of the form $\{x_1 \rightarrow y_1, x_2 \rightarrow y_2, \ldots, x_n \rightarrow y_n\}$ where (i) $\{x_1, x_2, \ldots, x_n\}$ includes all the variables common to both C and C' and (ii) $y_1, y_2, \ldots, y_n$ are distinct variables which do not occur in C or C'. The result of applying such a renaming substitution is that $\tau(C)$ and C' have no variables in common. For example, if $C = \{P(x), Q(f(x)), \overline{R(y)}\}$ and $C' = \{P(f(x)), \overline{P(g(y))}, R(a)\}$, then a possible renaming substitution is $\tau = \{x \rightarrow v, y \rightarrow w\}$. Then $\tau(C) = \{P(v), Q(f(v)), \overline{R(w)}\}$ and C' have no variables in common.

Consider two clauses C, C' in a set of clauses **C**. By applying a renaming substitution for C, C' (if necessary), we can assume that C, C' have no variables in common. If there exist two literals, $l \in C$ and $\overline{l'} \in C'$ such that there is an mgu μ which unifies $\{l, l'\}$, then we say that the two clauses C and C' *resolve* and that their *resolvent* is the clause

$$\mu(C - \{l\}) \cup \mu(C' - \{\overline{l'}\})$$

Theorem 6.2

If C and C' are simultaneously satisfiable then their resolvent is satisfiable.

Proof. If C and C' are simultaneously satisfiable then there exists some interpretation in which both C and C' are true. For this interpretation $\mu(C)$ and $\mu(C')$ must also be true. Now if $\mu(l)$ is true for this interpretation then

$\mu(\bar{l}) = \mu(\bar{l'})$ must be false. Hence $\mu(C' - \{\bar{l'}\})$ must be true for this interpretation and thus so must $\mu(C - \{l\}) \cup \mu(C' - \{\bar{l'}\})$. Similarly, if $\mu(\bar{l})$ is true for this interpretation, it follows that $\mu(C - \{l\})$ must be true and thus so must $\mu(C - \{l\}) \cup \mu(C' - \{\bar{l'}\})$. In either case, we have shown that the resolvent is satisfiable.

A corollary of this theorem is that if a resolvent of two clauses in **C** is unsatisfiable then **C** must also be unsatisfiable.

As an example of resolution, consider the two clauses $\{P(v), Q(f(v)),$ $\overline{R(w)}\}$ and $\{P(f(x)), \overline{P(g(y))}, R(a)\}$. In this case there are two possible resolvents. First we can construct an mgu for $\{P(v), P(g(y))\}$, e.g. $\{v \rightarrow g(y)\}$, and hence obtain the resolvent $\{Q(f(g(y))), \overline{R(w)}, P(f(x)), R(a)\}$. Second we can construct an mgu for $\{R(w), R(a)\}$, e.g. $\{w \rightarrow a\}$, and obtain the resolvent $\{P(v), Q(f(v)), P(f(x)), \overline{P(g(y))}\}$.

If all the literals in the set to be unified involve the predicate P then we say that we are *resolving on* P. Thus, for the above example, we have one way of resolving on P and one way of resolving on R.

The clauses C, C' are called the *parents* of their resolvent. Suppose that μ is the mgu used to construct this resolvent. Since we assume that C, C' have no variables in common, we can write $\mu = \lambda \cup \rho$ where λ is a substitution involving just those variables in C and ρ is a substitution involving just those variables in C'. Then, $\mu(C - \{l\}) \cup \mu(C' - \{\bar{l'}\}) = \lambda(C - \{l\}) \cup \rho(C' - \{\bar{l'}\})$. We can thus represent the construction of a resolvent diagrammatically as in Fig. 6.5.

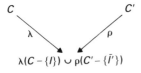

Fig. 6.5. Constructing a resolvent.

Another operation which we can perform on clauses without affecting their satisfiability is *factoring*. If C is a clause and l, l' are two literals in C such that there is an mgu μ of $\{l, l'\}$, then we say that $\mu(C)$ is a *simple factor* of C. For example, if $C = \{D(f(y), y), \overline{P(x)}, D(x, y), \overline{P(z)}\}$ then the following are all simple factors of C:

$\{D(f(y), y), \overline{P(f(y))}, \overline{P(z)}\}$
$\{\overline{P(x)}, D(f(y), y), D(x, y)\}$
$\{\overline{P(z)}, D(f(y), y), D(z, y)\}$

We define a *factor* of C recursively to be either (i) C itself or (ii) a simple factor of a factor of C. Thus the factors of our example are as follows:

(i) C itself, i.e. $\{D(f(y), y), \overline{P(x)}, D(x, y), \overline{P(z)}\}$;
(ii)   the three simple factors of C listed above;
(iii) any factor of the three simple factors, in this case just one, i.e. $\{D(f(y), y), \overline{P(f(y))}\}$.

If C is satisfiable then any simple factor of C is clearly satisfiable. Hence we can deduce by induction that any factor of C is satisfiable. As with resolution, we can represent factoring graphically. In Fig. 6.6, we illustrate the factoring of C using a substitution σ which may be the composition of several mgus.

C

$\sigma(C)$

Fig. 6.6. Factoring.

If a set of clauses contains an empty clause $\{\}$, the set is necessarily unsatisfiable. This observation suggests a simple strategy which we can use to attempt to show that a set of clauses **C** is unsatisfiable.

The Resolution Strategy

while $\{\}$ is not in **C**
do add to **C** some new clause which is either a resolvent of two clauses currently in **C** or a factor of one clause currently in **C**

From our comments about resolvents and factors, it is clear that if this strategy halts with the empty clause then **C** must indeed have been unsatisfiable. The strategy, as we have stated it, is *nondeterministic*, i.e. we have not defined a unique operation at each step. We have allowed the addition of any resolvent or of any factor. It can be shown, however, that provided that the correct choices are made, from any unsatisfiable set, the empty clause can indeed be deduced in a finite number of steps. The proof of this statement follows from our discussion of semantic trees. We know that for any unsatisfiable set **C** there exist two distinct clauses C, C' which have ground instances which are failing instances for sibling failure nodes. It can be shown that there is a resolvent of factors of these two clauses which will have a ground instance which is a failing instance for the corresponding inference node. It may even be that the inclusion of this resolvent in **C** would cause an ancestor of the inference node to be a failure node. In any case, however, if we select the two parent clauses correctly, construct the correct factors and resolvent and duly add this clause to **C**, the corresponding primary semantic tree for **C** must be reduced in size. The resolution strategy can iterate this process until the primary semantic tree is shrunk right down to a single node, i.e. the root. This can only occur when one of the clauses is empty. We have outlined the proof of the following important result.

Theorem 6.3

A set of clauses **C** is unsatisfiable iff the resolution strategy can halt with the empty clause in a finite number of steps.

The art of constructing refutations by resolution comes in the choice of which clause(s) to factor/resolve and for which literals to find an mgu. With the correct choice we can arrive quickly at the empty clause. Incorrect choices can delay matters (possibly infinitely!). Hence, we shall need to develop strategies for making these choices. Firstly, however, we shall illustrate some simple refutations by resolution using simple examples where the choices are obvious.

Refutations by resolution can be illustrated using a *refutation graph*. The original clauses in **C**, called the *base set*, are each represented by a node in this graph. When two parents are selected and a resolvent is constructed, the resolvent itself forms a new node and there is a labelled directed arc to it from each of its parents as shown in Fig. 6.5. If the parent clauses have variables in common so that a renaming substitution τ is required, this is represented as shown in Fig. 6.7(a) or (more commonly) in the abbreviated form of Fig. 6.7(b). Similarly, when a clause is factored, we introduce a new node for the factored clause joined to the original clause by a labelled directed arc as shown in Fig. 6.6.

Now, let us consider how we might use resolution to deduce 'Socrates is mortal' from the two statements 'All men are mortal' and 'Socrates is a man'. We use $D(x)$ to denote 'x is mortal', $M(x)$ to denote 'x is a man' and the constant s to denote 'Socrates'. Then 'All men are mortal' becomes $\forall x(M(x) \Rightarrow D(x))$, 'Socrates is a man' becomes $M(s)$ and 'Socrates is mortal'

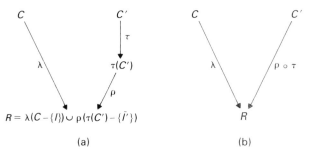

Fig. 6.7.

becomes D(s). To show $\{\forall x(M(x)\Rightarrow D(x)), M(s)\} \vdash D(s)$, it is sufficient to show that $\{\forall x(M(x)\Rightarrow D(x)), M(s), \sim D(s)\}$ is unsatisfiable. In clausal form, this becomes

$\{\overline{M(x)}, D(x)\}$
$\{M(s)\}$
$\{\overline{D(s)}\}$

A resolution refutation is given by the refutation graph of Fig. 6.8.

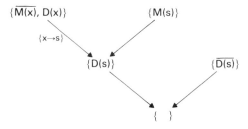

Fig. 6.8.

As a less simple example, we can deduce from 'All intelligent people understand logic' and 'Some computer scientists are intelligent' that 'Some computer scientists understand logic'. Representing 'x is intelligent' by I(x), 'x understands logic' by L(x) and 'x is a computer scientist' by C(x), we have to show that $\{\forall x(I(x)\Rightarrow L(x)), \exists x(C(x) \wedge I(x))\} \vdash \exists x(C(x) \wedge L(x))$. To do this, we show that $\{\forall x(I(x)\Rightarrow L(x)), \exists x(C(x) \wedge I(x)), \sim \exists x(C(x) \wedge L(x))\}$ is unsatisfiable. Converting to clausal form, we obtain the set of clauses

$\{\overline{I(x)}, L(x)\}$
$\{C(a)\}$
$\{I(a)\}$
$\{\overline{C(x)}, \overline{L(x)}\}$

Two possible refutations by resolution are given in the refutation graphs of Fig. 6.9.

In the above examples, factoring was not needed in the construction of a refutation by resolution. Factoring is essential in some cases, however. In Fig. 6.10 we give a refutation graph for the set of clauses

$$\{P(x),\ P(y)\}$$
$$\{\overline{P(u)},\ \overline{P(v)}\}$$

Without factoring, every deduced clause would always have two literals and hence $\{\ \}$ would never be deduced.

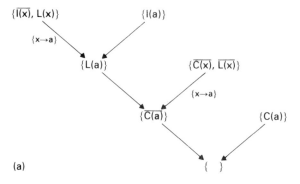

(a)

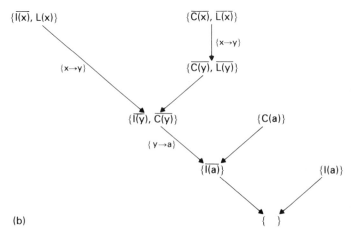

(b)

Fig. 6.9. Two refutations by resolution.

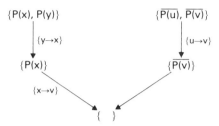

Fig. 6.10.

Simplification Strategies

There are various search strategies that can be used in an attempt to construct a refutation by resolution from an unsatisfiable set of clauses **C**. Before this we might first try to simplify **C** itself using one or more of a variety of simplification strategies. For example, any clause in **C** which contains a literal and its negation is simply a tautology. If we remove a tautological clause from a set of clauses, the satisfiability (or otherwise) of the set will remain unaffected. Hence one simplification strategy is to remove all tautological clauses from **C** and then also to discard any further tautological clauses that may arise during resolution.

Another simplification strategy which can considerably reduce the number of clauses which need to be considered is called *subsumption*. We say that a clause C *subsumes* a clause C' if there exists a substitution σ such that $\sigma(C)$ is a subset of C'. For example, $\{P(x), \overline{Q(f(y))}\}$ subsumes $\{P(f(x)), \overline{Q(f(a))}, R(z)\}$ using the substitution $\{x \to f(x), y \to a\}$. If C subsumes C' and C is satisfiable then, clearly, so is C'. Hence, if **C** contains C and C' where C subsumes C' then $\mathbf{C} - \{C'\}$ is satisfiable implies that **C** is satisfiable. Thus **C** is unsatisfiable implies that $\mathbf{C} - \{C'\}$ is unsatisfiable and we can deduce that if a refutation by resolution exists for **C** then it will also exist for $\mathbf{C} - \{C'\}$. We have thus justified the simplification strategy which states that if a clause C' in **C** is subsumed by some other clause C in **C** then C' can be eliminated from **C**.

One further simplification strategy which proves useful in practice is perhaps so obvious that it could be overlooked. In many applications the symbols we are using in the predicate calculus expressions have fixed semantic interpretations in the domain in which we are working. For example, the predicate D(x, y) can be used for the concept 'x divides y'. Therefore, with domain the natural numbers Nat we associate with D a Boolean function $\text{Nat} \times \text{Nat} \to \{T, F\}$. We might also be using function symbols such as *add, times* etc., and these are also naturally associated with functions defined over Nat. Finally, our expressions might involve the constant symbols 1, 2 etc. which have immediate interpretations as natural numbers. In such circumstances, some ground instances of literals are easily evaluated, e.g., D(2, *times* (2, 3)) evaluates to T, D(3, 7) evaluates to F. Any clause which contains a ground instance of a literal which evaluates to T can be eliminated since that clause is tautological. If a literal is a ground instance and can be evaluated to F then that particular literal can be eliminated from the clause. Thus this particular simplification strategy can sometimes be used to eliminate clauses and sometimes be used to eliminate literals from clauses. However, it should always be used with considerable care since it is completely dependent upon the chosen interpretation; many implementers choose to avoid it altogether. The subsumption and tautology elimination rules will often suffice as simplification techniques. However, some implementers generalize this approach still further, enabling the evaluation of some literals which contain variables. Depending upon the given interpretation, it is often possible to construct simple rules which can be used in such circumstances. In our example, for instance, we might perhaps add a rule that D(x, *times* (x, y)) evaluates to T. How many of these additional rules are included depends upon the particular interpretation under consideration. Be warned, however—checking literals to see whether they can be evaluated using some given set of rules can be a very time-consuming process.

Search Strategies

Having decided which simplification strategies to adopt, the next step is to decide exactly how to implement the resolution strategy. We need some procedure for deciding at each step whether to perform factoring or resolution and which clauses and literals contained within them are to be involved. A *search strategy* for resolution theorem proving provides answers to some or all of these questions. We say that such a strategy is *complete* if, when it is applied to an unsatisfiable set of clauses, it will guarantee to find a resolution refutation. This use of 'complete' is the same as that in Chapter 4; in this case the proof is by resolution and not by modus ponens. Unfortunately, complete search strategies tend to generate very large refutation graphs and will often work too slowly to be of much practical use. It is often better to adopt an incomplete strategy which, although it will not work for all cases, will quickly deduce the empty clause when applied to most unsatisfiable sets.

The most obvious complete search strategies will involve the systematic construction of every possible resolvent and factor (up to renaming of variables). One way of achieving this is by *breadth-first strategy*. The clauses in the original set, i.e. the base set, are defined to be at level 0. Those at level $i+1$ for $i \geq 0$ are defined recursively to be the resolvents of all possible (factors of) pairs of parents, one which occurs at the ith level and the other at the jth level where $j \leq i$. In Fig. 6.11, we give a refutation graph constructed using a breadth-first search strategy for the set of clauses

$$\{\overline{I(x)}, L(x)\}$$
$$\{C(a)\}$$
$$\{I(a)\}$$
$$\{\overline{C(x)}, \overline{L(x)}\}$$

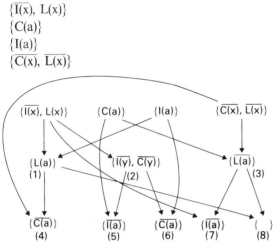

Fig. 6.11. Breadth-first search.

The numbers appearing under the resolvents indicate the order in which they were generated. Generation of level 2 resolvents ceases, of course, as soon as the empty clause is derived. In this example the mgus are obvious and hence are omitted from the graph.

It is possible to restrict breadth-first search by insisting that every resolvent in the refutation graph has at least one parent which is selected from among the clauses constructed from the negation of the goal WFF or their descendants. This set of clauses is called the *set-of-support* and this strategy is known as the set-of-support strategy. It can be shown that this strategy is complete. Although the depth of the search may be increased compared with breadth-first search, the overall search space is usually nevertheless significantly reduced. In Fig. 6.12 we use this strategy on our

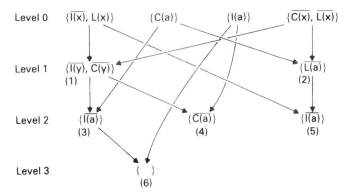

Fig. 6.12. Set-of-support strategy.

example. The set of support is $\{\overline{C(x)}, \overline{L(x)}\}$ together with any of its descendants.

A *linear-input form* search strategy is one where each resolvent has at least one parent, or a factor thereof, in the base set. Thus the refutation graphs of Fig. 6.9 could have been constructed using such a strategy. However, this strategy is not complete. A counter-example is the set of clauses

$$\{P(x), Q(y)\}$$
$$\{\overline{P(x)}, Q(y)\}$$
$$\{P(x), \overline{Q(y)}\}$$
$$\{\overline{P(x)}, \overline{Q(y)}\}$$

This set of clauses is clearly unsatisfiable, but every node constructed using a linear-input form search strategy must necessarily have one of its parents in the base set and hence contains at least one literal. Hence no node could possibly be the empty clause. Although incomplete, this strategy is simple to implement and is often used.

A complete strategy which can be viewed as a modification of the linear-input form strategy is the *ancestry-filtered form* search strategy. In this, each resolvent has a parent, or a factor thereof, in the base set or an ancestor of the other parent. The refutation graph for the above counter-example, given in Fig. 6.13, could have been constructed using such a search strategy.

Perhaps the most important and widely used search strategies are the *unit resolution* and *unit preference* strategies. A *unit* is a clause containing just one literal. If the parents of a resolvent R are a clause C and a unit clause, then R must contain fewer literals than C. To this extent R is closer

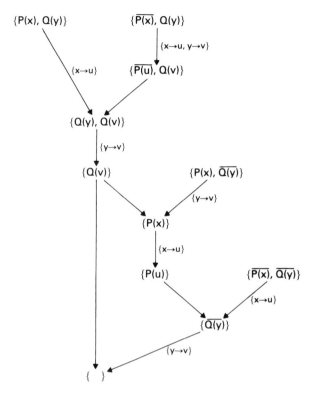

Fig. 6.13. Ancestry-filtered form strategy.

to the empty clause than *C* is. Hence an obvious heuristic ploy is to limit resolution to unit resolutions, i.e. to those which have one unit parent. The refutation graph of Fig. 6.9(a) involves just unit resolutions but this is not true of Fig. 6.9(b). A unit resolution strategy is clearly incomplete (consider the counter-example cited above). It is possible, however, to identify a class of clauses for which unit resolution will always suffice. We say that a clause is a *Horn clause* if it contains at most one non-negated literal. Provided that every clause in an unsatisfiable set of clauses **C** is a Horn clause, we can always find a refutation of **C** using unit resolution.

The unit preference strategy is a complete strategy which arranges the order in which resolvents are computed so as to favour resolving where one parent is a unit and, if this is not possible, to favour resolving on smaller rather than larger clauses. Details of this particular strategy together with a proof of the Horn clause result and considerable further discussion on a range of other strategies have been given by Loveland (1978).

Automatic Theorem Provers

Once a resolution search strategy is chosen, the computation of a refutation tree becomes a routine matter which can easily be automated. Because they can be allowed a large search space and can perform the basic operations so quickly, such programs would appear to have the capability of proving very complex theorems. Certainly, we might expect such programs to outperform even the most competent of human beings. To some extent this is indeed achievable. Provided that efficient search strategies are adopted and the properties of the domain in which we are working can be characterized by a reasonably simple axiom scheme augmented, as necessary, by previously derived theorems, we can expect considerable success. However, a person will often outperform an automatic theorem prover because he or she is able to make some major conceptual abstract step or use some sort of inspired guess. A person also improves his or her skill by practice. We need only see how an experienced algebraist is capable of quickly producing a neat argument to prove one of the basic results in group theory to appreciate this argument.

In this section we shall give some examples of the use of automatic theorem provers based on resolution. Since much of mathematics involves the proof of theorems from given rigorous axiom schemes, this seems a most promising application area for such automatic theorem provers. Indeed, many of the early successes of this approach were in the various branches of mathematics. One of the earliest pieces of research was in classical geometry (Gelertner *et al.*, 1963). In the late 1960s completely new results in mathematics were being established by computer. The SAMV project (Guard *et al.*, 1969) discovered the solution of a previously open problem in lattice theory. Since then, the use of computers by mathematicians has become more widespread and the automatic theorem prover has become a more common tool for researchers. An interesting comparison of various automatic theorem provers as applied in a variety of mathematical domains is given by McCharen *et al.* (1976).

As a simple illustration of the use of resolution theorem proving to establish a result in mathematics, we consider an example from group theory. Suppose that the binary operation of a group is $*$; then we shall use the predicate $P(x, y, z)$ to denote $x * y = z$. The axioms of group theory can then be written as follows:

(i) $\exists z P(x, y, z)$ (closure)

(ii) $\forall x \forall y \forall z [P(x, y, u) \wedge P(y, z, v)] \Rightarrow [P(x, v, w) \Leftrightarrow P(u, z, w)]$ (associativity)

(iii) $\exists x[\forall y P(x, y, y) \wedge \forall y \exists z P(z, y, x)]$ (existence of a left
identity and of left inverses)

In clausal form, these axioms become

$\{P(x, y, m(x, y))\}$
$\{\overline{P(x, y, u)}, \overline{P(y, z, v)}, \overline{P(x, v, w)}, P(u, z, w)\}$
$\{\overline{P(x, y, u)}, \overline{P(y, z, v)}, \overline{P(u, z, w)}, P(x, v, w)\}$
$\{P(e, y, y)\}$
$\{P(i(y), y, e)\}$

Now, suppose that we wanted to prove the result that every element of the group also has a right inverse. Then we need to show that the above axioms imply

$\exists x[\forall y\, P(x, y, y) \wedge \forall y \exists z\, P(y, z, x)]$

In clausal form, the negation of this WFF is

$\{\overline{P((x), j(x), j(x))}, \overline{P(k(x), z, x)}\}$

If we add this clause to the above clauses the resulting set of clauses should be unsatisfiable. This is established by the refutation graph of Fig. 6.14. This graph could have been generated using the set-of-support strategy. Some clauses, e.g. $\{P(e, y, y)\}$, occur more than once in this graph to simplify the presentation.

Once a computer is capable of solving problems, we can say that it has some form of 'intelligence'. We have discussed how computers can be programmed to prove theorems which no person has been able to prove. Are these machines more intelligent than people? Since these machines can only outperform people in such very limited environments, it would be wrong to answer yes. Nevertheless, we can begin to appreciate the possibilities afforded by a computer capable of reasoning. Any computer system with such an ability is said to possess some degree of *artificial intelligence* (AI). If we are to construct robots which can function as effectively as human beings then they must have the capability of solving new (unseen) problems. The AI research community has produced and refined several general techniques which enable machines to reason. Resolution theorem proving is one of these techniques which has a wide application. This approach to AI and other applications have been discussed by Nilsson (1980).

As an illustration of the use of resolution theorem proving in an AI

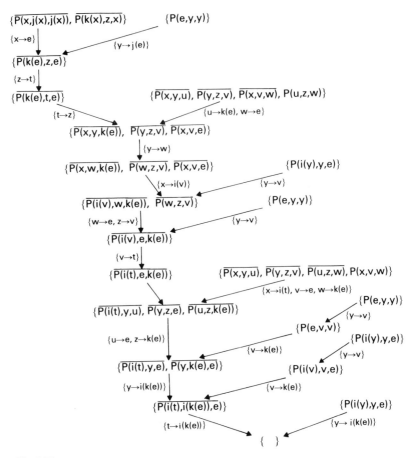

Fig. 6.14.

environment, we shall consider the classic 'monkey and bananas' problem. A monkey is on the floor of a room and a bunch of bananas is hanging from the ceiling too far away for it to reach even if it stood immediately under them. However, there is a chair in the room tall enough to enable the monkey to reach the bananas. If the monkey moves that chair under the bananas, climbs on it and thus gets the bananas we might say that it had some degree of intelligence. If a computer could deduce that action then we would say that it too was showing some degree of artificial intelligence.

To describe the situation in predicate calculus, we introduce the following predicates:

tall(x)	x is tall
climb(x, y)	x can climb y
close(x, y)	x is close to y
on(x, y)	x is on y
reach(x, y)	x can reach y
under(x, y)	x is under y
moves(x, y, z)	x moves y near z

We also use the constants b (bananas), c (chair) and m (monkey). We now consider the situation the monkey is in and the axioms it can assume. Firstly, if the monkey is close to something it can reach it, i.e.

$$close(m, x) \Rightarrow reach(m, x)$$

For the monkey to be close to the bananas, it must be on something tall under the bananas. Thus

$$tall(x) \wedge on(m, x) \wedge under(x, b) \Rightarrow close(m, b)$$

The chair is tall, i.e.

$$tall(c)$$

The monkey can climb the chair, i.e.

$$climb(m, c)$$

and the monkey can move the chair anywhere in the room, so that we have

$$moves(m, c, z)$$

As soon as the monkey climbs something, it will be on it; hence we have the axiom

$$climb(m, x) \Rightarrow on(m, x)$$

We also need to explain what is meant by 'near' in the definition of moves. We say that y is near z when either y is close to z or y is under z. Thus

$$moves(x, y, z) \Rightarrow close(y, z) \vee under(y, z)$$

Finally, since the bananas are attached to the ceiling and the chair is on the floor, we have

$$\sim close(c, b)$$

These eight axioms written in clausal form become

$$\{\overline{close(m, x)}, reach(m, x)\}$$

$\{\overline{\text{tall}(x)}, \overline{\text{on}(m, x)}, \overline{\text{under}(x, b)}, \text{close}(m, b)\}$
$\{\text{tall}(c)\}$
$\{\text{climb}(m, c)\}$
$\{\text{moves}(m, c, z)\}$
$\{\overline{\text{climb}(m, x)}, \text{on}(m, x)\}$
$\{\overline{\text{moves}(x, y, z)}, \text{close}(y, z), \text{under}(y, z)\}$
$\{\overline{\text{close}(c, b)}\}$

Now, we want to determine whether the monkey can reach the bananas, i.e. can we deduce reach(m, b). If we negate this, then we obtain the clause

$\{\overline{\text{reach}(m, b)}\}$

To show that the set of all nine clauses is unsatisfiable, we construct the refutation graph of Fig. 6.15. Note how the steps in the resolution correspond exactly to the tasks the monkey must perform if it is to reach the bananas. Techniques have been developed by AI researchers to extract such actions from refutation graphs once the latter have been constructed (Luckham and Nilsson, 1971).

Resolution theorem proving has opened up the possibilities of extensive use of computers to reason in specific domains, given a proper axiomatization. This not only gives exciting prospects in mathematics and AI but also opens up the possibility of a computer constructing its own programs! We have shown in Chapter 5 how we should specify programs using input and output predicates. The deduction of a computer program from a specification has many similarities to the construction of a formal proof in mathematics. The major problem with trying to automate this process is that we also require the resulting code to be efficient. If we can somehow link such a requirement into a logical statement of what we wish to be achieved by the program then we would have made considerable progress. The supporters of logic as a programming language believe that this is achievable and are making steady progress towards this goal. In the next section, we shall discuss logic programming with special regard to the programming language PROLOG.

Exercises

1 Say which of the following set of WFFs are satisfiable and which are unsatisfiable. Justify your answers.

(a) $\{\forall x(P(x) \vee P(f(x))), \sim\exists x P(g(x)), \sim\forall x P(f(g(x)))\}$

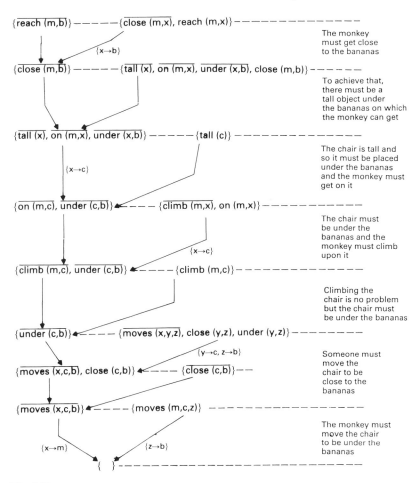

Fig. 6.15.

(b) $\{\exists x(P(x) \vee Q(x)), \forall x \sim P(x), Q(f(a))\}$ where a is a constant
(c) $\{\forall x \exists y G(x, y), \forall y \exists x G(x, y), \forall x(\sim G(x, x)), \forall x \forall y (G(x, y) \Rightarrow \sim G(y, x))\}$
(d) $\{\forall x(P(x) \Rightarrow \sim \exists y D(y, x)), \sim \forall x(D(x, x)), \sim \forall x(D(x, f(x))), \forall x P(f(x)), \sim \forall x P(x)\}$

2 Convert the following WFFs to clausal form:
   (a) $\sim \exists x(P(x) \Rightarrow P(a)) \wedge (P(x) \Rightarrow P(b))$, for constants a, b
   (b) $\forall x \forall y \forall z(P(x, y) \wedge P(y, z) \Rightarrow G(x, z))$
   (c) $\forall y \exists x P(x, y)$
   (d) $\sim \forall y \exists x G(x, y)$

3 Construct a semantic tree to show that the set of clauses constructed in Exercise 2(a) is unsatisfiable. Give a refutation by resolution of the same set of clauses.

4 Let $P(x, y)$ denote 'x is a parent of y' and $G(x, y)$ denote 'x is a grandparent of y'. Defining G in terms of P in the obvious way and assuming that everyone has a parent, use a resolution argument to show that everyone must have a grandparent. (Hint: see Exercises 2(b), 2(c) and 2(d).)

5 Consider each of the following sets of literals and construct an mgu if one exists:
   (a) $\{P(x, g(y), f(a)), P(f(y), g(f(z)), z)\}$
   (b) $\{P(x, f(x), g(y)), P(a, f(g(a)), g(a)), P(y, f(y), g(a))\}$
   (c) $\{P(x, f(x, y)), P(y, f(y, a)), P(b, f(b, a))\}$
   (d) $\{P(f(a), y, z), P(y, b, f(a)), P(x, y, f(z))\}$

6 Write a computer program to construct an mgu from a set of literals.

7 Represent the following statements in predicate calculus:
   (a) if a brick is on another brick, it is not on the table;
   (b) every brick is on the table or on another brick;
   (c) no brick is on a brick which is also on a brick.
Use resolution theorem proving to show that these statements imply that if a brick is on another brick then that second brick must be on the table.

8 Consider the following set of clauses:

$$\{P(x)\}$$
$$\{\overline{P(x)}, \overline{Q(y)}\}$$
$$\{Q(x), \overline{R(y)}\}$$
$$\{R(x), S(a)\}$$
$$\{R(b), \overline{S(x)}\}$$

   (a) Show that this set is unsatisfiable by constructing a refutation by resolution using (i) the breadth-first search strategy and (ii) the set-of-support strategy assuming that the final clause represents the negation of the goal WFF.
   (b) Consider the two (incomplete) strategies: linear input and unit. Which of these can be used successfully on this example?
   (c) What is the 'simplest' refutation tree that you can construct if (i) 'simplest' means 'of least depth' and (ii) 'simplest' means 'with fewest nodes'?

9 Consider the following WFFs:

$A(x) \Rightarrow (B(x) \lor C(f(x)))$
$B(x) \Rightarrow D(x)$
$B(x) \Rightarrow E(x)$
$C(x) \Rightarrow D(x)$
$C(x) \Rightarrow F(x)$
$A(g(x)) \lor B(h(x))$

(a) Express these WFFs in clausal form.

(b) Show that they imply that

$\exists x \exists y [D(x) \land E(x) \lor D(x) \land F(y)]$

by constructing a refutation tree using the set-of-support strategy.

(c) Construct an ancestry-filtered refutation tree showing that the same set of clauses is unsatisfiable. Compare the size of this tree with that constructed in (b).

10 Propositional calculus can be viewed as predicate calculus with 0-ary predicates only (see Chapter 3). Explain, in detail, how resolution can be used to prove theorems in propositional calculus, making simplifications to the technique wherever possible. Write a program to implement this method assuming that simple propositions are represented by single letters.

11 From the axioms of group theory given in this chapter, prove the following results using resolution.

(a) In a group G there exists a right identity.

(b) If G is an Abelian group then every element is self-conjugate, i.e. if $x * y = y * x$ for all x, $y \in G$ then $x * y * x^{-1} = y$ for all x, $y \in G$.

Chapter 7

Logic Programming

Declarative Languages

So far in this book we have concentrated on procedural programming languages and largely ignored declarative languages. The main characteristic of a procedural language such as Pascal is the assignment statement which assigns a value to a program variable. Control structures like loops and conditionals determine how to proceed from one set of assignments to the next. However, in a declarative language such as PROLOG the main characteristic is a rule statement which declares or describes a property which some structure must have. A program in such a language includes a list of such rules and expressions to be evaluated. The program is executed by repeatedly applying an appropriate rule to the expression until no further simplification of that expression is possible. The choice of rule and method of application is fixed for all programs in the given language. A logic programming language is a declarative language in which the rules can be interpreted as formulae in a predicate language, and the application of rules to simplify expressions can be understood in terms of using a set of inference rules to create a proof. We shall look in particular at a subset of PROLOG which forms a logic programming language and implements the main logical operators and connectives of predicate calculus.

Most languages contain both procedural and non-procedural aspects. In Pascal, for example, constant, type and variable declarations are non-procedural. They assert various properties which are always true throughout execution of the program. In contrast, PROLOG is a declarative language consisting mostly of predicate calculus like formulae but it also contains commands such as the 'cut' which affect how execution proceeds. These are used to control the direction of a computation by choosing which data and inference rules are used next.

Declarative and procedural programming languages are generally regarded to be as powerful as each other. Indeed, interpreters have been written which translate from procedural to non-procedural languages and vice versa. When this is possible the functions that they can compute must be the same. It is believed that algorithms can achieve the same time and space efficiency in both procedural and non-procedural languages, but in practice declarative programs contain much less procedural information and this tends to increase dramatically the execution time and space requirements. Careful choice of data for a declarative program will usually enable the same procedural information to be encoded and similar time and space efficiency to be achieved as with the corresponding procedural program.

The idea behind declarative languages is that it need not always be necessary to detail explicitly the algorithms or concrete data structures by which computation is performed. All that should be necessary is a formal description of the data types involved, e.g. a predicate calculus definition of the data types by means of formulae whose only model is that intended. A formula corresponding to the post-condition of the procedural program is then given to the system to be computed by inference rules given internally.

Although the declarative program lacks procedural information so that the system must spend time searching for the correct execution path, it does make it possible to test specification and design decisions much earlier in software development, before any code in a target procedural language is written. Efficiency of implementation is not as crucial at this stage but considerable savings can be made during development if testing can be done early enough to catch errors in design. In Chapter 5 our concern was with verifying that the code met the given specification. Here one use of logic programming is to check the stage before, i.e. the development, consistency, completeness and correctness of the specification. The inclusion of such a development step requires more discipline in programming than is normally encountered, and for this reason it is not yet the main use for languages like PROLOG. Currently it is in problems such as expert systems where there is a considerable knowledge base of data in the form of facts and general rules that PROLOG comes into its own. In those cases the natural software development process from specification to declarative and then procedural programs does not make sense and terminates with a declarative program. The procedural equivalent will save little in efficiency because the same searches through the database need to be made in both.

In this chapter we do not have space to offer a primer in PROLOG, but references are made later to such texts. The aim here is to give a flavour of logic programming—a theoretical rather than a practical ability to use logic as a programming language. This should indicate the importance of predicate calculus in that context. Interested readers are referred to Hogger

(1984) for further details. The overall view is that we need logic programming to enable (a) the early testing of specifications and (b) the manipulation of large quantities of data.

Logic Programs

Earlier in the book we encouraged the use of data invariants in procedural (e.g. Pascal) programs. These invariants consisted of comments against the various declarations consisting of predicate calculus formulae stating further properties of the declared object. These were viewed as parts of the specifications of the associated abstract data types, and it was hoped that they would be sufficient to specify the intended model completely. Together with pre- and post-conditions on procedures and functions and intermediate assertions a fairly well-documented program text is obtained. We can regard declarative and procedural programs as subtexts of this. In particular, the declarative equivalent of a given procedural program should be basically just the formal specification which comments on the procedural version together with the final post-condition.

Abstracting from this, for example, those parts of the comments and declarations concerned with the definition of natural numbers we might obtain the following information:

```
DataType NaturalNumbers;
Type    Nat;
Fns     0          :              → Nat;
        succ _     : Nat          → Nat;
        _ + _      : Nat × Nat → Nat;
Preds   _ < _      : Nat × Nat;
Var     a, b       : Nat;
Wffs    0 + b      = b;
        succ(a) + b = succ(a + b);
        0 < succ(a);
        a < b ⇒ succ(a) < succ(b)
End.
```

This description constitutes most of a logic program and is essentially part of a formal theory in a typed predicate calculus. The predicate language used is defined and the hypotheses given. The declarative language semantics will supply axioms in order to restrict the models suitably (e.g. to

Herbrand universes) and will also supply inference rules to complete the definition of the formal theory.

At run time a WFF is presented to the system and the inference rules are used to deduce a simple extra hypothesis which makes the WFF valid. This hypothesis usually consists of a list of equations giving values to variables in the WFF, such as

$$(x = 4) \wedge (y = 5)$$

i.e. it gives appropriate bindings to them. To perform useful computation, various expressions, i.e. terms in the predicate language, need to be evaluated in the specified model. This can be done by incorporating variables representing the required terms in the WFF. The run-time system will then reply as exemplified above with the desired conditions on the variable values. Therefore a logic program should compute bindings for variables.

With the environment of NaturalNumbers above we could give the post-condition

$$(z = succ(succ(0)) + succ(0)) \wedge (z < succ(0) \Rightarrow y = 0)$$
$$\wedge (\sim(z < succ(0)) \Rightarrow y = succ(0))$$

After applying the given WFFs the system should discover $z = succ(succ(succ(0)))$, from which $\sim(z < succ(0))$ will hold and so $y = succ(0)$. These values for y and z will be output. Alternatively, suppose we want to be able to have input and output files as in Pascal. They will be pre-declared variables of type list. Let us assume that lists are constructed using a built-in appending function '.' and a constant 'nil' for the empty list. Let the post-condition now be

$$(Input = x . y . nil) \wedge ((x = y \wedge Output = Succ(y) . nil)$$
$$\vee (x < y \wedge Output = y . nil) \vee (y < x \wedge Output = y + x . nil))$$

Then the machine will request input for x and y. Suppose that these are to be 2 and 1 respectively. Then we type in $succ(succ(0))$. $succ(0)$. nil because this is the notation that we specified for the input—we could, with more trouble, allow decimal numbers etc. The machine will complain that the post-condition cannot be achieved if the input condition is not met. In particular, the input must match the form x . y . nil. To satisfy the first clause x and y must be set to $succ(succ(0))$ and $succ(0)$ respectively. One of the last three clauses must be satisfied also. To test $y < x$ the machine will

$$y < x \equiv succ(0) < succ(succ(0)) \Leftarrow 0 < succ(0) \Leftarrow True$$

and so conclude that $y < x$ is true. To satisfy Output $= y + x$. nil the system must write out $y + x$. Therefore $y + x$ must be calculated. The first two WFFs are now used:

$$y + x \equiv succ(0) + succ(succ(0)) = succ(0 + succ(succ(0)))$$
$$= succ(succ(succ(0)))$$

Therefore succ(succ(succ(0))) . nil will be written to Output. A friendlier system could easily be built which would just print '3' for us.

Logic programming languages require a canonical method of writing terms in the universe in order to output bindings for variables. In the predicate language defined by a logic program, many terms such as Sqr(2), succ(succ(2)) and $2 + 2$ have the same value in the specified model and the system will have a chosen representative term for that element, presumably 4 for this example. It is this canonical representative which we wish to obtain in the output of the program. In PROLOG this is obtained by the predicate 'is' but often it is specified implicitly by the form of the WFFs in the program. Use of the inference rules may result in a formula $A \Rightarrow B$ being applied to cause an instance of B to be replaced by the corresponding instance of A, and the equation $s = t$ may cause a term matching s to be replaced by the appropriate instance of t. This way of rewriting formulae and terms makes the computation proceed towards the required answer, producing canonical representative terms for the bindings. Therefore the universe of the intended interpretation will almost always be a subset or all of the Herbrand universe, consisting of all the designated canonical terms.

Functional programming languages are logic programming languages in which we are unable to define or use predicates other than the pre-declared ones of the language. Programs consist mainly of definitions of functions and constants, often given by means of equations, and their execution mostly involves only the manipulation of terms. A standard way of computing in such languages is by treating equations as left to right rewrite rules, i.e. whenever a (ground) term matches the left-hand side of an equation (in the sense of unification) it is to be replaced by the right-hand side with the appropriate instantiation of variables. Given suitable equations, any term will then be rewritten eventually to a canonical representative. We did this when calculating succ(0) + succ(succ(0)). This term matched the left-hand side of succ(a) + b = succ(a + b) with a = 0 and b = succ(0). Therefore the term was replaced by succ(a + b), i.e. succ-

$(0 + \text{succ}(\text{succ}(0)))$. The implication $a < b \Rightarrow \text{succ}(a) < \text{succ}(b)$ was treated in essentially the same manner: replace the case $\text{succ}(0) < \text{succ}(\text{succ}(0))$ of the consequent by the corresponding case of the antecedent, i.e. $0 < \text{succ}(0)$. These methods of proceeding are just two of many inference rules that might be used by a logic programming system to create proofs as a method of calculation.

Functional programming languages can treat predicates satisfactorily although there is no syntactic difference between them and other functions. We simply define the required predicates as Boolean-valued functions and implement the logical connectives as Boolean operators. PROLOG works with the complementary part of logic to that used in functional programming languages. Although functions and constants can be defined and worked with as in functional programming languages, it is not as natural to do so. However, we can manipulate and define predicates with much greater ease. For the most part terms in a PROLOG program will always be canonical terms that cannot be further reduced except in the case of arithmetic expressions.

Usually the WFF presented to the logic programming system is known to be valid for certain values of the variables. If we define the predicate Add(x, y, z) to be true on the universe Nat exactly when $x + y = z$ and then ask if Add(3, 4, z) is valid, the reply should be the extra hypothesis $z = 7$. As we shall see with PROLOG, the resolution principles of Chapter 6 provide general techniques—the inference rules—for progressing to an answer. However, we observed there that, if the validity of the WFF presented to the system is suspect, then we cannot expect our program to terminate with a conclusion.

Horn Clauses

Although the resolution methods of Chapter 6 provide a general basis for computation in logic, performance is unacceptably poor if a complete strategy is chosen. This can be improved if the full expressive power of predicate calculus is sacrificed for that of Horn clause logic. In practice such a restriction is usually, at worst, only a minor irritation. The advantages of enhanced efficiency far outweigh the very slight practical restrictions.

Let us recall that a clause is a disjunction of literals (or atoms), i.e. of atomic formulae and negations of atomic formulae. It has the form

$$C_1 \vee C_2 \vee \ldots \vee C_m \vee \sim D_1 \vee \sim D_2 \vee \ldots \vee \sim D_n$$

where all the variables are implicitly universally quantified. The truth of this is identical with that of the equivalent formula

$$C_1 \vee C_2 \vee \ldots \vee C_m \Leftarrow D_1 \wedge D_2 \wedge \ldots \wedge D_n$$

In PROLOG-like notation it is written as

$$C_1; C_2; \ldots ; C_m :- D_1, D_2, \ldots , D_n .$$

Thus $\vee$, $\wedge$ and $\Leftarrow$ are written as semicolon, comma and :– respectively with a full stop denoting the end of the rule. As we saw in the previous chapter, everything can be written using clauses. The left-hand side of the rule, i.e. the disjunction which is implied, is called the *head* or *goal statement* of the clause and the other side is called the *body* or *tail* of the clause. Literals in the tail are called *subgoals* because resolution replaces the head or goal literal by the tail literals in its attempt to satisfy the original goal. The head is a disjunction of atomic formulae using the semicolon and the body is a conjunction of atomic formulae using the comma. Thus there are a number of alternative conclusions following from joint conditions.

A clause is a *Horn clause* when the head involves at most one conclusion, i.e. $m = 0$ or $m = 1$ in the above. In PROLOG only Horn clauses are used and they always have a head, so that $m = 1$ and the clause has exactly one positive atom. When the clause has no tail it is called a *fact*; otherwise it is called a *rule*. The terminology is clearly justified: with no tail the conclusions of the head hold unconditionally, but with a tail a rule is obtained for deciding when the head holds. A fact, therefore, is written more succinctly without the symbol ':–' in PROLOG. For example,

my_tank_is_full .

is a PROLOG fact, and

my_car_will_start :– my_tank_is_full, my_battery_is_charged .

is a PROLOG rule. The former states that 'my tank is full' is true, and the latter that 'my car will start if my tank is full and my battery is charged' is true. They will be hypotheses in the model of any PROLOG program containing them.

Headless clauses do come into the theory behind PROLOG. In particular, as PROLOG computes by constructing refutation proofs, the final goal is an empty clause. This has no head and no tail. How can a headless clause be read sensibly as a predicate formula containing an implication? The PROLOG fact

> my_car_will_start .

when negated will give the clause

> :− my_car_will_start .

in the notation above. The symbol ':−' is read 'if' because it corresponds to '⇐' in predicate calculus. If we put False on the left-hand side as the head, then for the rule to be true the predicate my_car_will_start must be false, as required. Observe that the disjunction $C_1 \vee C_2 \vee \ldots \vee C_m$ has exactly the same truth value as does False $\vee C_1 \vee C_2 \vee \ldots \vee C_m$ when m is positive. It is therefore reasonable to define the disjunction of no formulae to have the truth value of the second expression with $m = 0$, i.e. false. Since a head with no formulae is the disjunction of no formulae, the head of the above rule should be read as False.

In the same manner the fact

> my_car_will_start .

makes sense as a rule if we read the empty body as the logical constant True because the translation into a predicate formula which includes implication is then

> my_car_will_start⇐True .

We can justify this interpretation by noting that $D_1 \wedge D_2 \wedge \ldots \wedge D_n$ and True $\wedge D_1 \wedge D_2 \wedge \ldots \wedge D_n$ have the same truth values when n is positive. Defining the conjunction of no formulae in the same way using the second of these expressions yields True for that conjunction. Thus True is the correct interpretation for the empty body of a rule.

The rule with no head and no body is :−. which we now know how to interpret. The meaning is False⇐True if we translate the rule into the predicate language in the above manner. Thus such a sentence is always False. It is this empty rule that we try to obtain when applying resolution techniques.

Prolog and SL Resolution

Since PROLOG is probably the most widely used of the logic programming languages we concentrate on it. Currently its main use is in answering questions involving databases where the most frequent operation is searching through the data. Little procedural knowledge is involved in this, and wherever possible such knowledge is encoded as extra facts. Since many artificial intelligence and expert system applications can be written as structured databases of facts and rules, PROLOG is also well suited, in principle, to such areas of computing. We do not in any way wish to give the impression that writing an expert system is easy. However, the choice of a logic programming language is often appropriate for such a task, and a database with its management system can be viewed as a very simple example of an expert system.

The view of PROLOG presented here is not intended to be complete in any sense. What we are interested in is the close connection between it and the logic already studied in the earlier chapters. This should shed light on how the language has developed and how it is applied in practice. The name itself is derived from PROgramming in LOGic and belies its origin. The reader interested in a fuller account of the PROLOG language could consult, for example, Clocksin and Mellish (1981), Clark and McCabe (1984) or Kluzniak and Szpakowicz (1984).

PROLOG uses an untyped predicate calculus where the only WFFs are Horn clauses. Therefore the type declarations seen in a previous section can be ignored and identifiers can be and are declared by use. Each program has a number of rules and facts which are the hypotheses of the formal theory corresponding to the PROLOG program. This set of Horn clauses is called the *database*. As we have already mentioned, Horn clauses are much easier to deal with in resolution techniques. A linear resolution method described in the previous chapter can be used in a very simple form as the inference rule set of our formal theory.

The idea of computation in PROLOG is to give the system a goal statement which is a conjunction of positive (i.e. un-negated) literals only and containing definitions of the variables that are to be computed. Since proofs work by refutation, the system effectively negates this formula, which provides a new clause containing only negative literals, and tries to find values for any free variables which will yield a contradiction. Thus the clauses which have to be proved inconsistent are the base set, consisting of formulae in the database, together with the clause of the negated goal. To this goal clause and subsequent clauses obtained from it, SL resolution is applied. The L stands for *linear*. Thus, for any goal clause, the other parent of the resolving clause will be in the database. The S stands for *selected*, indicating that a particular literal to resolve on has to be chosen from the goal clause. This is the first literal in most PROLOG implementations.

Systematically, we construct resolving clauses until the empty clause is obtained, retracing steps to pick alternative rules or facts when the previous choice proved inadequate. The resolving clause keeps its literals in a specific order so that the correct literal is selected in the next resolution. This is usually given by replacing the selected literal in its clause by the body of the other clause. Thus the goal clause $\{\bar{A}, \bar{B}, \bar{C}\}$ and the ground clause $\{A, \bar{D}, \bar{E}\}$ have resolvent $\{\bar{D}, \bar{E}, \bar{B}, \bar{C}\}$ in which $\bar{D}, \bar{E}$ replaces the occurrence of $\bar{A}$.

Throughout the computation the goal clause always consists of negative atoms. This can be proved inductively. Certainly, we start with this property, but it is preserved at each resolution. In each database clause there is only one positive atom, i.e. the head literal. Resolving between such a clause and a clause of negative atoms can only be done by unifying the single positive atom with a negative atom of the other clause. Therefore the resulting clause again contains only negative atoms from each parent clause, with the unifying substitution made. This proves that the claimed property holds in general. The resolutions appearing in the refutation tree of Fig. 7.1 illustrate this.

At this point some qualifications on the use of resolution in PROLOG are necessary. Firstly, we shall look at completeness. SL resolution is complete in Horn clause logics without equality. This means that the negation of any valid Horn clause can be refuted using SL resolution. Thus, as long as we avoid possible traps with arithmetic operators by fully evaluating arithmetic expressions when they are encountered (so that syntactic equality between terms corresponds to equality in the model), then we can be sure that the refutation search tree will contain a finite branch which establishes the validity of a given valid WFF. Unfortunately, however, this does not cause every valid clause to be successfully recognized as such. As we saw in Chapter 6, any use of resolution has a strategy for traversing the refutation search tree attached to it. In the case of PROLOG a depth-first strategy is implemented. This is not complete because it may involve descending an infinite branch before the finite branch is reached. When that happens the system does not find the refutation of the given WFF because its search of the infinite branch does not terminate, and that search has to be completed first. The choice of strategy is again for efficiency reasons. The penalty is that the programmer must think carefully about the order of his database because this determines the order in which branches of the search tree are chosen.

Secondly, PROLOG is very expensive in time and space compared with

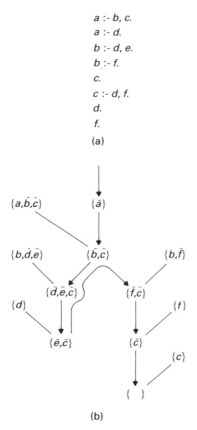

a :- *b*, *c*.
a :- *d*.
b :- *d*, *e*.
b :- *f*.
c.
c :- *d*, *f*.
d.
f.

(a)

(b)

Fig. 7.1. (a) A PROLOG database; (b) refutation of *a*.

procedural languages. To compete with them and enable real-time computation some shortcuts are usually made in the implementation of SL resolution and, as was noted in the previous paragraph, in the choice of strategy. To save time, the most expensive aspect of resolution, namely the unification, is often incorrectly coded with the occur check removed. This is the check which would make it impossible to unify the terms $f(x, g(y))$ and $f(g(x), z)$. This can cause termination problems owing to looping in the unification algorithm, and possibly incorrect confirmation of validity for invalid clauses.

To avoid the complications of unifying substitutions let us consider an example in which there are no variables. The PROLOG database of our program is given in Fig. 7.1(a). Commencing with the negated goal $\bar{a}$, the system resolves on the first appropriate clause in the database, creating a tree of subgoals as in Fig. 7.1(b) until the empty clause is obtained. Nodes in the tree are formed in the order given by the arrows: downward arrows represent successful resolutions and returning arrows represent backtracking to look for alternative clauses on which to resolve when a subgoal cannot be further simplified to the empty clause. Note how the order of literals in the goal clauses are obtained: replace the first literal by the tail of the other parent. The refutation in Fig. 7.1(b) is a proof of a in the sense defined in Chapter 1 for a formal theory. Thus, a PROLOG run-time system proves theorems by inferencing, using SL resolution for its inference rule set. The model theory and proof theory of logic provide the mathematical semantics of the non-procedural aspects of PROLOG.

Notice in this example that the selected clause is not always the best. Reordering the database by interchanging the clauses with head b will produce the empty clause more quickly from the initial goal a because the system always iterates through the database from top to bottom looking for clauses with which to resolve. Successful resolutions result in children of the given node born in the order that they appear in the database. With the depth-first strategy, all their descendants are investigated before the next child is generated. Thus, when resolution can no longer be applied to the current goal clause because no negative literal matches the head of a rule or fact in the database, the system backtracks to previous goals, trying to resolve them with alternative clauses further on in the database than the one previously tried. The order of choice of facts and rules by the theorem-proving system and the structuring of the data make the difference between programs which run in an acceptable time and those which appear to, or do indeed, take infinitely long to complete. Because of its incomplete search strategy and the time and space that such searches occupy, PROLOG includes some procedural aspects which control the database search. In PROLOG two such aspects are the order of the database itself and the 'cut' by which branches of the refutation search tree can be pruned.

It is very easy to write programs which have infinite branches that will be investigated. The rule $g_1 := g_1, \ldots$ will automatically cause looping if it is the first rule with head g_1 in the database. The goal g_1 will always generate g_1 as its first subgoal, causing an infinitely long branch. If the second rule with head g_1 is the fact g_1, then the system misses a possible resolution and consequent refutation with that clause.

Variables and Quantification

Let us introduce an example in which constants, functions and variables
appear. As in predicate calculus the PROLOG syntax for terms and
predicates is the usual prefix notation except for arithmetic operators which
have their standard syntax. A car maintenance expert system might include
a predicate *is_part_of* through which car parts are structured into
subassemblies. From the constants *car*, *engine* and *crankshaft* we can form
the statements

    is_part_of(crankshaft,engine) .

and

    is_part_of(engine,car) .

Constants commence with a lower-case letter or digit. We require a general
rule which enables us to deduce from the above PROLOG facts the
property is_part_of(crankshaft,car). More explicitly, a rule that states
is_part_of is a transitive relation. This requires variables, say Part1, Part2
and Part3, which are declared by use; the initial capital letters distinguish
them as variables from constants. The required predicate formula is

    Part1 is_part_of Part2 ∧ Part2 is_part_of Part3
      ⇒ Part1 is_part_of Part3

which is written in PROLOG as the rule

    is_part_of(Part1,Part3):−
        is_part_of(Part1,Part2), is_part_of(Part2,Part3).

As with all clauses, this rule is understood to be quantified universally over
all its variables. If we want to express the fact that the crankshaft itself
consists of parts we need to assert the existence of something which is a part
of the crankshaft. This can be done by means of the PROLOG fact

    is_part_of(somepart,crankshaft).

where *somepart* is a constant not previously used. Existential quantifiers are
thus replaced by the explicit choice of a constant which satisfies the required
formula.

The database can be questioned using ?− as follows:

    ?− is_part_of(crankshaft,car).

More generally, any tail of a PROLOG rule can be used to query the system. Suppose that we have included all the rules and facts given above. The system will then try to apply rules to deduce the truth of this formula. It will find that the implication above is satisfied when Part1, Part2 and Part3 are instantiated as *crankshaft*, *engine* and *car* respectively, and so respond with 'yes'. If we assume termination, for a constant *piston* the answer to

>   ?– is_part_of(piston,engine).

is 'no', which really means 'I don't know' because the database does not yet contain any rule or fact from which it can deduce the truth or otherwise of this query. 'No' means that the system has failed to prove the validity of a query. It may or may not be true, depending on the choice of model. The predicates are only partly defined because, although we may have stated by rules and facts all those points in the Herbrand universe where each predicate is to be true, we cannot state that at other points the predicates are to be false. We shall return to this point later. In fact, the query ?– is_part_of(piston,engine) fails to terminate. This is because the literal does match the head of a clause, i.e. that expressing the transitivity property. Part1 is set to *piston*, Part3 is set to *engine* and the new goal is_part_of(piston,Part2) then recurs infinitely often as it always matches the same clause again.

It is possible to ask questions in which variables occur, such as

>   ?– is_part_of(CarPart,car).

This means 'is there a value for CarPart which makes is_part_of(CarPart, car) true?' PROLOG responds with CarPart = engine if this is the first constant it finds in the database which answers the question positively. If the question is posed again by prompting PROLOG with a semicolon for an alternative the reply CarPart = crankshaft would be given if that were the next solution obtained by continuing the search through the refutation tree. Therefore questions are implicitly existentially quantified over their variables and replied to with values of those variables which satisfy the problem. The negated query which forms the goal clause for the refutation proof is therefore implicitly universally quantified over its variables, just as the other clauses are. As we would expect, the answer 'no' is received when no solutions or no more solutions to a query can be found. We need to be sure that the database has complete information at least before concluding that there really are no more solutions when 'no' is the answer. PROLOG, then, can be prompted into providing all choices of variables which will make the initial goal true.

The resolutions used in answering CarPart = crankshaft to this last query are as follows. Taking parent clauses

> is_part_of(Part1,Part3):– is_part_of(Part1,Part2), is_part_of(Part2, Part3).

and

> :– is_part_of(CarPart,car).

yields the clause

> :– is_part_of(CarPart,Part2), is_part_of(Part2,car).

by instantiating the variable Part3 as car. This is resolved with the clause

> is_part_of(crankshaft,engine).

to give

> :– is_part_of(engine,car).

by instantiating CarPart as crankshaft and Part2 as engine. Finally, this last clause together with

> is_part_of(engine,car).

have the empty clause as their resolvent. PROLOG prints out the instantiated value of each variable in the original query

> CarPart = crankshaft.

When prompted with a semicolon (i.e. 'or') the system reacts as if it had so far failed to answer the problem and continues to try to resatisfy goals with alternative choices of clauses with which to resolve. It continues in its depth-first search for another refutation.

A Procedural Description of Resolution

For a procedural interpretation of resolution, consider resolving the clauses $\{\bar{A},\bar{B},\bar{C}\}$ and $\{A,\bar{D},\bar{E}\}$ in which the literals A, B, ... may contain variables. We have the goal $A \wedge B \wedge C$ to satisfy and the implication $A \Leftarrow D \wedge E$ given. Cases of the goal hold if the subgoal $D \wedge E \wedge B \wedge C$ holds with variables chosen to unify the occurrences of A in the two clauses. This subgoal corresponds to the resolvent obtained, i.e. $\{\bar{D},\bar{E},\bar{B},\bar{C}\}$, with appropriate bindings on the variables. By thinking of each literal as a procedure we can interpret the rule $A:-D, E$ as a statement that the body of procedure A consists of sequential calls to procedures D and E. The order of calling is the result of the selected literal for resolution always being the first one. These procedure calls pass information via their arguments, i.e. the arguments of the literal, which can therefore be regarded as parameters. The occurrences of A and its negation in the two clauses result in the unification of their arguments. Thus the call to A in $A \wedge B \wedge C$ is accompanied by the instantiation of some variables appearing as parameters, and the completion of the call (via procedures D and E) causes a return of information by variables bound by further unifications within D and E. At the end of the refutation the empty clause $\{ \}$ is obtained, which we consider from the procedural viewpoint as the null statement (or the procedure 'True'). This means there is no more computation to do. The values of the parameters in the original procedure call are then returned to the user.

If a call to some procedure, say E, fails because we cannot find an appropriate rule (through either there being no rule with head E or an inability to unify the arguments), then the system retreats to the calling procedure (A in this case) and attempts to find an alternative rule. This is called *backtracking*. The next matching rule in the database is chosen if there is one, say $A \Leftarrow G$. Thus the call on A actually invokes a repetition of the execution of successive right-hand sides of rules (which have head A) until success is obtained. Success here means completing all relevant procedure calls by finding rules which can be resolved.

In order to imitate standard procedural techniques, we just have to break a problem into a sequence of subtasks, make each into a predicate and use arguments to pass all the information to subsequent predicates. To take a simple arithmetical example, define predicates *add*, *subt* and *mult* so that with argument list (X,Y,Z) they are true when $X + Y = Z$, $X - Y = Z$ and $X * Y = Z$ respectively. If *goal*(X,Y,Z) holds when $Z = ((Y * 2) + X) - Y$ then a call to *goal* defined by

goal(X,Y,Z):– mult(Y,2,A), add(A,X,B), subt(B,Y,Z) .

would pass partial evaluations of the expressions via A and B along to the last predicate, which returns a value for Z. The construction of *goal* clearly mirrors precisely that of the expression it has to calculate.

Rather than use the built-in PROLOG predicate *is* to evaluate the arithmetic expression above, let us use our usual function succ to define *mult, add* and *subt*. We shall therefore write 2 as succ(succ(0)) in the definition of the predicate *goal*. A PROLOG database for these predicates is given in Fig. 7.2. In that figure, and in PROLOG generally, the symbols /* and */ denote the start and finish of comments. Note how the clauses correspond exactly to Peano's axioms. In both cases we are defining addition and multiplication in terms of the successor function. Rule 1 is just the axiom R + succ(S) = succ(R + S), fact 2 is just T + 0 = T and rule 5 is the axiom R * succ(S) = R + (R * S). In the last case, we can see this in two steps from R * succ(S) = T = R + U = R + (R * S). Thus specification and program are very closely related.

```
/* 0 */     goal(X,Y,Z) :- mult(Y,succ(succ(0)),A), add(A,X,B), subt(B,Y,Z).

/* 1 */     add(R,succ(S),succ(T)) :- add(R,S,T).

/* 2 */     add(T,0,T).

/* 3 */     subt(succ(R),succ(S),T) :- subt(R,S,T).

/* 4 */     subt(T,0,T).

/* 5 */     mult(R,succ(S),T) :- mult(R,S,U), add(R,U,T).

/* 6 */     mult(R,0,0).
```

Fig. 7.2. Some definitions of predicates.

Let us compute $((Y * 2) + X) - Y$ when X is succ(succ(0)) and Y is succ(0). We pose the question ?– goal(succ(succ(0)),succ(0),Z). This elicits the following sequence of goals in PROLOG's attempt to reach the empty clause:

/*G1/*/ goal(succ(succ(0)),succ(0),Z)

/*G2*/ mult(succ(0),succ(succ(0)),A),
        add(A,succ(succ(0)),B),
        subt(B,succ(0),Z)   /*resolvent of G1 & 0*/

/*G3*/ mult(succ(0),succ(0),U),
        add(succ(0),U,A),
        add(A,succ(succ(0)),B),
        subt(B,succ(0),Z)   /*resolvent of G2 & 5*/

/*G4*/ mult(succ(0),0,U'),
        add(succ(0),U',U),
        add(succ(0),U,A),

	add(A,succ(succ(0)),B), subt(B,succ(0),Z)	/* resolvent of G3 & 5 */
/* G5 */	add(succ(0),0,U), add(succ(0),U,A), add(A,succ(succ(0)),B), subt(B,succ(0),Z)	/* resolvent of G4 & 6 */
/* G6 */	add(succ(0),succ(0),A), add(A,succ(succ(0)),B), subt(B,succ(0),Z)	/* resolvent of G5 & 2 */
/* G7 */	add(succ(0),0,T), add(succ(T),succ(succ(0)),B), subt(B,succ(0),Z)	/* resolvent of G6 & 1 */
/* G8 */	add(succ(succ(0)),succ(succ(0)),B), subt(B,succ(0),Z)	/* resolvent of G7 & 2 */
/* G9 */	add(succ(succ(0)),succ(0),T'), subt(succ(T'),succ(0),Z)	/* resolvent of G8 & 1 */
/* G10 */	add(succ(succ(0)),0,T''), subt(succ(succ(T'')),succ(0),Z)	/* resolvent of G9 & 1 */
/* G11 */	subt(succ(succ(succ(succ- (0)))),succ(0),Z)	/* resolvent of G10 & 2 */
/* G12 */	subt(succ(succ(succ(0))),0,Z)	/* resolvent of G11 & 3 */
/* G13 */	. with Z = succ(succ(succ(0)))	/* resolvent of G12 & 4 */

PROLOG now writes the value of Z to the output file. In this example the choice of the initial database makes the computation entirely 'deterministic'. This means that at any point in the calculation there is only one choice of clause with which successful resolution is possible. The choice of clause is determined. Calculations should then be as fast as in an imperative or procedural language (except for a constant multiplication factor). Unification is used to find the values of the variables at each stage. In the original goal as rewritten in G2, the value of A is passed as a parameter from the call on *mult* to that on *add* in G8, at which point it has been transformed by various substitutions to A = succ(T) = succ(succ(0)). Similarly the value of B had to be found, and it is passed on to the third procedure of G2 when control reaches G11. Its successive values, when the appropriate substitutions are made, are $B = succ(T') = succ(succ(T'')) = succ(succ(succ(succ(0))))$. Finally, the last procedure of G2 returns an instantiated value for Z when the empty clause is reached in G13. Unification of G12 with axiom 4 of the database yields the binding $Z = succ(succ(succ(0)))$ with which PROLOG will respond at the end of the computation. The goal clauses above always contain the sequence of procedures still to be performed in the order that they are executed and with the bindings calculated so far.

Whereas this procedural viewpoint with passing of parameters is more comforting to those used to imperative languages, it does cover up the pure logic of the deductive approach which ensures that the computations are correct. The database contains hypotheses about the required model and, whatever rule or fact is applied, if it can be applied then the deduction made is sound. It is the proof-theoretic view via refutations that guarantees the results and obviates the need for verification in the sense required for procedural programs and considered in Chapter 5.

The Search Space

In Fig. 7.1 we saw just part of the search space for a refutation proof using resolution. The tree produced contains just those nodes encountered before successfully obtaining the empty clause when traversing the search tree by resolving on the first available literal. The route over the tree is given by *pre-order* depth-first traversal. This is defined recursively by

```
procedure ProcessTree(N:Node);
var Child:Node;
begin
        ProcessNode(N);
        Child:= FirstSon(N);
        while Child < > Nil do
        begin
                ProcessTree(Child);
                Child:= Next(Child)
        end
    end;
```

For a given node N corresponding to some goal there is a child for each rule or fact in the database which can be successfully unified with the first literal of the current goal, and they occur in the order given by the database. The complete search space for the example of Fig. 7.1 is indicated in Fig. 7.3. Note that it is always the first literal in the goal clause that is resolved. When continually prompted by semicolons, PROLOG will normally continue traversing the search tree from one refutation to the next, finding all possible proofs of *a*. In all there are three such proofs here, one for each path from the root to a leaf marked by an empty clause. However, in this case the system has been given a query with no variables. It knows that further proofs will not yield different values for the variables in the query and so it will stop after the first refutation proof is obtained. A literal is said to have *succeeded* in a clause when control reaches the end of that literal or any literals introduced into the goal clause by that literal. Otherwise the literal is said to have *failed*. In particular, in Fig. 7.3 the goal *a* has succeeded when control reaches any of the empty clauses and *b* in the goal $\{\bar{b},\bar{c}\}$ succeeds when the goal has been reduced to $\{\bar{c}\}$, but *a*,*b* and *e* all fail in the leftmost branch of the tree because control is always at the head literal of the goal clause.

If PROLOG were to allow the selection of any literal rather than just the first then the search tree would be considerably broadened. In that case there would be additional children for each node. These would correspond

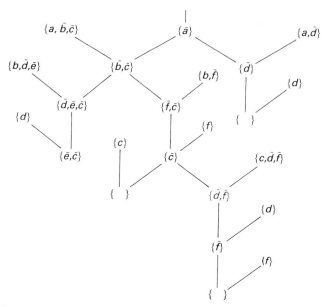

Fig. 7.3. The complete search tree for ?— *a*.

to resolving on clauses of the database whose heads matched literals in the goal clause other than the first. However, the computation rule by which the first literal is always chosen is large enough to give a complete search space, i.e. it will always contain a refutation down some branch when one exists. Therefore there is no need to consider this larger search tree.

In a logic programming language the deductions made by the system always follow a more or less fixed strategy so that the programmer does not need to worry very much about how to perform his calculation. Even if the strategy is incomplete, as in PROLOG, the user has little to worry about other than the possible non-termination of his program. If an answer to a query is obtained then it will be correct provided that the input is correct. As a secondary consideration he or she is usually able to make use of *extralogical* directives and features to speed up the program without affecting the truth of results, perhaps thereby obtaining a solution when the built-in strategy would not otherwise terminate.

One such feature in PROLOG is the order of the database, and in most cases a good programmer will be able to achieve at least a program which is guaranteed to terminate. By rearranging the order of the rules potentially infinite branches can usually be moved to the right of the tree, enabling the finite branch of a refutation to be accessible to PROLOG.

A second feature is the choice of rules and facts which determine the required predicates. There are usually many different ways of expressing the same relationships. It is a good policy to make a choice of clauses in which only a few clauses will match the head of a given goal. This makes the search tree very narrow so that very few choices or points for backtracking are encountered, and the system should converge rapidly towards a solution. This was done in the example of the previous section with the definitions of *add*, *mult* and *subt* given in Fig. 7.2. For any pair of clauses with the same head literal, the goal clause can match at most one of the head literals. This proves that in the associated search tree there is only ever one (or no) descendants of any node. The tree is as narrow as possible. Therefore, if there is a refutation, then PROLOG will find it as it descends the branchless tree deterministically.

A third way of controlling the search through the refutation tree is by means of the 'cut', denoted !. This is of most benefit when we are looking for only one solution to a particular subproblem which, if it fails later on, signals that the current method for attacking the whole problem should be abandoned in favour of another, rather than generating further solutions to the subproblem. We would want to do this when resatisfying the current goal would not give another useful solution. For example, suppose that two sets of data are to be processed and that two methods are available. If the first method works sometimes but not always when the two sets intersect and the second method is very expensive, then we ought to test for the first method initially. Thus:

process(Set1,Set2):— commonitems(Set1,Set2,Z), method1(Z,Set1,Set2).
process(Set1,Set2):— method2(Set1,Set2).

(Here Z is returned as a common member of the two sets.) Our interest centres on the case when the success of *method1* is independent of the actual value of Z. Suppose that in a particular application *method1* fails. If the sets have a large intersection then the call to the first of these clauses could be very costly. It would be much better to cut out all those branches corresponding to further values of Z satisfying *commonitems* in order that after the first value of Z we can progress to the second method. This is achieved by using the cut so that *commonitems* returns a single value of Z before failing when the system next backtracks to this predicate. If *commonitems* is defined by

commonitems(Set1,Set2,Z):— element(Set1,Z), element(Set2,Z).

then a cut should be put at the end of the clause, as follows:

acommonitem(Set1,Set2,Z):— element(Set1,Z), element(Set2,Z), !.

and this new procedure *acommonitem* should be used in the first clause for *process* instead of *commonitems*.

The effect of a cut is to commit the system to all the choices of clauses, and hence all the variable bindings, made in resolutions since and including the choice of the clause containing the cut. Therefore if the clause succeeds so that the cut is reached, then upon backtracking for further solutions the system does not attempt to resatisfy either call to *element* in the clause or even resatisfy the call to *acommonitem* by picking another matching clause (if there were one) with *acommonitem* in its head literal. This achieves the desired result. If *acommonitem* succeeds then any attempt to resatisfy it will immediately fail because all alternatives are automatically pruned from the search space. In our call to *process*, *method1* is attempted once with the chosen value of Z and backtracking will not produce any other value for Z. When *method1* fails, no attempt is made to resatisfy *acommonitem* so that control passes directly to the second *process* clause and *method2*.

To illustrate the cut further, we shall introduce the predicate *write* which takes a string as its parameter and always succeeds. Strings are written as in Pascal. In effect there is a built-in clause

write(X) .

which makes *write* always succeed, but it has the side effect of writing the value of X to the output file. Similarly, the predicate *nl* (newline) succeeds, appending a carriage return and line feed to the end of the output file.

Consider the database

```
/*1*/  conjugate(X)   :- subject(Y), verb(Y,X), nl, fail.
/*2*/  conjugate(X)   :- write('Finished. ').
/*3*/  subject(1)     :- write('I ').
/*4*/  subject(2)     :- write('you ').
/*5*/  subject(3)     :- write('he ').
/*6*/  verb(1,'be')   :- write('am ').
/*7*/  verb(2,'be')   :- write('are ').
/*8*/  verb(3,'be')   :- write('is ').
/*9*/  verb(3,X)      :- write(X),write('s ').
/*10*/ verb(Y,X)      :- write(X),write(' ').
```

This should write out the conjugation of some verbs. By default, the undefined constant predicate *fail* will fail. Therefore clause 2 will be reached when all solutions to clause 1 have been tried. Clauses 9 and 10 are required when the second parameter of verb is not 'be'. In response to ?– conjugate('be') the output is

```
I am
be
you are
be
he is
bes
be
Finished.
yes
```

In fact we only wish one call on the predicate *verb*. Further calls for the same value of the parameter of *subject* should be suppressed. This is done by a cut after each call to *verb*, giving the new database

```
/*1*/ conjugate(X)    :− subject(Y), verb(Y,X), nl, fail.
/*2*/ conjugate(X)    :− write('Finished. ').
/*3*/ subject(1)      :− write('I ').
/*4*/ subject(2)      :− write('you ').
/*5*/ subject(3)      :− write('he ').
/*6*/ verb(1,'be')    :− write('am '), !.
/*7*/ verb(2,'be')    :− write('are '), !.
/*8*/ verb(3,'be')    :− write('is '), !.
/*9*/ verb(3,X)       :− write(X), write('s '), !.
/*10*/verb(Y,X)       :− write(X), write(' ').
```

Now if any clause for the predicate *verb* succeeds, then backtracking will not involve resatisfying *verb*. The new output for ?− conjugate ('be') is

    I am
    you are
    he is
    Finished.
    yes

and for ?− conjugate('think') it is

    I think
    you think
    he thinks
    Finished.
    yes

If clause 1 is replaced by

    /*1'*/ conjugate(X) :− subject(Y), verb(Y,X), nl, !, fail.

then the output for ?− conjugate('be') becomes

    I am
    no

Since the cut in 1' is reached after the first line of output none of the predicates in that clause is retried, nor is *conjugate* itself re-attempted by applying clause 2. Putting the cut slightly earlier in the clause with

    /*1″*/ conjugate(X) :− subject(Y), !, verb(Y,X), nl, fail.

yields the same output, i.e.

    I am
    no

for the same query. If *verb* had allowed further solutions then these would have been obtained. lastly, repositioning the cut to the front of the clause to yield

/∗ 1‴ ∗/ conjugate(X) :─ !, subject (Y), verb(Y,X), nl, fail.

means that if the head of 1‴ can be unified with the current goal then the system is committed to pursuing this clause only, and clause 2 will not then be used. The output will therefore be

I am
you are
he is
no

A pictorial representation of the effects of a cut is given in Fig. 7.4. Here Fig. 7.3 based on the program of Fig. 7.1(a) has two branches cut off when a cut is added to give the clause

a :─b, c, !.

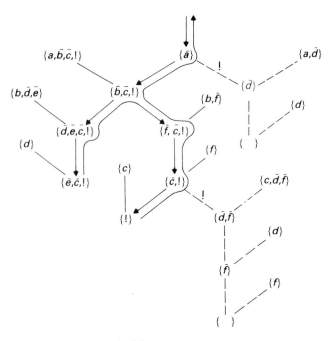

Fig. 7.4. The effect of a cut on Fig. 7.3.

All branches between the clause introducing the cut and that in which the cut has moved to the front of the goal clause are pruned.

The main advantages of the cut are to increase the efficiency of the program and decrease the set of obtainable solutions without affecting the logical properties. The penalty for this speed up is that some or all successful refutations may be removed from the search space. However, in practice most programs are sufficiently deterministic to require no cuts, or cuts are carefully inserted as in the above examples so that if there is a refutation it is not removed. In the conjugation example the cuts are easily removed to give a more logically transparent program:

```
/* 1 */ conjugate(X)    :— subject(Y), verb(Y,X), n1, fail.
/* 2 */ conjugate(X)    :— write('Finished. ').
/* 3 */ subject(1)      :— write('I ').
/* 4 */ subject(2)      :— write('you ').
/* 5 */ subject(3)      :— write('he ').
/* 6 */ verb(1,'be')    :— write('am ').
/* 7 */ verb(2,'be')    :— write('are ').
/* 8 */ verb(3,'be')    :— write('is ').
/* 9 */ verb(3,X)       :— not(X = 'be '), write(X), write('s ').
/* 10 */verb(Y,X)       :— not(X = 'be'), not(Y = 3), write(X), write(' ').
```

Here equality is syntactic identity, and the operator *not* has the obvious action. It is clear that exactly one of the clauses for the predicate *verb* will have a head that can be unified with a call to *verb*. We have thus achieved the same result as the original cuts.

Negation by Failure

Negation is implemented in PROLOG in a form called 'negation by failure' and is invoked by the Boolean operator *not*. This is not true negation in the logical sense of the predicate calculus $\sim$ except when the interpretation of our database is restricted to a particular model. For a formula A the call $not(A)$ succeeds in PROLOG if and only if no attempt to satisfy A succeeds. This call cannot instantiate any variables.

The difference between this form of negation and true negation is noted by using 'yes'/'succeed' and 'no'/'fail' in PROLOG rather than the 'true' and 'false' of logic. Use of *not* may involve evaluating formulae in a manner that does not correspond precisely to the substitution of the logical $\sim$ for *not*.

Therefore, from now on, we must refer to predicates succeeding or failing rather than as being true or false.

Continuing the car maintenance example we would like to add a fact to the database, namely that a spark plug is not made up of smaller components. Thus we must deny that any part is a part of a spark plug. This might be done using PROLOG notation by

:— is_part_of(AnyPart,sparkplug).

but this is not PROLOG because every rule must have a head containing one literal. If it were possible, then certainly whatever value were chosen for AnyPart the predicate would be false as intended. This problem is solved using the fact that if PROLOG cannot establish the truth of is_part_of (AnyPart,sparkplug) for any choice of the variable then it deems that predicate to have failed. Thus PROLOG is picking a particular model in which to compute rather than any model satisfying the hypotheses stated in the database. It assumes a model in which predicates are effectively false if they cannot be proved to be true. Users have two choices in such circumstances: either to avoid using *not* entirely, or to ensure that the model used by PROLOG coincides with that intended. In the latter case it is necessary to ensure that predicates are as fully defined as possible by stating every case in which they are true. If we consider only that part of PROLOG so far described, i.e. the purely logical aspects, then it is really only if negation is used in a PROLOG program that verification in the sense of Chapter 5 may be required. Every use of *not* ought to be accompanied by a proof that when *not(A)* succeeds, i.e. *A* fails, then *A* is indeed false in the intended model.

One difference between the negations of logic and PROLOG is that, although *A* and *not(A)* are mutually exclusive in both cases, it is not the case that one or other must always be true in logic although this is the case in PROLOG. This is because in logic there may be some models of the hypotheses in the database in which *A* is true and some in which *A* is false, but in PROLOG a particular model is chosen in which either *A* or *not(A)* is always the case. If for a given choice of variables the formula *A* fails, then PROLOG works in a model of the database in which *not(A)*, with the appropriate variables instantiated, is assumed true.

It is possible that we may wish to pose a question which includes a universally quantified variable. Previously it was noted that variables in questions were implicitly existentially quantified because their logical negations must be clauses, and clauses are universally quantified. Thus the query ?– q(X,Y,Z) yields the clause ~ q(X,Y,Z) for the refutation proof, and this means ∀X∀Y∀Z ~ q(X,Y,Z). This is shown to be false with values of X, X, Y and Z for which it does not hold. Thus ~ ∀X∀Y∀Z ~ q(X,Y,Z) is shown to be true, i.e. ∃X∃Y∃Z q(X,Y,Z), with values of the variables returned for which q(X,Y,Z) holds. Returning to the example, let us pose the query 'are all car parts part of the engine?'. Recalling that the existential quantifier is defined using negation and a universal quantifier, we could try to re-express this in PROLOG as

  ?– not(is_part_of(Any,engine)).

Unfortunately, this is not the correct solution. PROLOG will first try to make is_part_of(Any,engine) succeed, just as it would if the query were part of the body of any goal statement. It would instantiate Any = crankshaft, which makes is_part_of(Any,engine) succeed, and so not(is_part_of (Any,engine)) would fail with PROLOG returning the answer 'no'. This is clearly not the answer we wished for. The explanation is that the implicit quantification over variables is always as local as possible. The evaluation of a negated predicate involves trying all possible values of the local (i.e. so far uninstantiated) variables to see whether the predicate can succeed. Therefore the above query is the same as asking for the truth value of

  ~ ∀Any (is_part_of(Any,engine)).

Thus the implicit quantification seen previously in the normal forms of Chapter 6 does not quite correspond to that used here. In rules, facts and queries the implicit quantifiers appear *within* negated expressions wherever possible. To make the quantifier come outside the use of *not* we must declare it more globally by using it in an earlier predicate of the query before the *not* is encountered. If we use good programming practices then we have already introduced enumerated types by having unary predicates, one for each type, and making declarations of the elements in each type by means of PROLOG facts such as

  part(piston).
  part(battery).
  . . .

These would define a type called *part*. Then the query, rephrased as 'is there any part which is not in the engine?', is written as

  ?– part(Any), not(is_part_of(Any,engine)).

where *Any* is now necessarily interpreted as globally existentially quantified. Each time PROLOG finds a value of *Any* which makes part(Any) true it then has to satisfy the second predicate with that instantiated value of *Any*. Therefore if part(crankshaft) succeeds PROLOG then checks whether is_part_of (crankshaft, engine) succeeds. If it does, then the negated predicate fails and PROLOG backtracks to look for an alternative value for *Any*. If it fails, then the negated clause succeeds and the query succeeds with the response Any = crankshaft.

By posing questions we can easily interrogate the database to see what its view of the universe is, and incrementally add or change rules and facts in the database using further extralogical commands of PROLOG, i.e. edit the database interactively, until the model is correct and complete. We shall not describe how to do this, but let us observe that in preparing the specification of some program a programmer will normally start with a few facts and rules about the problem domain and add to this database as his knowledge and understanding increases. Adding facts and rules restricts the set of models of the database. We can make use of the difference between 'false' and 'no' in this development process in the following manner. It was noticed above that 'no' was the answer to

?— is_part_of(piston,car).

because incomplete information was given. This does not mean that a piston is not a part of a car, but just that this property cannot yet be deduced from the database. Clearly the answer ought to be 'yes' and this is achieved by inserting the fact

is_part_of(piston,engine).

to the database. In this way the programmer can discover how the machine's model of a car compares with the real article and augment the database to improve the model.

Although in predicate calculus we know that not(not(A)) has the same value as A, this does not generally happen in PROLOG. When a goal fails then the variables become undefined. This means that variables instantiated by the call A are not instantiated in the call not(not(A)). If A is

is_part_of(CarPart,engine)

then A succeeds with CarPart = crankshaft, so that not(A) fails, *CarPart* loses its value and not(not(A)) succeeds but with no value for *CarPart*. Thus ?— A yields the answer CarPart = crankshaft but ?— not(not(A)) just has the reply 'yes'. This emphasizes the need for an associated verification proof when *not* is used.

The discussion of negation was postponed until after that of the cut because PROLOG's *not* can be implemented using the cut. It can be defined by the rules

not(A) :– A, !, fail.
not(A).

Here *not* is a logical operator and takes a predicate as a parameter, so that A will be instantiated as a predicate with its parameters, but otherwise the rules work in the same way as before. The predicate *fail* fails because there are no clauses defining it. If a call to not(A) is made, then the first clause is entered with a call to A. If this succeeds then the cut is encountered and *fail* fails. Since the cut was processed, the alternative clause on which to resolve *not* cannot be chosen. Therefore not(A) fails. However, if A itself fails, then the cut is not reached and control moves to the second clause which states that not(A) succeeds.

Functions and Structures

Finally, in our brief look at PROLOG, we must make some remarks about terms. The predicates of PROLOG can take terms as parameters, and not just variables or constants. Functions are available, although the typical applications of the language deny any computational aspect and they are therefore called *structures* rather than functions. Indeed, we want to know how to store data in a clause, and the answer is by using terms, i.e. structures. The closest parallel in Pascal is the idea of a record. For student records the term st_rec(mary,date_of_birth(13,jan,75)) holds information and any variable instantiated to the value of this term can be used to process the data. The fact that this student is in second year computer science could be expressed by

student(2,compsci,st_rec(mary,date_of_birth(13,jan,75))).

Selecting a field of the record is the same as obtaining the value of an argument in the term. This is very easily done, e.g.

birthdate(st_rec(Name,X),X).
name(st_rec(Name,X),Name).

When the goal birthdate(S,X) is presented with S instantiated then S is

unified with st_rec(Name,X) in the above fact, and this gives X the value
desired. For S = st_rec(mary,date_of_birth(13,jan,75)) the successful call to
birthdate will set X to date_of_birth(13,jan,75). Thus the parameters of a
structure or predicate are just the field entries that would be put in a Pascal
record. For example, we might be ordering a class by merit instead of name.
Progressively, a binary tree is built up:

> order(noone).
> order(name(mary,27,noone,noone)).
> order(name(mary,27,noone,name(john,24,noone,noone))).
> etc.

The structure called *name* has entries for the pupil, the mark and the
subtrees of pupils with higher and lower marks respectively. By using the
four arguments of *name* to annotate the node and form the two subtrees, it is
fairly simple to draw the appropriate binary tree for the last term above.

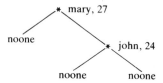

Nevertheless, despite having created a binary tree, the predicate *order* has
one argument which is a term composed from many applications of the
function *name* and the constants *mary, john, noone*, 24, 27 etc. Naturally, as
in a procedural language, we would have rules for appending another name
to the tree, thereby extending the structure. Thus

> create_tree(name(X,Mark, Left,Right),X,Mark,Left,Right).

can be used not only to select *Right* from a tree by supplying a value for the
first argument, but also, by supplying the last four arguments to a call on
create_tree, to instantiate a variable in the first position to the tree formed
from those values. It should be clear that representing data structures in a
predicate language is just as easy as in a procedural language, and the same
richness is available in both.

Verification

Our description of the predicate logic aspect of PROLOG is now complete.
There are, of course, many other predicates and operators available in the

various implementations of the language which help with input and output, arithmetic, searching etc. These are not so fundamental to the ideas of logic programming. What we have covered are the direct equivalents of the elements in the alphabet of our chosen predicate language: the constants, functions, predicates, variables, quantifiers and logical connectives.

Verification is just as important in logic programming as in any imperative language. The same problems arise and the techniques are very similar. However, by programming in logic it is possible to come closer to the definition of a function or predicate than in conventional procedural languages. There is less difference between the specification of a program and the code for it; hence there is less to prove and less chance for error. This is true especially in intelligent knowledge-based systems like the car expert system above where the specification would include rules about the various parts in a subassembly. These are precisely the rules in the database and the specification is virtually identical with the PROLOG program. Sometimes, as in the example of Fig. 7.2, more work is necessary in choosing the database so that the choice of rule will make the computation progress. Then algorithmic information has been included, perhaps at the cost of a less natural specification, but the specification has become executable.

Proofs of correctness are just as necessary in logic programs as in procedural programs but should be easier to achieve. The advantages in logic programming are that the specification and program are closer and the program is shorter. Partial correctness is almost immediate because the facts and rules of the database should be easily derived from the specification, and only sound results can be obtained by applying these rules. The disadvantages are that the proof of total correctness, i.e. showing that the program terminates, depends critically on the algorithm of the inference engine and other extralogical features of the language such as the order of rules in the database. With a good logic programming language it is as easy to ensure termination as with an equivalent program in a procedural language.

Exercises

1 The infix PROLOG predicate *is* can be used as an assignment statement: X *is* $Y + Z$ will assign the value of $Y + Z$ to X. Thus the predicate *mult* in the text could have been defined by

$\quad$ mult(X,Y,Z) :- Z is X*Y.

The relational operators $<$, $=:=$ (equality), $=/=$ (inequality), $=<$, $>=$ and $>$ are infix predicates which will evaluate and then compare their two arguments, just like their procedural equivalents.

Write a PROLOG program to calculate the following functions:

(a) $f(X)$ $= X(2+X)$;
(b) $g(X,Y)$ $= X^3 + 3XY + Y^3$

(c) $abs(X)$ $= \begin{cases} X \text{ if } X > 0, \\ -X \text{ otherwise}; \end{cases}$

(d) $fact(X)$ $= \begin{cases} 1 \text{ if } X \leqslant 0, \\ X*fact(X-1) \text{ otherwise}; \end{cases}$

(e) $exp(X,Y) = X^Y$, using the arithmetic operator$*$;

(f) $hcf(X,Y) =$ the highest common factor of X and Y—use Euclid's algorithm which depends on $hcf(X,Y) = hcf(X \bmod Y, Y)$.

Predicates should be constructed which are true if and only if the last argument has the value of the function at the point given by the other arguments.

In each case write down the successive goal clauses reached when the system is asked to calculate the value of the function when $X = 3$ and $Y = 2$.

In cases (e) and (f) demonstrate that your program will always terminate for positive integer values of the arguments.

2 Take the database
   is_part_of(crankshaft,engine).
   is_part_of(engine,car).
   is_part_of(Part1,Part3) :— is_part_of(Part1,Part2),
       is_part_of(Part2,Part3).
used in the text.
   (a) Construct the search trees for the queries
       (i) ?— is_part_of(piston,engine).
       (ii) ?— is_part_of(CarPart,car).
to show that they have infinite branches.
   (b) What will PROLOG respond to each query in (a) when prompted by semicolons?
   (c) Answer the first two parts again when the clause
   is_part_of(Part,Part).
is added to the database just before the last clause.

3 Constants such as *smith*, *kennedy*, *jones* and *macdonald* can be compared for their relative lexicographic order using the infix predicate @ <. We can build lists (which are terms) using the notation [ ] for the empty list, [a,b,c] for the list with elements a, b and c, and [Head|Tail] for the list with element *Head* at the beginning and *Tail* as the rest of the list. In particular, Head = a and Tail = [b,c] for the list [a,b,c]. Write down a list containing the four constants given above.

Define a predicate *sort* which will take two lists as arguments and be true when the second list is the lexicographically sorted permutation of the first. Trace the calculations made in sorting the list just constructed.

4 Use the cut to define a unary predicate *neuter* which is true precisely when its argument does not satisfy either of the unary predicates *male* or *female*.

5 For each of the four subsets of the database
is_part_of(heater,coolingsystem).
is_part_of(heater,engine).
decide what PROLOG's response would be to the two queries
?– is_part_of(CarPart,coolingsystem), not(is_part_of(CarPart,engine)).
and
?– not(is_part_of(CarPart,engine)),is_part_of(CarPart,coolingsystem).
Write down predicate calculus formulae corresponding to these questions in which the quantifiers are made explicit.

6 Consider the PROLOG database

```
happy     :– birthday, christmas.
happy     :– christmas.
happy.
birthday  :– pigscanfly.
christmas :– pigscanfly.
christmas :– christmas.
```

(a) Construct the search tree for the query ?– happy, and show how PROLOG traverses it.
(b) Rearrange the database so that the query is answered in finite time.
(c) Insert a cut to make the search tree finite but as large as possible.
(d) Using the two clauses given in the text for defining *not* using the cut, construct the search tree for ?– not(pigscanfly), happy as far as the first refutation.

(e) Describe the effect of inserting a cut in the first clause in any of the three possible positions.

7   The Towers of Hanoi game starts with discs numbered 1 to *n* arranged in order to form one tower. Using the list notation given in Exercise 3, define a predicate full_tower(N,T) which returns the list T = [N,. . .,3,2,1] of elements which make up this tower. The head of such a list represents the lowest disc in the tower.

Using a second tower as temporary storage, all the discs have to be transferred to a third tower. Only the top disc in a tower is available to be moved at any one time and it may not be placed above a disc of lower number. The solution to the game is the list of moves required. Write a PROLOG program to solve the game, writing the moves one at a time in the correct order to the output file using the predicates *write* and *nl*. It may be useful to consider in your solution the predicate move(T,I,J) which writes to output the moves required to transfer the discs in list T from tower I to tower J. It is most easily defined in terms of moving the head and tail of T separately.

Test the program by working through the case of three discs. Prove that it terminates and provides a correct solution.

Modify your program so that the output from the program is an explicit list of moves rather than a side effect on the screen.

References

Alagić, S. & Arbib, M. A. (1978) *The Design of Well-structured and Correct Programs*, Springer, Berlin.

Berg, H. K., Boebert, W. E., Franta, W. R. & Moher, T. G. (1982) *Formal Methods of Program Verification and Specification*, Prentice-Hall, Englewood Cliffs, NJ.

Boolos, G. S. & Jeffrey, R. C. (1980) *Computability and Logic*, Cambridge University Press, Cambridge.

Clark, K. L. & McCabe, F. G. (1984) *Micro-PROLOG: Programming in Logic*, Prentice-Hall, Englewood Cliffs, NJ.

Clocksin, W. F. & Mellish, C. S. (1981) *Programming in PROLOG*, Springer, Berlin.

Enderton, H. B. (1970) *A Mathematical Introduction to Logic*, Academic Press, New York.

Floyd, R. W. (1967). Assigning meanings to programs. In *Proc: Symp. on Applied Mathematics*, Vol. 19, Mathematical Aspects of Computer Science (ed. J. T. Schwartz), pp. 19–32, American Mathematical Society.

Foley, M. & Hoare, C. A. R. (1971) Proof of a recursive program: Quicksort. *Computer Journal*, **14**, 391–395.

Gelertner, H., Hansen, J. R. & Loveland, D. W. (1963) In *Computers and Thought* (eds E. Feigenbaum & J. Feldman), McGraw-Hill, New York.

Glaser, Hankin & Till (1984) *Principles of Functional Programming*, Prentice-Hall, Englewood Cliffs, NJ.

Guard, J R., Oglesby, F. C., Bennett, J. M. & Settle, L. G. (1969) Semi-automated mathematics. *Journal of the Association for Computing Machinery*, **16**(1), 49–62.

Henderson, P. (1980) *Functional Programming*, Prentice-Hall, Englewood Cliffs, NJ.

Hoare, C. A. R. (1969) An axiomatic basis for computer programming, *Communications of the Association for Computing Machinery*, **12**, 576–580.

Hoare, C. A. R. (1971) Procedures and parameters; an axiomatic approach. *Symposium on Semantics of Algorithmic Languages* (ed. E. Engeler), Lecture Notes in Mathematics, Vol. 188, Springer-Verlag, Berlin.

Hoare, C. A. R. (1971) Proof of a program: Find, *Communications of the Association for Computing Machinery*, **14**, 39–45.

Hoare, C. A. R. (1972) Proof of correctness of data representation, *Acta Informatica*, **1**, 271–281.

Hoare, C. A. R. (1972) Proof of a structured program: The sieve of Eratosthenes, *Computer Journal*, **15**, 321–325.

Hogger, C. J. (1984) *Introduction to Logic Programming*, Academic Press, New York.

Jones, C. B. (1986) *Systematic Software Development Using VDM*, Prentice-Hall, Englewood Cliffs, NJ.

Kleene, S. C. (1967) *Mathematical Logic*, Wiley, New York.

Kluzniak, F. & Szpakowicz, S. (1984) *Prolog for Programmers*, Academic Press, New York.

Lind, L. F. & Nelson, J. C. C. (1977) *Analysis and Design of Sequential Digital Systems*, Macmillan, New York.

Loveland, D. W. (1978) *Automatic Theorem Proving: A Logical Basis*, North-Holland, Amsterdam.

Luckham, D. C. & Nilsson, N. J. (1971) Extraction of information from resolution proof trees. *Artificial Intelligence*, **2**(1).

McCharen, J. D., Overbeck, R. A. & Wos, L. A. (1976) Problems and experiments for and with automated theorem-proving programs. *IEEE Transactions on Computers*, **25**(8), 773–782.

Manna, Z. & Pnueli, A. (1974) Axiomatic approach to total correctness. *Acta Informatica*, **3**, 243–264.

Mano, M. M. (1984) *Digital Design*, Prentice-Hall, Englewood Cliffs, NJ.

Mavor, J., Jack, M. A. & Denyer, P. B. (1983) *Introduction to MOS LSI Design*, Addison Wesley, Reading, MA.

Mead, C. & Conway, L. (1980) *Introduction to VLSI Systems*, Addison Wesley, Reading, MA.

Mendelson, E. (1979) *Introduction to Mathematical Logic*, Van Nostrand, Princeton, NJ.

Nilsson, N. J. (1980) *Principles of Artificial Intelligence*, Tioga Press, Palo Alto, CA.

Robinson, J. A. (1979) *Logic: Form and Function*, Edinburgh University Press, Edinburgh.

Tanenbaum, A. S. (1984) *Structured Computer Organization*, Prentice-Hall, Englewood Cliffs, NJ.

Index